THE
WINDTURBINE
COMPANY

basic
electronics
for
hydraulic
motion
control

by Jack L. Johnson, PE

published by the editors of HYDRAULICS & PNEUMATICS magazine

Library of Congress Catalog Card Number 91-77995

Basic Electronics for Hydraulic Motion Control

ISBN 0-932905-07-2
Copyright © 1992 by J. L. Johnson.
Copyright © 1992 by Penton Publishing Inc.
1100 Superior Avenue, Cleveland, OH 44114

Current printing (last digit):
10 9 8 7 6 5 4 3 2 1

Printed in the United States of America

Dedicated to: **Russell and Eunice**

Foreword

Control of hydraulic systems has evolved from those *bang-bang* systems that depended on the actuator reaching the end of its stroke to provide position control. Current hydraulic system design relies on systems integration of the total automation cycle. Today, the circuit-design engineer must be proficient in using mathematical modelling to provide stable force and motion control of the system.

It is generally agreed that effective control of a hydraulic system often requires the inclusion of sensors to monitor the state of the system, using the electrical/electronic data as input to computers programmed to provide the control signals needed to achieve the desired forces, transverse velocities, and positioning with the required stability.

The use of electrical/electronic sensors to control hydraulic systems is becoming more common as hydraulic system circuit designers become familiar with the available sensor hardware — and how to optimize its application to their projects.

It is expected that the growth in the application of such systems will accelerate as circuit designers become more adept in applying them, and as users of machines incorporating electronically controlled motion controls become convinced of their reliability and superior performance.

To that end, this volume provides a very effective means of instruction in the design, application, and maintenance of electronically controlled hydraulic equipment. And, although this work is titled as dealing with *Basic Electronics for Hydraulic Motion Control*, it is also an excellent primer on mathematical modelling of hydraulic systems.

In my opinion, fluid power systems are rapidly evolving to the point where the majority will be electronically controlled with an electrically controlled-and-powered proportional 3-way valve in each actuator port. Circuit force and motion control will be governed by suitably programmed microcomputers. This work serves to hasten the day when such systems will be developed and become commonly used.

The author, Jack Johnson, is especially well qualified to teach electrohydraulic motion control. He has had solid experience in such applications in industry and has effectively applied that exposure to his natural propensity to be an effective teacher in the preparation of this work.

Z. J. Lansky
retired Vice President & Chief Technical Director, Parker Hannifin Corp., and present Chairman, Technical Committee TC 131, Fluid Power Systems, of the International Organization for Standardization.
Sarasota, Florida
February 1992

About the author

Jack L. Johnson, PE, is a Senior Lecturer in the Milwaukee School of Engineering Mechanical Engineering Graduate School, and Manager of Advanced Concepts, IDAS Engineering Software, also in Milwaukee. With his BSEE from MSOE and graduate study in automatic controls at Marquette University, his professional specialization has been the electronic and computer control of hydraulic systems.

Several of his previous positions include: Chairman and Delegation Leader of the U. S. Technical Advisory Group to the International Organization for Standardization, Fluid Power Systems Technical Committee 131, Subcommittee 8, Product Testing and Contamination Control; Executive Vice President, Fluid Power Society; Director, Fluid Power Insitute, MSOE; and Engineering Manager, HPI Div., W. H. Nichols Co.

An internationally recognized authority on hydraulic fluid power, Johnson has specialized in the development of methods for the prediction and control of the dynamic performance of hydraulic and electrohydraulic systems. His education and experience have accustomed him to develop the basic data for mathematical modeling and application of the digital computer to analyze, design, and control the final system.

In addition to this book, Johnson also is the author of *Design of Electrohydraulic Systems for Industrial Motion Control*, © 1991.

Preface

Electronic control of fluid power systems has been with us since the days of World War II, but until recently was primarily limited to military and aerospace applications. Reasonable people will disagree about the exact causes for the now-increasing use of electronic controls in industrial applications, but the advent of extremely powerful, versatile, and inexpensive electronic devices must rank as one of the more important ones. Add to that the pressures on industry to reduce cost while at the same time improving quality, and we see that in many instances this is accomplished best with electronic controls which direct the impressive power of hydraulic equipment with finesse and precision.

Today, the fluid power practitioner is faced with a need to know hydraulic circuits and systems and also to know how to control that machinery with electronic equipment. The time is rapidly coming when the fluid power specialist will need to be a *systems specialist*, whose knowledge spans a multitude of technical specialties. I am occasionally asked whether industry should hire electronic technicians and engineers and train them in the ways of fluid power, or hire fluid power engineers and technicians and train them in the ways of electronics? This book does not answer that question. But upon reflection, I believe that I have assumed that we could teach our present fluid power technicians and engineers the methods for dealing with electronic devices and circuits. Toward that end, there are occasional references to hydraulic-circuit concepts that I felt would help bridge the gap from fluid power to electronics. But I hope the electrical circuit analysis techniques will show how one can more effectively apply those concepts to hydraulic circuits and systems as well. Hydraulic system analysts and designers would be well-served by adopting the analytical ideas that have been so well developed by our electrical sisters and brothers.

This book, then, is intended to serve as a cross-training tool to bridge from hydraulics to electronics. The early chapters provide the basic physical foundations of electronic theory; the later chapters proceed to the practical application of both analog and digital devices. One problem with electronic text books written specifically for electronic specialists is that they become too involved in the analysis of very complex circuits that we, as practitioners of the fluid power art, will never be called upon to solve. The fact of the matter is that almost every circuit we encounter will be either a simple series circuit, a parallel circuit, or a bridge circuit. Therefore, I have refrained from stressing the analysis of complex electrical networks. Kirchoff's and Ohm's Laws are necessary because they have analogous application to both hydraulic and electronic systems, however, the example problems are basic. It also is true that the interconnection of electronic devices requires at least a qualitative understanding of a few operational amplifier circuits, so that servo and proportional valve amplifiers can be correctly interfaced.

During my years of involvement in the fluid power industry, I encountered many non-electronic technicians and engineers who have developed considerable competence in the design of useful electronic control circuits. In their cases, it was art born of necessity. Not everyone who must learn about electronics will be required to — or even want to — design electronic circuits. But in the event they do, I have in many instances derived the necessary design equations for the circuits at hand. The text therefore has some value as an engineering reference should the reader choose to use it that way.

Transducers are covered from the standpoint of principles of operation because with a little insight, knowledge of a few underlying ideas can help the reader's understanding expand into other devices I have neglected, or perhaps that have not yet been invented. The most important interfacing consideration is the idea of loading error. The uninitiated user must be ever mindful of the possibility that the connection of the transducer output to the amplifier input, for example, may result in unexpected loading error. The error is insidious because it may be unexpected, and even more so because every attempt to measure the effect of loading error in electronic circuits will fail to reveal its presence. And yet it is there!

There are other important interfacing considerations such as those that occur when using an LVDT that requires AC excitation and produces AC output but must connect to a DC amplifier. This and other ideas are covered as *data format* concepts in which the most common forms of data signals that arise in electrohydraulic circuits are presented. If one knows the format in which the data exists, many times the interfacing method is established. Furthermore, the format of the data many times is dictated by the nature of the transducer. Therefore, the principles of transduction and data formats are covered together in consecutive chapters.

Digital circuits, like many of the other topics in the book, have been covered in thousands of excellent electrical engineering textbooks. In the limited space available, I have attempted to present those concepts I have found to be most important to the fluid power community. There are three very important ones:
- the time delay that is inherent in all digital devices
- the limited resolution that accompanies all digital devices, and
- the need for *handshaking* between communicating digital devices.

To show why these limitations exist, some basic principles are covered along with elementary circuits, such as gates, analog-to-digital and digital-to-analog converters, and electronic counters. The treatment is by no means exhaustive, but the reader should gain some insight regarding some of the more common digital control elements.

In the name of completeness, I have included Chapter 13 to survey some of the ways in which various inventors and designers have created proportional electrohydraulic interface devices (PEHIDs). These devices receive electronic signals and convert them into proportional hydraulic output(s). The most common are the servo and proportional valves, but electrical strokers for pumps and motors also are included.

Ending the book are two chapters which deal with systems. These chapters provide an overview of how the electronic and hydraulic elements come together to form a system. They include the use of feedback or closed loop control, and explain how that concept is used to solve the industrial motion-control problem. Both speed-control loops and position-control loops are discussed.

In closing, I offer my most sincere thanks to all the fine people at the Milwaukee School of Engineering for sponsoring the industrial seminars that sparked the first pages of this book.

Warm personal regards go to Jeff Cullman and Larry Schrader of Parker Hannifin Corp., who expanded an industrial training program that permitted me to further develop and refine many technical details, and that also provided much of the focus. Parker Hannifin Corp. deserves a special acknowledgement for allowing me to expand upon basic materials that appear in their *Handbook of Electrohydraulic Formulae* into Chapter Ten herein.

I extend a special thank you to Prof. G. Toet, Eindhoven Technological University, Netherlands, for allowing me to use his materials on flow transduction.

But most of all, I must extend the most sincere and warmest personal thanks to Ned Stull, executive editor of HYDRAULICS & PNEUMATICS magazine, for his countless hours spent in editing this text. Because of his effort, this book is far, far better than it might have been.

Finally, I thank my good friend and mentor, Dr. Z. J. Lansky, retired Vice President and Technical Director, Parker Hannifin Corp., who provided the Foreword for the book as well as years of advice, counsel, and inspiration.

Jack L. Johnson, PE
East Troy, Wisconsin
May 1992

Contents

Chapter One — Essential Ideas About Calculus / 1 /
Inverses / 1 / Integration / 2 / Physical interpretation / 4 / Devices that integrate / 8 /

Chapter Two — Electrical Meters and Measurement / 10 /
Moving charges / 11 / Voltage / 13 / Absolute zero pressure / 14 / Ohm's Law / 15 / Basic voltage, current relationships / 22 / Voltage measurement / 24 / Intrusiveness / 26 / DC current measurement / 27 /

Chapter Three — Basic Electrical Circuit Analysis / 31 /
Circuit concepts and conventions / 32 / Circuit laws / 34 / Voltage Law example / 36 / Example problems using Ohm's and Kirchoff's Laws / 41 / Series circuits / 44 / Parallel circuits / 44 / Equivalent resistance / 46 / Voltage-divider equation / 51 / Circuit loading / 53 / Terminal voltage problems / 55 / Leakage coefficient problem / 59 / Power / 60 / Maximum power transfer / 71 / Impedance matching / 73 /

Chapter Four — Capacitance and Inductance / 79 /
Summary of capacitance / 85 / Inductance / 85 / Summary of inductance / 89 /

Chapter Five — Alternating Current Circuits / 90 /
Current and voltage in resistive circuits / 93 / Current and voltage in capacitive circuits / 94 / Current and voltage in inductor circuits / 97 / The complex operator and impedance / 100 / Basic concepts of complex algebra / 102 / Current and voltage in R/L/C circuits / 103 / Transformers / 108 /

Chapter Six — Diodes, Rectifiers, and Power Supplies / 110 /
Conversion function / 111 / Heating values / 113 / Circuit over-powered / 115 / Voltage regulator characteristics / 118 /

Chapter Seven — Transistors, Amplifiers, and Other Signal Processing / 119 /
Transistors / 120 / Voltage amplifier conversion / 122 / Voltage

gain calculation / 123 / Transistor characteristics / 128 / Hydraulic transistor / 129 / Pump amplifier / 130 / Transistor amplifier summary / 134 / Operational amplifiers / 136 / Op-amp characteristics / 137 / Equivalent circuit / 140 / The ideal amplifier / 141 / Operational amplifier comparator circuit / 143 / Basic inverting amplifier / 146 / Inverting amplifier circuit input, output impedances / 149 / Basic non-inverting operational amplifier circuit / 151 / Gain of the basic non-inverting amplifier circuit / 152 / Basic non-inverting amplifier circuit input, output impedances / 153 / Non-inverting amplifier with input attenuator / 153 / Attenuated non-inverting amplifier input, output impedances / 154 / Two-input differential amplifier / 155 / Inverting summing amplifier / 158 / Single-ended to differential conversions / 165 / Noise sensitivity of the op-amp comparator / 167 / Schmitt trigger / 168 / Mono-stable multivibrator / 174 /

Chapter Eight — Special Circuits for Electrohydraulic Control / 178 /
Power output stage / 179 / Triangular wave oscillator / 183 / PWM modulator / 187 / Ramp generator / 189 / Deadband eliminators/correctors / 193 / Limit adjustments / 197 / Proportional valve amplifier / 201 / Servo amplifier / 204 /

Chapter Nine — Digital Electronics / 207 /
TTL logic / 208 / CMOS logic / 209 / Logic circuits and gates / 210 / Internal construction of the logical inverter / 210 / Two-input AND gate / 213 / Two-input OR gate / 215 / Other gates / 216 / Circuits with memory / 217 / RS flip-flop / 218 / Electronic counters and the JK flip-flop / 221 / Multi-stage counters / 223 / Numbering systems / 226 / Decimal numbering system / 227 / Notation scheme / 228 / Binary numbering systems / 228 / Conversion of decimal to binary / 230 / Hexadecimal numbering systems / 232 / Bits, bytes, and high-level languages / 233 / Digital-to-analog conversion / 234 / Analog-to-digital conversion / 236 / Commercial D/A and A/D converters / 238 /

Chapter Ten — Challenges of the Control Chain: Measurement, Data Transmission, and Noise Control / 240 /
Three elements / 243 / Selection questions / 244 / Forms and methods for data transmission / 245 / Analog data forms / 246 / DC data transmission forms / 246 / AC data transmission forms / 249 / Amplitude modulation, carrier present / 250 / Amplitude modulation, suppressed carrier, double sideband / 253 / Phase modulation / 254 / Digitization of a PWM signal / 257 / Frequency

modulation / 258 / FM, deviation-from-center frequency / 259 / FM, carrier is the data / 260 / Digitization of frequency / 260 / Period digitization / 262 / Frequency-to-voltage conversion / 263 / Frequency-measurement summary / 265 / Noise control in electronic systems / 265 / General rules for controlling noise / 266 / Parasitic capacitance and electrostatic interference / 266 / Electrostatic shielding / 269 / Killing the parasitic feedback path / 271 / Ground loops — cause and control / 272 / Differential signal transmission / 274 / Opto-isolation / 274 / Electromagnetic interference / 274 / Radio-frequency interference / 275 /

Chapter Eleven — Physical Principles of Transduction — Part I / 277 /

Changes in electrical properties / 277 / Resistance changes / 277 / Inductance and inductive coupling changes / 282 / Change in capacitance / 287 / Summary of inductive and capacitive transducers / 288 / Electrical generation and energy conversion / 290 / Photo-electric generation / 290 / Photo-voltaic cell / 290 / The photo transistor / 291 / Comparisons / 292 / Incremental encoders / 293 / Absolute encoders / 294 / Thermo-electric generation / 296 / Piezoelectric generation / 297 / Hall effect / 299 / Faraday-induced voltages / 300 / DC tachometer / 300 / Drag-cup tachometer / 301 / Alternators, AC generators / 303 / Mechanically variable impedance devices / 305 / Potentiometer / 306 / Pot linearity / 308 / Adjustable voltage dividers / 310 / Potential-measuring circuit / 311 / Autotransformers / 312 /

Chapter Twelve — Physical Principles of Transduction — Part II / 313 /

Gas ionization / 313 / LEDs / 313 / Electrical resistance and current / 314 / Thermoelectric cooling / 314 / Mechanical reaction / 315 / Thermal expansion / 317 / Electromechanical energy conversion / 318 / Mechanical reaction / 320 / Positive displacement / 321 / Turbines and propellors / 323 / Flow-to-pressure conversion / 325 / Laminar flow tube / 325 / Pitot tube / 327 / Drag-body flow sensor / 328 / Annubar flow sensor / 329 / Variable-area flow meter / 330 / Orifice pressure drop / 330 / Thermofluidic processes / 331 / Hot-wire flow transducer / 331 / Heater-coil flow meter / 332 / Electrofluidic processes / 333 / Electrofluidic electrical generation / 333 / Electro-rheological fluids / 333 / Sonic and ultrasonic wave transmission / 334 / Ultrasonic position transducer / 334 / Doppler flow transducer / 336 / Magnetostriction / 338 /

Chapter Thirteen — Proportional Electrohydraulic Interface Device Fundamentals / 342 /

Valves as bridges / 342 / Electromechanical actuators / 344 / Electrohydraulic valves / 345 / Direct-acting valves / 345 / Pilot-operated valves / 347 / Torque motors / 347 / Force motors / 352 / Proportional solenoids / 353 / Device comparisons / 355 / Summary of pilot-operated valves / 356 / Sliding -spool valves / 356 / Positioning the main spool / 359 /

Chapter 14 — Electrohydraulic Feedback Control Systems / 361 /

The open-loop plant / 362 / Simple gain block / 365 / Combining cascaded blocks / 366 / Closed-loop plant / 367 / Feedback control / 368 / Feedback system delivery / 370 / Electrohydraulic positional servomechanism / 371 / Rotary speed-control loops / 374 / Hydrostatic-transmission control of motor speed / 376 / Swash-plate feedback / 378 / Valve control with integrating amplifier / 379 / Errors in positional servomechanisms / 380 / Systematic and random errors / 382 / Closed-loop bandwidth of the first order model / 384 / Electronic deadband correction / 388 / Phasing the positional servomechanism / 388 /

Chapter Fifteen — Motion Control / 390 /

Two methods of hydraulic control / 392 / Motion-control profiles and system response / 396 / System specifications and performance / 398 / Factors affecting overshoot / 398 / Factors that increase lag / 400 / Solutions to the motion-control problem / 401 / Positional servo and profiling / 404 /

Appendix A * / A1 /

Glossary / A1 / Electric-Hydraulic Analogies / A23 /

*Reprinted from *Lexicon III, Directory of Electrohydraulic Terms and Electrohydraulic Analogies*, Copyright © 1991 Milwaukee School of Engineering, Milwaukee, Wis. Used with permission.

Chapter One
Essential Ideas About Calculus

The goal of this chapter is to provide an intuitive feel for the process of integration and differentiation rather than instruct in the use of calculus. If one understands how time enters into the control of acceleration, velocity, and position, there can be a better appreciation of why motion control is such a challenging problem.

The study of electrohydraulic motion control is concerned with input-output relationships, that is component gains and/or transfer functions. For example, voltage applied to the input of a servo amplifier produces a current in the valve's coils. This current, reacting to the command voltage, is established almost instantaneously. We say that the amplifier has a gain of so many output amperes per input volt.

A hydraulic cylinder receives input flow and responds by providing output velocity. This reaction also is nearly instantaneous. But what if we are interested in the cylinder position more than its velocity? Now, time enters into the process because the position does not simply depend upon the amount of input flow, but also upon how long that flow exists.

This is true because the cylinder **integrates** or accumulates molecules of oil; the more molecules that enter, the farther the cylinder rod travels. Thus, the cylinder is an integrator in every sense of the word. The discussion that follows treats another well-known integrator, the automotive odometer. The discussion about this well-known mechanism should help develop a feel for the physical interpretation of calculus.

Inverses

Calculus has many variations and new theories continue to advance the concept and expand the body of knowledge. Usually introduced in college mathematics courses, the two branches of calculus considered at that time are: integral and differential. These branches are the inverse of each other, just as addition and subtraction are the inverse of one another, multiplication and division are the inverse of one another, logarithms and

1

antilogarithms are the inverse of one another, and so on. Integration and differentiation are the inverse of one another.

Mathematical operations frequently are indicated through use of symbols:

$$A = X + Y. \tag{1.1}$$
$$C = Z - X.$$
$$D = R \times S, \text{ and}$$
$$N = I/Q,$$

where the $\times$, $/$, $+$, and $-$ are called operators. Each operator requires a *right* and a *left* hand operand. That is, in Equation 1.1, X is the left operand, Y is the right operand, and $+$ is the operator.

Having considered this method of denoting these operations, another whole set of theories follows; for example, commutative characteristics:

$$X + Y = Y + X.$$
$$X - Y \neq Y - X.$$
$$A \times B = B \times A, \text{ and}$$
$$A/B \neq B/A,$$

and so on.

Some operations have only one operand:

$$y = \log(x), \text{ and}$$
$$z = \sin(\theta).$$

And so it is with the two basic operators of calculus:

$$y = dx/dt,$$

where d/dt is the **differential** operator. This means that:
- d/dt operates on x, that is dx/dt, and
- the dx/dt operation evaluates the slope or steepness of the graph or curve of x vs. t.

Consider a graph of x vs. t, Figure 1.1. The differential operator dx/dt states that we are performing the operation of **differentiation**, and the value of dx/dt (actually the graph) is called the **derivative of x**.

Integration

For integration,

$$y = \int_o^t x \, dt,$$

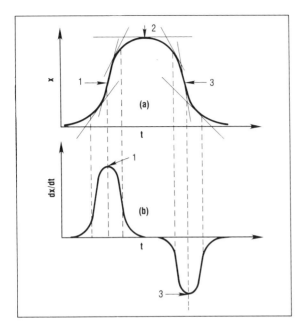

Fig. 1.1 The original curve, (a) has greatest positive steepness at point 1, is horizontal or neutral at point 2, and has greatest negative steepness at point 3. The derivative curve, (b), is highest at point 1 when curve (a) is steepest, and is at its most negative value, point 3, when the steepness of curve (a) is at its most negative.

where $\int_o^t (\ )\, dt$ is the **integral** operator. This means that:
- the integral operator $\int_o^t (\ )\, dt$ operates on x which is a graph
- in the operation $y = \int_o^t x\, dt$, y is called the **integral of** x
- mathematically, the **process of integration** is an operation of **infinite summation**, and
- geometrically, the integral can be interpreted as the area under the graph.

A formal course in calculus deals with formulas or **functions** as they are called in the calculus. For example, if we have the formula

$$y = A(\sin x), \qquad\qquad 1.2$$

then we are interested in finding new formulas or functions, namely the derivative and the integral of Equation (1.2).

Determining such integrals and derivatives is the purely abstract, mathematical application of calculus, and it occupies a very important place in a technical education. The process is used in the proof of many concepts and also in the design of dynamically complex systems. However, this purely mathematical side of the calculus has only limited usefulness in understanding the practical applications of electrohydraulic control systems.

Engineers often use digital computers to perform integrations and

3

differentiations. As more control systems make use of microprocessors, this method of implementing calculus becomes more important. Further discussion about use of computers is beyond the scope of this work.

Although integration is a mathematical process as we have seen, it also occurs as natural physical relationships in our universe. For example, the distance one travels can be correctly defined as the integral of velocity. There are countless physical devices which perform integration: capacitors, motors, cylinders, inductors, and odometers.

It is easy to see that integrators are normal elements of power machinery as well as the systems that control that machinery. The integrations these physical devices perform result in system **time lags**. The control system designer is concerned with all the system time lags and designs the controller with additional time lags and their complements, **time leads** in order to enhance dynamic performance of the system. Sometimes, this can be done intuitively; in other cases, more sophisticated means must be used.

Physical interpretation

Consider a simple time-velocity problem as an example of the physical interpretation of integration. How far would a car travel in two hours when operated at 50 mph?

$$distance = (velocity)(time), \qquad\qquad 1.3$$
$$= (50 \; mph)(2 \; hr),$$
$$= 100 \; miles.$$

Take a more extensive example where the car's speed takes on different values over different time intervals. What is the total distance covered using these times and speeds: 10 mph for 12 min., 30 mph for 15 min., 60 mph for 60 min., 45 mph for 30 min., and 0 mph for 10 min?

Using Equation 1.3, we all know intuitively that the total distance is the sum of all the distances covered in each time interval. That is:

$$distance = [(10)(1/5)] + [(30)(1/4)] + [(60)(1)] + [(45)(1/2)] +$$
$$[(0)(1/6)],$$
$$= 2 + 7.5 + 60 + 22.5 + 0,$$
$$= 92 \; miles.$$

The graph of velocity vs. time for this problem, Figure 1.2*(a)*, clearly shows the graphic or physical interpretation of integration. The total distance covered in the 127-minute trip can be calculated by noting the **area under the speed-vs.-time curve.** If we view each segment of the trip as a rectangle with a base that represents a measure of time and a height which represents a measure of the car's speed, it follows that:

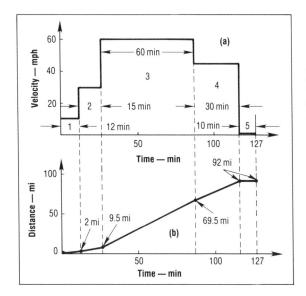

Fig. 1.2 The graphic interpretation of the time-vs.-velocity curve, (a), provides a total trip time of 127 minutes. Totalling the sum of the five areas under the curve calculates the 92 miles covered during the trip, indicated by the miles vs. velocity curve, (b). These curves are the inverses of one another: curve (a) is the derivative while (b) is the integral.

$Area\ 1 = (10\ mph)(12\ min)(1\ hr/60\ min)$
$= 2\ miles,$

$Area\ 2 = (30\ mph)(15\ min)(1\ hr/60\ min)$
$= 7.5\ miles,$

$Area\ 3 = (60\ mph)(60min)\ (1\ hr/60\ min)$
$= 60\ miles,$

$Area\ 4 = (45\ mph)(30\ min)(1\ hr/60\ min)$
$= 22.5\ miles,\ and$

$Area\ 5 = (0\ mph)(10\ min)(1\ hr/60\ min)$
$= 0\ miles.$

This information and its interpretation can be used to construct a graph of the distance as a function of time, Figure 1.2(b). (For the moment, we will refer to the (a) or (b) curves of Figure 1.2.) The (b) curve is a plot of the instantaneous position of the car as it progresses through the various speed-vs.-time intervals. On the other hand, the (a) curve is a measure of the steepness of the (b) curve and, therefore, is the derivative of the (b) curve. Furthermore, the (b) curve is the inverse of the (a) curve and is its integral.

This example used a velocity-vs.-time curve in which the car's speed

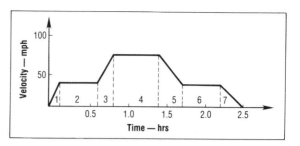

Fig. 1.3 This velocity-vs.-time profile could almost represent an actual case. Notice that the units of time have been changed to hours to eliminate multiplication by 1/60.

changed instantaneously, clearly an impossibility. Practically, the car will undergo periods of constant speed as well as periods of acceleration and deceleration, Figure 1.3.

Using the velocity vs. time profile of Figure 1.3, the same question is posed: how far did the car travel in 2.5 hours? If we use the purely geometrical interpretation of the area under the curve being the integral of the function, the sum of these areas will again determine the distance. Recall that the area of a triangle is *(½)(base)(height)*. Now:

$$Area\ 1 = (½)(⅒\ hr)(40\ mph)$$
$$= 2\ miles,$$

$$Area\ 2 = (½\ hr)(40\ mph)$$
$$= 20\ miles,$$

$$Area\ 3 = [(⅕\ hr)(40\ mph)] + [(½)(⅕\ hr)(35\ mph)]$$
$$= 23.5\ miles,$$

$$Area\ 4 = (⅗\ hr)(75mph)$$
$$= 45\ miles,$$

$$Area\ 5 = [(³⁄₁₀\ hr)(28\ mph)] + [(½)(³⁄₁₀\ hr)(47\ mph)]$$
$$= 15.45\ miles,$$

$$Area\ 6 = (⁶⁄₁₀\ hr)(28\ mph)$$
$$= 16.8\ miles,\ and$$

$$Area\ 7 = (½)(³⁄₁₀\ hr)(28\ mph)$$
$$= 4.2\ miles.$$

The total distance traveled, of course, is the sum of these areas:

$$distance = 2 + 20 + 23.5 + 45 + 15.45 + 16.8 + 4.2$$
$$= 126.95\ miles.$$

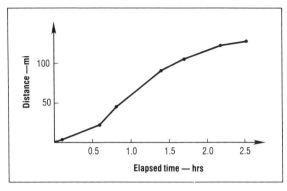

Fig. 1.4 Using the elapsed time values and odometer readings of Chart 1.1, the distance in miles can be shown graphically.

We also can plot the progression of the odometer reading, Figure 1.4, if we note the accumulated mileage at the end of each time interval, Table 1.1. During a real automobile trip, speed and acceleration rarely are constant; they change continuously. If we made a continuous strip chart recording of an actual trip, it might look like Figure 1.5.

If we were to ask how far the car would go if it followed the time-vs.-velocity plot in Figure 1.5, we would have several courses of action:

● write an equation or series of equations which would fit the curve and then go into the calculus tables for an analytical solution. This is not worth the effort and rarely is in any situation

● **digitize** the graph and use a computer to perform the integration by approximating the graph as a series of very small rectangles

● convert the speed into a voltage and then use an **operational amplifier**

Table 1.1 — Accumulated mileage

Elapsed time-hrs	Odometer reading-miles
0	0
0.1	2
0.6	22
0.8	45.5
1.4	90.5
1.7	105.95
2.2	122.75
2.5	126.95

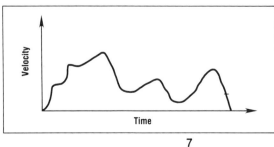

Fig. 1.5 An actual velocity-vs.-time profile of an automobile may look like this. The integration of this curve would take special effort.

7

integrator to integrate the velocity to find the distance, or
● read the odometer at the start and end of the trip.

Devices that integrate

Odometer. As noted earlier, the odometer accurately totals the mileage accumulated throughout time. When the car moves, the odometer is totalizing, and the rate at which it totalizes is the car's velocity. When the car stops, totalizing stops, too. Further, the odometer never resets itself.

Fluid power cylinder. When input to the cylinder is hydraulic flow and the output of the cylinder is rod position, the cylinder is a true integrator. It does so by **accumulating** the incoming volume of fluid. Consider the flow into a hydraulic cylinder, Figure 1.6.

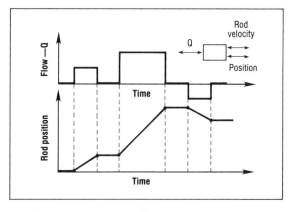

Fig. 1.6 Graph indicates the integral and derivative of pressure fluid flow into a cylinder.

Accumulator. A hydraulic accumulator is an integrator when the input is hydraulic flow and the output is the resulting pressure.

Capacitor. By accumulating electrical charges, the capacitor integrates its input current and the integral is reflected in the resulting voltage.

Now, the essential properties of integrators and differentiators can be stated:

● **integrators** have the property that when their inputs are exactly zero, their outputs remain fixed at their last value. For exampe, the odometer in your car remains at its last value whenever the car is parked. Similarly, when the input is not zero, the output **must** be changing, and

● **differentiators** are the inverse of integrators and produce an output only when the input is changing. Think of a hydraulic cylinder whose position you manually change: there will be output flow **only** when you change position of the rod, that is, when piston velocity is not zero. A differentiator calculates the rate at which its input changes.

8

These properties are true whether the integration/differentiation takes place in a physical component such as a hydraulic cylinder, or if we elect to use an operational amplifier or numerical techniques in the software of a computer. It can become confusing because sometimes we can change from an integrator to a differentiator merely by redefining input and output.

Chapter Two
Electrical Meters and Measurement

All material is comprised of atoms. The simplest model of an atom, Figure 2.1, has a tightly packed nucleus of positively charged protons with negatively charged particles — electrons — spinning around. The electrons continuously orbit the nucleus like a tiny solar system. The numbers of electrons and the shapes of their orbits characterize the material as indicated on the chemist's periodic table.

In some materials such as the metals, the electrons in the outer ring(s) are loosely bound to the parent nucleus and are relatively free to wander from atom to atom. Electrically, materials with these loosely bound electrons are called **conductors**. Other materials have electrons strongly bound to the nucleus so the electrons cannot freely move from one atom to the other. These materials are classed as **insulators**.

As implied by their names, conductors are used to conduct or transmit electricity while insulating materials are used to prevent electricity from going where it is not wanted. The most common conductor in commercial use is copper. It is an excellent conductor, is found in abundance throughout the world, and can be refined at an acceptable cost. Precious metals such as gold, silver, and platinum are better conductors, but their cost limits their use only to the most critical applications.

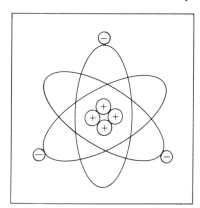

Fig. 2.1. This simple model of an atom illustrates how electrons with their negative charge orbit the positively charged protons in the atomic nucleus.

Many commercial insulating materials are compounds of the plastic

10

family and are available in almost endless variety. They are selected because of their ability to prevent current or arc-over between conductors and to maintain their insulating properties at higher temperatures.

Time and temperature cause insulating materials to deteriorate; the higher the temperature, the more rapid the deterioration. Insulation deterioration in wire-wound equipment such as electric motors, solenoids, and transformers is a common failure mode.

Moving charges

Electrical current results when the loosely bound electron in a

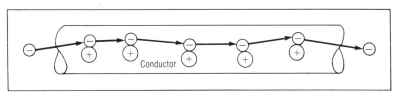

Fig. 2.2 An entering electron at one end of a conductor displaces another electron at the other end.

conductor have a net movement from atom to atom, Figure 2.2. Due to an **external** motivating force, an elron enters a conductor at one end and with a tumbling, domino action, forces a different electron out the other end of the conductor. Electrical **current** is the net movement of electrical charges past a point. This movement occurs at the speed of light, that is 186,000 miles/sec or 3×10^8 meters/sec. Thus, in most industrial electronic control systems, conductor length is not a factor. Later, we will see that time delays resulting from electrical inductance and capacitance are indeed a factor in control system performance.

The standard, internationally recognized unit of electrical current, the **ampere**, is defined as the number of electrical charges passing a given point over a specified time period: 1 ampere of current $= 6.28 \times 10^{18}$ electrons/sec. I is the algebraic symbol of current in units of amperes, A.

Obviously, one cannot count passing electrons any more than one can count the molecules of oil leaving a pump. Therefore, experimental verification of the standard ampere is done by measuring the rate at which metal is deposited on an anode in an electroplating process. The ampere is standardized using mass and time, parameters which otherwise are unrelated to electrical charge.

An **ammeter** — sometimes mistakenly called an ampmeter — measures current. Ammeters come in a variety of ranges and a set of names has evolved:

● ammeter — generic

11

• milliammeter — used to measure current ranging from about 10^{-4} amps to about 1 ampere
• microammeter — used to measure current ranging from 10^{-7} amp to about 1 milliamp, and
• galvanometer — used to measure current ranging from 10^{-12} to 10^{-9} amperes.

All these devices are ammeters and are identical in principle. Their names suggest their measurement ranges.

The galvanometer is said to be more sensitive than, for example, the milliammeter because it responds to smaller currents. **Sensitivity** is often confused with **accuracy** which is a totally different issue. Nearly all current measurements required when dealing with electronic fluid power controls can be made with a milliammeter. Occasionally, there is need to measure an ampere or two.

There are two practices involved in defining current direction: **conventional current**, and **electron flow**. Unfortunately, these two practices assign exactly opposite direction to charge motion. Physical evidence has proved that the mobile charge carrier is the negative electron.

However, conventional current ideas assume that the mobile charge carrier is positive. This is patently erroneous. Yet, conventional current ideas, perpetrated by the fictitious mobile positive charge carrier, persist in the literature and are the basis for standard electrical engineering practice.

Even though we know it is wrong, we will use the engineering practice of defining current direction as consistent with that of conventional current. The notable exceptions to this erroneous practice are the military services of the United States. Note that it is immaterial which carrier convention is adopted, because either one yields the same results. It is important, however, that one does not switch convention in mid-problem.

In summary, these points apply to electrical current:

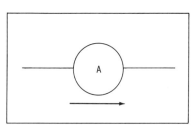

Fig. 2.3. The symbol of an ammeter.

• conventional current notation will be used which presumes the mobile charge carrier to be positive
• the schematic symbol of an ammeter, Figure 2.3, is an A within a circle accompanied with an arrow
• the ampere, or amp is the unit of measure; its abbreviation is A
• the algebraic symbol for current is I for steady-state or DC current, and i for instantaneous or time-varying current, and
• a current source is an electrical generator of some sort whose output

12

current depends only on the generator and not on its load. This ideal generator exists only approximately in the real world. Nonetheless, there are two conventional symbols for current sources, Figure 2.4, used in the literature. These sources also are called constant-current sources or constant-current generators although current output may vary with time. Positive-current source, like the hydraulic term positive displacement, would have been a better name.

Voltage

If the charge carriers are to move, some motivating force must propel them. The archaic name for this force is **electromotive force**, or EMF for short. The modern name is **voltage**. (Note that voltage is an accepted technical term while its counterpart, amperage, is uncivilized language.) The algebraic symbols for voltage are E (from EMF) as well as V. These designations are used interchangeably.

Voltage creates a force on the mobile charge carrier causing it to move from a region of higher voltage to a region of lower voltage. A perfect analogy exists between hydraulic pressure and voltage in an electrical system: pressure acts on oil molecules and attempts to push them to a region of lower pressure. If a path exists, most assuredly fluid molecules will find it and travel along the path from higher to lower pressure.

For example, a hole in the inlet side of a pump will allow air molecules to enter, having been motivated by the higher external atmospheric pressure; a hole in the pump outlet will push oil out of the hydraulic system onto the floor,

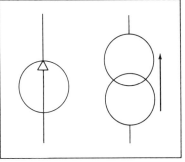

Fig. 2.4. Although these are con-ventional symbols for current sources and do appear in texts and the literature, they are not included in ANSI Y32.2-1975, Graphic Symbols for Electrical and Electronics Diagrams, as amended.

motivated by the higher internal pressure. Analogously, voltage and current play the same roles in electrical circuits that pressure and flow, respectively, play in fluid power circuits.

Electrical current and hydraulic flow are easy concepts to grasp because one can visualize the physical transportation of particles from one place to another. Voltage and pressure, on the other hand, are more abstract. They simply exist, and are the driving force in their systems.

The instrument for measuring voltage, not surprisingly, is a **voltmeter**. It has two leads and measures the voltage or potential difference betweeen two points in a circuit. A differential pressure transducer or gage has two physical ports which the user connects into a circuit. The resulting output is a measure of the pressure difference between the two ports. Again, the voltage/pressure analogy is perfect: pressure-measuring instruments also have two ports although in gage instruments, one is made for us and is therefore implicit.

For example, the conventional Bourdon-tube pressure gage has only one plumbing port while ambient pressure is applied to the implicit port. Therefore, a pressure gage measures the difference in pressure between the point of the fluid connection and atmospheric pressure. Thus, even gage pressure is a differential pressure, contrary to popular interpretation. Actually, **all pressures** are differential pressures because they are measures of the potential differences between two points in space (or in a system). In like manner, voltage also is a differential measurement.

Absolute zero pressure

The voltage/pressure analogy fails when considering absolute zero pressure. One can readily imagine a condition in which every last molecule of fluid has been removed from a closed volume. At that time, the internal pressure would be absolute zero. While absolute zero pressure does exist at least in theory, there is no such thing as absolutely zero voltage. One cannot visualize the analogous situation for voltage; in fact, the idea is nonsensical.

This failure in the analogy is not merely philosophical. There are profound consequences of this when comparing the hydraulic medium to the electric medium. For example, the hydraulic circuit concepts of meter-in and meter-out have no parallel in the operation and control of electrically powered machinery whether loads are overrunning or not.

If one attempts to control the speed of a DC motor with a series resistance (analagous to meter-out control of a hydraulic motor), it makes no difference whether the resistor is in the high voltage line or the low voltage line. When deceleration is commanded by resistance change, the voltage to the motor will change to whatever positive and negative values are necessary to cause the deceleration. The hydraulic circuit designer, in contrast, must make sure the deceleration controller is in the motor outlet port because pressure in the motor inlet can only go to slightly below atmospheric before cavitation takes place.

In summarizing voltage, recognize that:

● there is no schematic symbol for a voltmeter. An arrow notation will be used herein

● the unit of measure is the volt with the symbol V or v

● the algebraic symbol for voltage is V or v but E and e also are used, and

● the schematic symbol for a votage source implies its physical construction, Figure 2.5.

Practical voltage sources are available which approximate the ideal

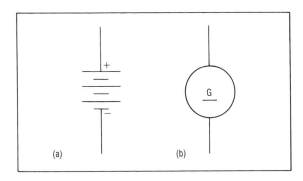

(a)   (b)

Fig. 2.5. Voltage source symbols include (a), a battery, and (b) a generator.

voltage source. A fully charged and otherwise healthy wet cell automotive battery, for example, is capable of delivering hundreds of amps to a short-circuit load. Regulated power supplies also can deliver rated current at almost no decrease in voltage.

Ohm's Law

Electrical circuit current and voltage are related to each other through circuit **resistance**. While an increase in voltage increases current, an increase in resistance decreases current. The discovery of this relationship is attributed to an 18th century German physicist named Georg Ohm[1]. His formula is called Ohm's Law:

$$I = E/R.$$

In Ohm's Law, the current, I, is in amperes, E is in volts, and R is in ohms. Whereas voltage is the force to increase current, resistance is a measure of the opposition to current. When 1 volt of voltage is *impressed across* or *dropped across* a 1 ohm resistor, 1 ampere of current results. Note that current does NOT FLOW. It simply exists, because current is the flow of electrons. *A current is flowing*, is commonly used language but

---

[1] *The son of a poor locksmith, Ohm's 1827 work was so controversial that peer criticism forced him to resign his teaching position in Cologne and earn a meager living as a private tutor in Berlin for the following six years. By 1833, his discoveries were gaining acceptance and he was awarded a professorship in Nuremberg. He died in Munich in 1854 and was finally vindicated by the International Electrical Congress in Paris in 1881 when they adopted the standardized practical unit for resistance and named it the ohm.*

15

is needlessly redundant. Substituting **electron flow** for **current** indicates the needless redundancy. Correct language is to say, *There is a current in the circuit.*

Ohm's work also established that the resistance[2] of a resistor at a fixed temperature was directly proportional to the resistor's length, inversely proportional to its cross-sectional area, and dependent on its material. This is expressed by:

$$R = (\rho L)/A,$$

where R is the resistance in ohms, ρ is the resistivity of the material used in constructing the resistor, L is the length of the resistor, and A is the cross-sectional area transverse to the flow path.

Note that ρ is a material property and L and A are geometric factors; shape and material are important. Contrast that with output voltage of, say, a generator. The value of voltage certainly has geometric and material components, but it also depends on an intensity factor, that is, how fast the generator is turned. Resistance has no intensity factor. Resistance value is a characteristic of the resistor whether it is on a shelf or in a powered or unpowered circuit. For this reason, resistance has become an important engineering quantity.

We shall see later that the open-loop gain or amplification of one integrated circuit operational amplifier chip may vary as much as 5:1 from one chip to another. When applying these chips in a circuit, amplifier gain may be made dependent only on the user's choice of external resistors. The inexpensive, external resistors make the complete circuit perform in a predictable, stable way.

Because of the importance of resistance, equipment to measure it with high accuracy has been developed. Laboratory-quality measurements are made with Wheatstone bridge circuits specifically designed and calibrated for resistance measurement. Measurement to six significant digits is routine and to eight digits is not rare. Field measurement of resistance usually is made with an ohmmeter using the popular digital and analog multimeters which are available at modest cost.

Resistor manufacturing skills also have evolved to produce high-quality products. An electronic circuit designer's major job is to select commercial resistors to support the integrated circuit chips, capacitors, and other elements of the circuit. The almost endless variety of commercially available resistors imposes little constraint on designers. This variety not only enhances their creativity, it also asssures that their

---

[2]*He obviously did not have the advantage of a standard ohm at the time, but instead worked with a more rudimentary dimensional analysis.*

circuits remain commercially viable.

In our modern, high-tech electrohydraulic world, many fluid power application and sales engineers find it necessary to select a resistor now and then. While total resistor selection criteria are beyond our scope, basic insights can be gained by inspecting some of the more important resistor specifications:

● resistance value
● tolerance on that value
● power rating
● temperature coefficients of resistance, and
● cost.

The Resistor Family, Table 2.1, puts some of the commercial resistor variety into perspective. While the Table is incomplete, it may be helpful in determining the appropriate resistor for an application.

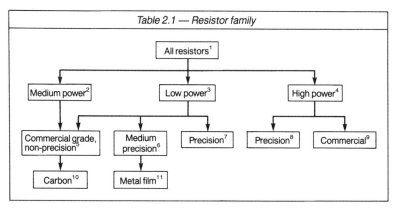

Table 2.1 — Resistor family

[1]While the All Resistors label is presumptuous and/or erroneous, a look in an electronics catalog will show the vast variety which comprises the universe of commercial resistors; it is much larger than this simple Table. The Table does, however, cover a substantial portion of those resistors which will be typically encountered and needed by the electrohydraulic applications engineer/technician.

[2]Power less than 2 watts.

[3]Power less than ½ watt.

[4]The divisions of power into high, medium, and low are the author's and do not reflect industrial standard terminology. The chart should help as a guide when searching through a local parts store or an electronics catalog. **Power rating is that power which the resistor must dissipate due to its own current under standard ambient conditions.** When higher ambient temperatures are encountered, the power dissipation must be derated. This subject is beyond our scope.

[5]Tolerance of 5% and 10%.

[6]Tolerance less than 3%.

[7]*Precision resistors are usually wire wound, and thus have a positive temperature coefficient of resistance. They are available at lower power levels only. Their cost depends primarily on the resistance tolerance, starting at about 30 cents at 1% to several dollars each at 0.001%.*

[8]*Tolerance less than 3%. When precision in resistance value is required as well as power capacity above ½ watt, precision power resistors are required. There appears to be little commercial selection between ½ and 3 watts. Thus, the price of a high power (3 watts), 10K, 1% (precision) wire-wound resistor is about $2.00; at ½ watt, it is only about 50 cents. Maximum off-the-shelf power capacity is about 50 watts and each resistor will cost several dollars — some even as high as $11.00 or $12.00.*

[9]*Commercial-grade power resistors are available from a low of 5 to greater than 200 watts. Price is affected primarily by power rating since off-the-shelf tolerance is ± 10%. At the low end, prices are about $1.50 to $2.00 each to about $20.00 at 25 watts. They also are available in adjustable versions. The variety of available values in power resistors is more limited than in the low to medium powered carbon types.*

[10]*The large majority of resistors (billions annually) fall into this area of the Table. They are inexpensive — 3 or 4 cents each at low power (¼ watt and popular 10K, 100K, 22K, 56K, etc.) and in quantity, to 50 cents each at high power. The important characteristic of these resistors is that they have a negative temperature coefficient of resistance, meaning that their resistance decreases with temperature rise. The change in resistance with temperature is substantial, precluding their use in many critical cases when operating temperature variations may exceed ± 40° F. They are available in low power (⅛ watt) to medium power (2 watts). The cost differential between 5% and 10% tolerance is 10% to 20%.*

[11]*Metal film resistors are the preferred choice for applications requiring wide ranges in ambient operating temperature. Temperature coefficients are specified as ± amounts indicating that the resistance of one specimen may increase with a temperature increase while a nominally identical specimen may have a decreasing resistance with rising temperature. Nevertheless, the percent of resistance change per degree of temperature change is far less than the carbon counterparts and so these resistors are less sensitive to temperature variations. They are usually not available in any but the lowest power ranges, and their cost is about 3 to 5 times the carbon variety.*

Standard Nominal Resistance Values, Table 2.2, may at first look like a cross between chaos and disorder, but there is a system. The confusion occurs because there is more than one system. The most common system of setting and marking resistor values is applied to carbon resistors. This is the resistor family that carries the familiar **resistor color code**, Figure 2.6, and Table 2.3, **Color Coding for Resistors**. In Table 2.2, note that there is greater variety in 5% resistors than in the 10% variety. This is because of marketplace demand.

Further, there are a number of military standards or MIL-Specs which state permitted resistance values. Manufacturers have catered to the government's needs and supply the same resistors in the commercial

Table 2.2—Standard nominal resistance values.							
Boldface figures are ± 10% values. All values available in ± 5% tolerance.							
Ohms							
1.0	**5.1**	**27**	130	**680**	3600	**18,000**	91,000
1.1	**5.6**	30	**150**	750	**3900**	20,000	**100,000**
1.2	6.2	**33**	160	**820**	4300	**22,000**	110,000
1.3	**6.8**	36	**180**	910	**4700**	24,000	**120,000**
1.5	7.5	**39**	200	**1000**	5100	**27,000**	130,000
1.6	**8.2**	43	**220**	1100	**5600**	30,000	**150,000**
1.8	9.1	**47**	240	**1200**	6200	**33,000**	160,000
2.0	**10.0**	51	**270**	1300	**6800**	36,000	**180,000**
2.2	11.0	**56**	300	**1500**	7500	**39,000**	200,000
2.4	**12.0**	62	**330**	1600	**8200**	43,000	**220,000**
2.7	13.0	**68**	360	**1800**	9100	**47,000**	
3.0	**15.0**	75	**390**	2000	**10,000**	51,000	
3.3	16.0	**82**	430	**2200**	11,000	**56,000**	
3.6	**18.0**	91	**470**	2400	**12,000**	62,000	
3.9	20.0	**100**	510	**2700**	13,000	**68,000**	
4.3	**22.0**	110	**560**	3000	**15,000**	75,000	
4.7	24.0	**120**	620	**3300**	16,000	**82,000**	
Megaohms							
0.24	0.43	0.75	1.3	2.4	4.3	7.5	13.0
0.27	**0.47**	**0.82**	**1.5**	**2.7**	**4.7**	**8.2**	**15.0**
0.30	0.51	0.91	1.6	3.0	5.1	9.1	16.0
0.33	**0.56**	**1.0**	**1.8**	**3.3**	**5.6**	**10.0**	**18.0**
0.36	0.62	1.1	2.0	3.6	6.2	11.0	20.0
0.38	**0.68**	**1.2**	**2.2**	**3.9**	**6.8**	**12.0**	**22.0**

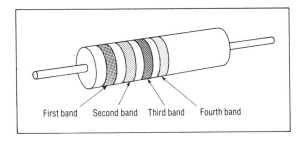

First band   Second band   Third band   Fourth band

Fig. 2.6 Four bands indicate resistance values for carbon resistors. For example, the resistance of a resistor whose bands are red, red, red, and silver, according to Table 2.3, is 22×10^2, or 2.2 kΩ ± 10%.

marketplace. The complete range of multipliers, Table 2.4, **Military Values of Resistance**, has 96 entries. Further inspection shows that with a ± 1% tolerance, the ranges meet and in some cases, overlap. The consequence is that any available resistor falls into one of the standard ranges. It appears that manufacturers have a sorting rather than a manufacturing problem. So much for standardization.

The most important parameter of a resistor is, of course, its resistance value. The second most important parameter is its power rating. When a resistor is placed in an electrical circuit, it naturally carries a current. Resistors always convert electrical power into thermal power which then can increase the temperature of the resistor. If the resistor cannot radiate this heat energy into the atmosphere at least as quickly as it converts the electrical energy into thermal energy, temperature of the resistor will rise and two harmful things can happen:

• the resistor resistance value will change by an intolerable amount causing circuit malfunction, and/or

• the resistor will burn up.

Because of this, choice of a resistor includes selection of the proper resistance value and the correct power rating. As power ratings increase, resistors get physically bigger. This has two beneficial effects:

• the power conversion is distributed over a larger volume, eliminating

Table 2.3—Color coding for resistors.			
Color	First band	Second band	Third band
Black	0	0	10^0
Brown	1	1	10^1
Red	2	2	10^2
Orange	3	3	10^3
Yellow	4	4	10^4
Green	5	5	10^5
Blue	6	6	10^6
Violet	7	7	10^7
Gray	8	8	10^8
White	9	9	10^9
Gold	—	—	10^{-1}
Silver	—	—	10^{-2}

Fourth band: Silver indicates $\pm$ 10% tolerance
Gold indicates $\pm$ 5% tolerance
No band indicates $\pm$ 20% tolerance

Table 2.4—Military values of resistance																
Ohms																
10.0	11.5	13.3	15.4	17.8	20.5	23.7	27.4	31.6	36.5	42.2	48.7	56.2	64.9	75.0	86.6
10.2	11.8	13.7	15.8	18.2	21.0	24.3	28.0	32.4	37.4	43.2	49.9	57.6	66.5	76.8	88.7
10.5	12.1	14.0	16.2	18.7	21.5	24.9	28.7	33.2	38.3	44.2	51.1	59.0	68.1	78.7	90.9
10.7	12.4	14.3	16.5	19.1	22.1	25.5	29.4	34.0	39.2	45.2	52.3	60.4	69.8	80.6	93.1
11.0	12.7	14.7	16.9	19.6	22.6	26.1	30.1	34.8	40.2	46.4	53.6	61.9	71.5	82.5	95.3
11.3	13.0	15.0	17.4	20.0	23.2	26.7	30.9	35.7	41.2	47.5	54.9	63.4	73.2	84.5	97.6

hot spots in the resistance medium, and
- the larger outside area helps conduct heat energy to atmosphere.
   In summary, the facts about resistors and resistance are:
- the ohm is the unit of resistance and the graphic symbol for ohm is the Greek capital omega, Ω
- the algebraic and schematic symbol is R
- the schematic symbols for resistance are shown in Figure 2.7
- a Wheatstone bridge is used to measure resistance in the laboratory; an ohmmeter is used in the field, and
- Table 2.5, **Typical Resistance Values**, indicates typical resistances.
Note that the first five entries in the Table comprise coincidental resistances, that is, a proportional valve solenoid coil is designed, installed, and made effective because of its magnetic inductance characteristic. But because the coil is wound of wire, it coincidentally has

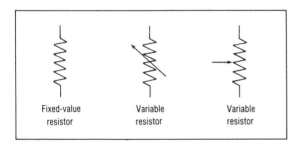

Fig. 2.7. Schematic symbols for resistance.

| Fixed-value resistor | Variable resistor | Variable resistor |

Table 2.5—Typical resistance values

Device	Typical resistance at room temperature
Proportional valve coil	5 to 50 ohms
Servovalve coil	20 to 300 ohms
100-watt light bulb	10 ohms cold 144 ohms operating
One winding of 100-hp 440-V induction motor	0.01 ohm
Resistance of the human body from one hand to the next	60,000 to 200,000 ohms depending on the contact, skin oil, salt, etc.
Resistors used in electronic devices	A few hundred to several thousand ohms comprise the majority. Thus, electronic circuits tend to have high impedances (resistances).

resistance. In contrast, the resistors in electronic circuits are selected exclusively for their resistance value which is not just coincidental.

Basic voltage, current relationships

Alternating current (AC) measurements sometimes can be important in electrohydraulic controls such as when making evaluations in the AC portions of electronic power supplies. The general topic of AC measurements of all types is a complex subject and is not covered here. Fortunately, AC power comes from the local electric power company, which has expended great effort to supply voltage with a sinusoidal wave shape. The voltage, which continuously varies with time, is described by a sine wave. A sine wave, Figure 2.8, is the simplest motion achieved in

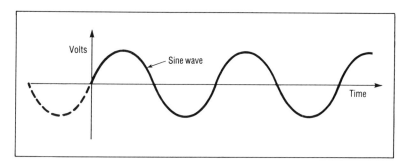

Fig. 2.8. Sine wave of voltage. Power companies design their alternators specifically to generate sinusoidal voltage.

nature and is easy to analyze.

Even though the voltage varies with time and has a different value at each instant, the supplies commonly are called 120 V, 220 V, or a 440 V, depending on whether they are intended for domestic consumer use, domestic consumer use for high-power equipment such as water heaters, ranges, etc., or industrial power, respectively. How, then, do we speak of **constant line voltage**, when the voltage always varies?

The answer lies in the concept of root-mean-square or RMS for short. This mathematical procedure arises when evaluating power (heating) equivalents in AC and direct current (DC) circuits, Figure 2.9. For example, a 100-watt bulb connected to a 120 V RMS AC source will glow with a certain intensity. That intensity requires a certain filament temperature and power consumption. If the same bulb is connected to a 120 V DC source, it will glow with the same intensity, meaning that the power draw and the filament temperature also are the same. The relationship between the RMS value of a sine wave and its peak equals 0.707 E_{max}, Figure 2.10.

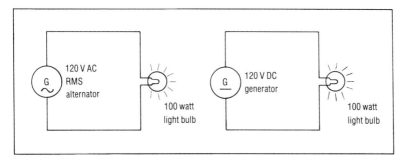

Fig. 2.9. The light intensity (power dissipation and filament temperature) of a 100-watt bulb connected to a 120 V RMS AC source is the same as when the bulb is connected to a 120 V DC source.

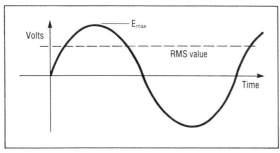

Fig. 2.10. The relationship between E_{max} and the equivalent RMS value is that $E_{RMS} = 0.707E_{max} = E_{max}/(2)^{1.2} = E_{max}/1.414$. The peak (maximum) value can easily be read with an oscilloscope. The RMS value is the indication that would be presented on a typical commercial AC voltmeter.

There are AC voltage-measuring instruments which provide true RMS readings regardless of the wave shape, but they are most often found in the laboratory. A typical commercial digital or analog multimeter, often seen in the technician's tool kit, has an AC voltage and current measuring ability.

Understand that these low-cost instruments satisfactorily measure voltages only when the voltage waveform is sinusoidal. Measurement of other wave shapes result in erroneous readings. This is because the instrument converts the unknown AC voltage or current into a rectified AC (converts the AC to DC by flipping the negative halves of the wave up), measures the resulting pulsating DC, and displays the DC value mutiplied by a scaling or form factor. This form factor is only correct when the wave shape is sinusoidal. Low-cost AC multimeters also have an upper frequency limit, some as low as 400 hertz. Measurement of voltages at higher frequencies can result in serious measurement error.

While these comments have been directed at voltage measurement, the relationships are completely applicable to current measurements with appropriate changes in notation, that is

$$I_{RMS} = I_{MAX}/(2)^{1/2}.$$

Voltage measurement

As indicated earlier, all voltmeters have two leads. The way these leads are connected into a circuit when making DC measurements determines the algebraic sign of the reading. One of the most elusive concepts in electrical circuit analysis is the mental organization needed to keep the algebraic sign correct. This may seem like the pursuit of trivia, but the sign can become very important when phasing feedback control systems. If the feedback is phased wrong, the output will run away instead of obeying the desired control inputs.

On commercially available multimeters, the leads are usually removable and made to be inserted into two jacks on the instrument. One jack will be red or marked with a + sign; the other will be black and be marked with a common or − sign. GET INTO THE HABIT OF PUTTING THE RED LEAD INTO THE RED (+) JACK AND THE BLACK LEAD INTO THE BLACK (−) JACK. Failure to do so does

Fig. 2.11. When the red lead or jack of the voltmeter is connected to the positive side of a battery (a), the voltmeter gives a positive reading. When the leads of a voltmeter are reversed (b), it displays a negative reading.

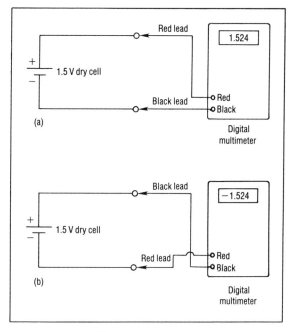

not damage the instrument, it merely confuses the algebraic sign. When assessed incorrectly, damage could result if feedback controls for a system are under construction.

Given compliance with the lead/jack rule, the voltmeter is phased so

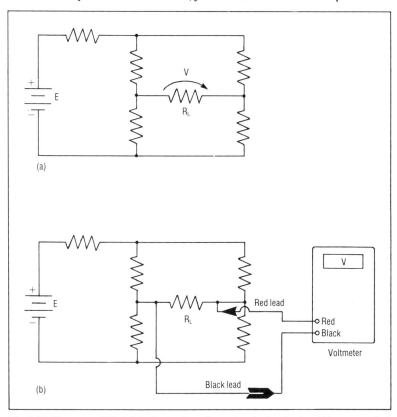

(a)

(b)

Fig. 2.12. The arrow, V in (a), indicates how the voltmeter leads should be connected to insure that the voltmeter gives the proper algebraic sign on the reading. The feathers on the tail of the black lead in (b) and the arrow on the head of the red lead correspond to the arrow in (a). The two schematics are equivalent; the positive red lead should be connected to the right side of R_L.

that when the red lead is connected to the positive side of a DC voltage and the black lead is connected to the negative side, a positive indication is displayed on the instrument. Lead reversal will result in sign reversal, Figure 2.11. To help with the algebraic sign and to ease the sketching of schematic diagrams herein, we will adopt an arrow notation. The arrow will indicate the way in which the voltmeter should be connected into the circuit in which the measurement is to be made, Figure 2.12.

A DC voltmeter indicates the average value, that is:

$$Indicated\ value = 1 \Big/ T \int_o^T e\,dt,$$

where T is the arbitrary time period over which the average is to be made, and e is the time-varying voltage being measured.

Thus, if a DC voltmeter is connected to an AC voltage source such as an AC power line, it will indicate zero because that is the average value of the AC line. If one measures another, more complex wave shape that has an AC component superimposed on top of a DC component (not unusual in electronic circuits), the meter indicates only the average DC component. If, in this case, the meter is switched to AC, the reading will be totally wrong unless the meter is a true RMS model.

Digital multimeters usually are not as sensitive to range-selection errors as are analog meters. If one sets a digital multimeter on the 10-V range, for example, and then proceeds to connect it to a 100-V source, instrument damage is unlikely. On the other hand, selecting the 10-V range on an analog meter and then measuring a 100-V source could destroy the instrument.

This is especially true of the less expensive ($20 - $30) analog meters on the market. If one selects a voltage range of 10 V on an analog meter, for example, and then connects it to a 120 V AC line, there will be excessive voltage across the meter. The voltage will have zero average value and give no reading, yet will burn out the instrument. A digital multimeter will likely survive such abuse and so is more forgiving.

Intrusiveness

All electrical measurements (all measurements, in fact) are somewhat intrusive. That is, the simple act of connecting the instrument into the circuit to make a measurement alters the value being measured. Different instruments have different degrees of intrusiveness. The amount of voltmeter intrusiveness depends on the meter's input resistance or impedance as it probably is called in the manufacturer's specifications.

The higher the input resistance, the better the meter. The ideal voltmeter would have infinite resistance and would not intrude at all; such a wonderful instrument does not exist. However, the typical digital multimeter will have an input impedance of a few megaohms and will intrude negligibly into most measurements.

On the other hand, analog instruments draw the energy for meter deflection directly from the circuit being measured. Thus they offer the greatest degree of intrusion. Furthermore, the input resistance of the meter varies with voltage range selection. The key value is the ohms/volt specification which usually is printed in the corner of the display window.

The higher the ohms/volt rating, the better the meter. A typical reading of modern low-cost analog meters is 20,0000 ohms/volt. On the 1-V range, the meter will have an input resistance of only 20,000 ohms; on the 10-V range of 200,000 ohms; and on the 100-V range of 2 megaohms which approaches the digital multimeter's input resistance.

Actually, an analog voltmeter is a microammeter with a number of resistors in series with it. As the operator selects the voltage range, the appropriate resistor is switched into the circuit. A 20,000 ohms/volt voltmeter has a 50 microamp ammeter as its heart (50 microamp = 1 V/ 20,000 Ω). Thus, the lower the current sensitivity, the higher the ohms/volt rating and the better the instrument.

It should be clear that digital multimeters are more forgiving and less intrusive than their analog counterparts. The digital versions eliminate the human uncertainty when estimating the exact position of a pointer as well as parallax reading errors which, of course, do not occur with digital displays.

It would be easy to conclude that analog meters have no place in the electronic troubleshooter's tool box, but that notion would be incorrect. In situations where the voltage fluctuates, the digital roll-by of the indicator is difficult to read. An analog meter permits a mental averaging that may be sufficiently accurate for the situation at hand. When tuning a system for null such as zeroing a spool-position LVDT transducer and proportional-valve spool, an analog meter is far friendlier than the constantly moving digital display. Both types of meters have their place; a well-equipped tool box includes both of them.

DC current measurement

DC ammeters also have two leads. On some multimeter packages, the ammeter leads and jacks may be the same as those used for voltage measurement. On others, there is a special jack for current measurement On those instruments, THE COMMON (BLACK) LEAD STAYS PUT.

Whatever the specific style of instrument, the ammeter/milliammeter function has two leads: one for a red (+) jack and one for a black (−) jack. Meter convention has established that when conventional current (not electron current) enters the red lead, the display shows an upscale, positive current reading. Reversing the leads yields a negative indication.

Schematically, when it is necessary to make a current measurement, it may be indicated by putting an arrow in or along the line whose current is to be measured, Figure 2.13. When first beginning to analyze an electrical circuit, it may be impossible to tell actual current direction. For example, the two currents to be measured in Figure 2.11 could be either positive or negative as measured. This is not a problem. If the initial guess is wrong, it only provides a negative reading. This text also will use an arrow convention to indicate the way an ammeter should be connec-

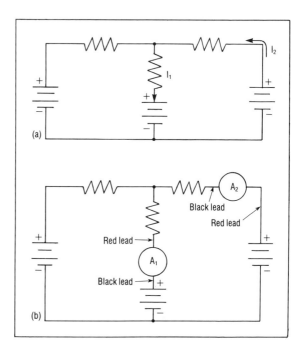

Fig. 2.13. I_1 and I_2 arrows in (a), give simplified notation for ammeter insertion. Redrawn (b)shows actual ammeter insertion into the circuit.

ted into a circuit.

Like voltmeters, ammeters intrude into the circuit in which the measurement is made. In order to insert the ammeter, it becomes necessary to physically break the electrical line at the point of measurement. Besides this physical intrusion, there is quantitative intrusion as well. Because the ammeter has some internal resistance, the meter's placement into the circuit alters the circuit and the current. The current with the meter in place is not the same as the current without the meter.

Because an ammeter is installed in series with the elements whose current is to be measured, it is desirable that the meter have minimum internal resistance. The non-existent ideal ammeter would have zero internal resistance; such an instrument would make no intrusion at all. Real ammeters have internal resistances of a fraction of an ohm in the ampere range and of several ohms in the milliampere ranges. Even though commercially available multimeters have current measurement capabilities, they are rarely used for this. The primary reason is the nuisance factor.

To make current measurements on an electronic circuit board is especially difficult. Because the ammeter must be inserted into the circuit, wires or resistors have to be desoldered or board traces may have to be cut, leads soldered on, and then resoldered in reverse order after the measurement is completed.

Sometimes current measurement is required. When troubleshooting servovalve circuits, for example, it is not always sufficient to establish that there is a voltage across the torque motor coils. Measuring currents off-board is usually not highly problematic. In the servovalve case, the torque motor leads usually can be disconnected at the terminal strip screw lugs, temporary leads can be attached, and the ammeter inserted. After the measurement is taken, the circuit can be restored with little problem.

Commercial multimeters also have an ohmmeter function. It is important to know that all ohmmeters have an integral electrical supply, usually a dry-cell battery. Therefore, they are never (or rarely) used to make resistance measurements in a powered circuit. Instead, they are used to measure the resistance of isolated devices.

Sometimes, it becomes necessary to make resistance measurements on a printed circuit-board circuit. If so, two precautions are necessary:

• ALWAYS remove or turn off electrical power to the circuit for the safety of the instrument and also FOR THE OPERATOR. Power which is not disabled may overpower the ohmmeter (and the operator) and damage it (them), and

• always disconnect at least one lead of the device whose resistance is to be measured. This disconnection eliminates the possibility of unseen parallel resistances affecting the measurement; disconnecting one lead assures that only one resistance will be measured. Even experienced electronic troubleshooters have trouble recognizing all parallel paths in complex circuits. Disconnection will require desoldering if the questionable resistor is on a circuit board.

Of the three functions on a multimeter, resistance measurement is the easiest to perform if these two precautions are followed. However, resistance measurements place the instrument in its most *precarious* condition; that is, it can easily be damaged. Always place the function selector off the ohms function when putting the meter away. It is too easy to use the meter later and inadvertently begin to make voltage measurements in the resistance mode. Even a digital multimeter could be damaged in this case.

Analog multimeters have simple, non solid state internal circuits. The resistance mode actually is a current-measuring mode but the meter has a scale calibrated to read the resistance value of the unknown. When in the resistance mode, the internal battery voltage powers the resistance function, and so battery condition directly affects the measurement.

Thus, analog meters have a *zero ohms* control. This is used to compensate for inevitable battery discharge. To zero the ohmmeter, the leads are shorted together and the control is turned until the reading zeros. Zeroing must be repeated for each range. Failure to reach zero indicates the battery must be replaced.

On digital multimeters in the resistance measurement mode, battery voltage is isolated from the resistance measuring circuit by an on-board voltage regulator. This regulator, using electronic feedback, assures a very stable measurement-circuit voltage even though the battery may have been partially discharged. Excessive battery discharge is indicated on the display. In that event, the battery must be changed before accurate measurements can be made.

Chapter Three
Basic Electric Circuit Analysis

A complete study of the electrical aspects of electrohydraulics would consist of a complete course in electronic engineering, but that clearly is not the scope of this text. Instead, the goal is to present sufficient electrical and electronic concepts to strengthen the confidence of the electrohydraulic practitioner. If one is not engaged specifically in the design of electronic control circuits, the majority of the electronic circuits encountered in a work-a-day world are of the relatively simple series or parallel variety. On occasion, bridge circuits must be considered.

The reader is most likely not an electronic control system designer, but must deal with real-world interfacing challenges of electric, electronic, and hydraulic systems. A list of all those challenges would be extensive, but a few examples provide a feeling for the intent of this text:

- making the ± 10 V output of a feedback transducer interface correctly with a computer which delivers a command of 0 to $+5$ V
- deciding if a replacement servovalve will interface properly with an existing servoamplifier
- selecting, assembling, and debugging the components of an electrohydraulic control system
- sizing a DC power supply based upon the electronic circuit cards which the supply must power, and
- selecting a potentiometer as a voltage scaler or as a feedback transducer.

Making these decisions requires at least a rudimentary understanding of electrical circuits, and that necessarily requires some circuit-analysis ability. This ability involves application of the following electrical theorems and laws along with some notational conventions to help understand the concepts:

- Kirchoff's Current Law
- Kirchoff's Voltage Law
- Ohm's Law, and
- power consumption in electrical circuits.

31

Circuit concepts and conventions

Modern electrical engineering texts cling to the archaic notion that the mobile charge carrier is positive. We know that the electron or the negative charge carrier is the particle free to move. The only rational justification for this tenacity is that the conclusions reached when designing and analyzing electrical circuits are not dependent of the erroneous mobile charge-carrier assumption.

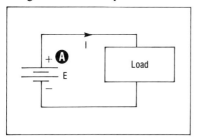

Fig. 3.1. Voltage source and positive current indication for conventional (positive mobile charge) current supplying an unspecified load.

It is important that whichever convention is adopted (conventional or electron-current), the circuit analyst must not change convention in mid-problem. This text follows the traditional method and assigns positive current as leaving the positive terminal of its motivating source, Figure 3.1. Imagine that a *clump* of electrical charges leave the positive battery terminal headed toward some arbitrary load. The charges always will move toward the negative side of the source which originally motivated it, in this case the negative battery terminal. This phenomenon will be important to recall when tracing currents in bridge rectifier circuits.

With the speed of light, the charges that leave the positive terminal of the source are replaced with other charges entering at the negative terminal. The actual migration velocity of individual charges usually is no more than a few m/sec. This electron flow is analogous to hydraulic fluid flow where molecules of oil, displaced out of the pump's high-pressure port, are replaced with the speed of sound by other oil molecules at the pump's inlet port, cavitation notwithstanding.

Understand that it is not the departing molecules that immediately enter the inlet port. It may take several seconds or even minutes before a departing molecule eventually recirculates into the pump inlet. Circulation time depends upon the physical length of the hydraulic circuit and plumbing cross-sectional areas, as well as system flow rate.

It also is important to realize that the charged electrical particles returning to the negative terminal do not recharge the battery. It would be the answer to the alchemist's dream if that were the case, because then flashlights would become ever brighter the longer they burned. Experience with burning car lights with the engine (and alternator) off proves clearly that is not the case.

Instead, returning charge carriers have been relieved of the potential energy they had while resting in the battery. That potential energy left the circuit in the form of heat, or was transferred to the load by some other conversion process such as the movement of a load by an electric motor. The battery *does* revitalize the returning charges and raises their potential energy so they again can circulate and carry more energy to the load, but in the process, the battery discharges. This charge revitalization in a battery is a chemical process; alternators and generators are mechanical-to-electric energy convertors. A battery is analgous to a hydraulic pump whose hydromechanical energy conversion process imparts energy to the oil molecules which enter its inlet. The invigorated oil particles then carry that energy to the load.

In an electrical circuit, kinetic energy is stored in the mass of the moving charges but that energy is so small when compared to the potential energy of the circuit, that kinetic energy is ignored in most situations. The most notable exception to this concerns vacuum tubes, especially cathode ray and tv picture tubes, where charge carriers' kinetic energy is converted to light energy on a phosphorescent screen.

Analogously, kinetic energy of hydraulic fluid power circuit oil molecules also can easily be ignored when compared to the molecules' potential energy. But some special cases require consideration of fluid momentum and/or its kinetic energy. For example, kinetic energy is important when analyzing the flow forces in valves, when designing the nozzles of flapper-nozzle and jet-pipe pilot valves, or when contending with turbulence in a reservoir. Otherwise, the ability to ignore kinetic energy in electrical and hydraulic circuits greatly reduces the complexity of analysis problems.

The current arrow, Figure 3.1, indicates the way an ammeter should be inserted into a circuit to measure current. The arrow should point away from the positive (red) terminal of the meter. Because this is the same direction charges should emerge from a battery, it follows that a meter connected that way will give a positive reading.

That is what happens as long as the load is passive rather than active. If the load in Figure 3.1 included a generator or another battery that could override battery *A*, current could be forced into the positive terminal to drive the ammeter downscale. Under that condition, the *load* would be charging the battery.

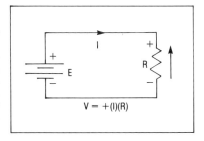

Fig. 3.2. A simple resistive circuit with notations that will be used in this text. Arrowhead by I indicates direction of conventional current. Plus sign above resistor R shows side of resistor that conventional current enters and is always positive; minus sign below resistor is side that current leaves and always is negative. Arrow beside resistor indicates how voltmeter should be connected.

If the load of Figure 3.1 is simply a passive resistor, Figure 3.2, the charge carriers will lose voltage as they pass through the load. That is, there will be a voltage drop across the load resistor. Voltage-drop polarity is such that the side of the resistor the current first encounters is more positive than the side from which current emerges. This relationship is indicated by the + and − polarity markings at the two ends of resistor R.

It is important to note that these signs are placed at the ends of the resistor on the basis of the assumed current direction. Once a current direction is established, then the +, − labeling across the resistor is fixed. That conceptual trick will assure that the current-to-voltage conversion at each resistor always has the correct sign.

But there is a second issue: How to connect a voltmeter to make a voltage measurement? The arrow notation answers the question. Because the voltmeter has two leads, the red + lead can be connected to the top or to the bottom of the resistor. Recall from earlier conventions that the plus lead is connected to the + side of the resistor. When connected that way, there will be a positive indication on the meter. (But the voltmeter does not have to be connected this way. The plus lead could have been connected to the bottom of the resistor and give a negative reading.)

Circuit laws

Ohm's Law. A profound discovery was made by Georg Simon Ohm (1787 — 1854) of Cologne University in 1827. Although it was controversial at the time, Ohm's contention that electrical-circuit current and voltage are linearly related has prevailed and now is universally accepted by engineers and physicists throughout the world. In fact, Ohm's work is

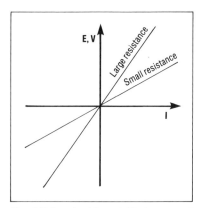

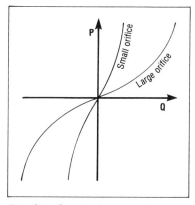

Fig. 3.3. Graph of E = (I)(R) for two different resistances. Voltage is a linear function of current and when current changes sign, resistive voltage drop changes sign too.

Fig. 3.4. Graph of the nonlinear relationship between pressure and flow in a hydraulic orifice. Pressure drop, ΔP, relates to the square of the flow, Q^2.

so inviolable that the relationship is called Ohm's Law, not Ohm's Theorem. Mathematically, the relationship is stated in the now familiar terms:

$$E = (I)(R).\tag{3.1}$$
$$I = E/R, \text{ and}\tag{3.2}$$
$$R = E/I.\tag{3.3}$$

where E is the voltage in volts, I is the current in amperes, and R is the resistance in ohms.

A representative graph of the linear Ohm's Law relationship, Figure 3.3, is in contrast with the analogous pressure-flow graph for a hydraulic orifice, Figure 3.4. Although the pressure-voltage and current-fluid flow analogies are helpful as well as useful, the analogies fail when considering the mathematical relationships. A quite different kind of formula is needed to relate pressure to flow in a hydraulic resistive circuit:

$$Q = (K_v)(P)^{1/2}\tag{3.4}$$
$$P = Q^2/(K_v)^2, \text{ and}\tag{3.5}$$
$$K_v = Q/(P)^{1/2}.\tag{3.6}$$

where Q is in in^3/sec, P is in psid, and flow area is in in^2. Thus K_v is in $in^3/sec/psi^{1/2}$.

Merritt[1] has shown that for *typical* mineral based hydraulic fluids and for an orifice discharge coefficient of about 0.6, K_v reasonably can be estimated as 100 times the cross-sectional flow area of the orifice.

These facts have deterred progress toward a universally accepted method for analyzing hydraulic circuits. Countless texts have been written on the general subject of electrical circuit analysis but few coherent volumes are devoted to hydraulic fluid power circuit analysis. The mathematical intractability of equations describing the more complex hydraulic circuits discourages engineers from pursuing their analysis. Digital computers and numerical solution methods for non-linear equations now are helping expand hydraulic circuit analysis, but much work remains. That is another subject.

Kirchoff's Voltage Law. Gustav Robert Kirchoff (1824 — 1887) was a German physicist who discovered the principles of spectrum analysis and mechanical thermodynamics. His work in electricity, of greatest interest to circuit analysts, produced these well-known laws: Kirchoff's Voltage Law and Kirchoff's Current Law.

In its most basic form, his Voltage Law states: **The algebraic sum of the voltage rises around a closed circuit must equal the algebraic sum**

---

[1] *Herbert E. Merritt, Hydraulic Control Systems, p. 42*

of the voltage drops around the same closed circuit. When adopting a notational convention such as the use of arrows to indicate how a voltmeter is to be connected, wording the Voltage Law can be reduced to: **The algebraic sum of the voltages around a complete loop must be zero.**

Arrows help keep the algebraic sign straight, and there need be no concern that the potential rise of a voltage source is different from a voltage drop. **All voltages are treated the same way.** It is unnecessary for the algebraic summing loop to form a closed circuit; it only is necessary for the algebraic loop to be complete. This is helpful when defining the output voltage, for example, from an electrical bridge circuit even when there is only a pair of measuring terminals with no physical output circuit present.

Voltage Law example

A simple example points out how to put the Voltage Law to work. There is an arbitrary voltage source, E, Figure 3.5, connected to four series resistors, R_1, R_2, R_3, and R_4, with current direction as shown. Each resistor accounts for its own voltage drop, V_1, V_2, V_3, and V_4, respectively. Note that the current-induced voltage drops are indicated by the succession of $+$, $-$ signs associated with each resistor.

The procedure makes use only of the voltage arrow notations, so there is no need to worry about sources and drops:

● begin at any point on a given loop (Figure 3.5 only has one loop) and establish the rule that when proceeding around the loop, if an arrow is passed <u>in the direction</u> of the arrow head, that voltage is assigned a $+$.

Fig. 3.5. Kirchoff's Voltage Law requires that $E - V_1 - V_2 - V_3 - V_4 = 0$. *Ohm's Law requires that* $V_1 = +(I)(R_1)$, $V_2 = +(I)(R_2)$, $V_3 = +(I)(R_3)$, *and* $V_4 = +(I)(R_4)$.

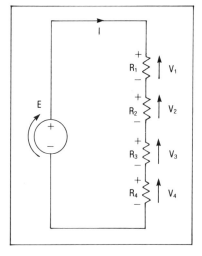

When passing through an arrow <u>opposite</u> to the way it points, that voltage is assigned a $-$; and when returning to the point of origin the summation is set to zero. Application of the procedure to the circuit of Figure 3.5 yields:

$$E - V_1 - V_2 - V_3 - V_4 = 0 \qquad (3.7)$$

Ohm's Law requires that

$$
\begin{aligned}
V_1 &= (+I)(R_1), & (3.8) \\
V_2 &= (+I)(R_2), & (3.9) \\
V_3 &= (+I)(R_3), \text{ and} & (3.10) \\
V_4 &= (+I)(R_4). & (3.11)
\end{aligned}
$$

Substituting Equations (3.8) through (3.11) into Equation (3.7) results in

$$E - (I)(R_1) - (I)(R_2) - (I)(R_3) - (I)(R_4) = 0, \text{ or} \qquad (3.12)$$
$$E = (I)(R_1) + (I)(R_2) + (I)(R_3) + (I)(R_4). \qquad (3.13)$$

Factoring the current provides

$$E = (I)(R_1 + R_2 + R_3 + R_4). \qquad (3.14)$$

Now, solving for current yields:

$$I = E / (R_1 + R_2 + R_3 + R_4). \qquad (3.15)$$

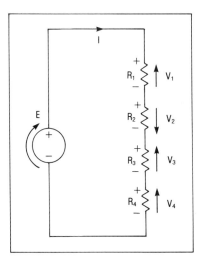

Fig. 3.6. The V_2 definition is reversed when compared with Fig. 3.5 to show that the algebraic sign on V_2 does not affect the outcome when rigidly adhering to the procedure.

Figure 3.6 contains the same electrical circuit as Figure 3.5, but the definition of the voltage drop across resistor R_2 has been reversed. If the algebraic signs are carefully analyzed and the procedure rigidly followed, the outcome of using the definitions of Figure 3.5 when compared with Figure 3.6 will be the same. Note that use of the sign rule and Kirchoff's Voltage Law produces

$$E - V_1 + V_2 - V_3 - V_4 = 0. \qquad (3.16)$$

But, because of the redefinition of V_2, Ohm's Law requires that

$$V_1 = (+I)(R_1), \qquad (3.17)$$
$$V_2 = (-I)(R_2), \qquad (3.18)$$
$$V_3 = (+I)(R_3), \text{ and} \qquad (3.19)$$
$$V_4 = (+I)(R_4). \qquad (3.20)$$

When Equations (3.12) through (3.20) are substituted into Equation (3.16),

$$E - (I)(R_1) - (I)(R_2) - (I)(R_3) - (I)R_4) = 0, \qquad (3.21)$$

which is exactly the same as Equation (3.12), the algebraic sign on the R_2 voltage drop having taken care of itself as a matter of procedure. If it is not now obvious that further work on Equation (3.21) must produce results identical to those produced using Equation (3.12), the student should review the procedure until understanding is gained.

There is a direct analogy between electrical and hydraulic circuits in that Kirchoff Voltage Law applies directly to hydraulic circuits without

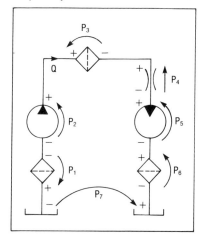

Fig. 3.7. When an arrow notation is adopted for differential pressure drop, then Kirchoff's Pressure Drop Law can be applied directly to hydraulic circuits in exact analogy to electrical voltage; $-P_1 + P_2 - P_3 - P_4 - P_5 - P_6 - P_7 = 0$.

modification when treating pressure analogously to voltage. In a simple hydraulic pump/motor circuit, Figure 3.7, individual differential pressure drops across the circuit elements can be indicated by a ΔP arrow just as voltage drops are indicated with arrows in an electrical circuit.

Indicated hydraulic flow Q emanates from the pump, proceeds to the motor and finally re-circulates through the reservoir. The +, − notations at each circuit element indicate the polarity of the pressure drops, and each is labeled consistent with the assumed direction of flow Q. That is, the side of the element which the flow enters is given a plus sign while the departure side is labeled with a minus sign. This is intuitively attractive, because one would expect the inlet of a motor, for example, to be at higher pressure than its outlet during normal operation.

Note that the polarity of the pump differential pressure, P_2, indicates that the pump discharge port is more positive (higher pressure). Again, it is intuitive that this is correct because the pressure at a pump's outlet should be higher than at its inlet.

In particular, look at differential pressure, P_7, Figure 3.7. This is an assumed pressure gradient within the reservoir; in most hydraulic systems this gradient is so close to zero that it can be ignored. It is included here to emphasize that:

• it is <u>not</u> necessary to consider a reservoir's internal pressure gradient is zero; it can be included in the Voltage Law, and
• inclusion of the reservoir pressure-drop arrow completes the circuitous loop necessary for the formation of the pressure-drop loop.

Interpretation of Figure 3.7 and application of what can be called Kirchoff's "Pressure-drop Law" yields the loop equation:

$$-P_1 + P_2 - P_3 - P_4 - P_5 - P_6 - P_7 = 0, \qquad (3.22)$$

in which P_7 is very nearly zero. In the usual case where the reservoir differential pressure is zero, P_7 drops out of the equation.

Kirchoff's Current Law. Kirchoff's Current Law deals with the way currents combine and/or separate when encountering a node (electrical junction). The Law says: **The sum of the currents entering a node must equal the sum of the currents leaving the node.**

The drawing of an arbitrary electrical node, Figure 3.8, has six branches. Application of Kirchoff's Current Law requires that

$$I_1 + I_3 = I_2 + I_4 + I_5 + I_6. \qquad (3.23)$$

All electrical circuit analysis problems begin with the use of Ohm's and Kirchoff's Laws. Using a systematic approach, the very simple circuits as well as those with much more complexity can be solved. Mathe-

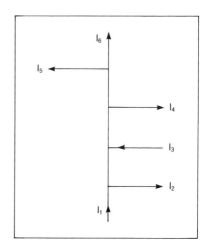

Fig. 3.8. Electrical node or junction, having six branches, each with different current to show the application of Kirchoff's Current Law: $I_1 + I_3 = I_2 + I_4 + I_5 + I_6$.

matical solutions to the equations generated when following the laws usually involve matrix methods and the simultaneous solutions of sets of equations. Intuitive methods can be used for simpler circuits, however, as is the case for examples used in the balance of this text.

As was true with Kirchoff's Voltage Law, there is near perfect correlation between electrical and hydraulic circuits for his Current Law: **The sum of the hydraulic flows entering a junction must be equal to the sum of the hydraulic flows leaving the junction.** The imperfection of the analogy is because hydraulic fluid is partially compressible.

Compressibility causes a fluid to become more dense in the high-pressure portions of a circuit which, in turn, leads to reduced volumetric flow in the high-pressure regions when compared to the volumetric flow of low-pressure regions. If the hydraulics technology used mass flow rather than volumetric flow, continuity would demand that the mass flow into the junction be exactly equal to the mass flow leaving the junction. But volumetric flow is used because the result, when multiplied by pressure, is power. Use of mass flow would require use of pressure-dependent fluid density in all power calulations. Furthermore, many flowmeters used in industry inherently measure volumetric rather than mass flow.

The result is that Kirchoff's Current Law can be directly applied to hydraulic systems that have pressures less than a few thousand psi. There are ways, however, to analyze other systems in which compressiblity is significant with manageable margins of error. Most notable of these systems involve time-changing pressure in which the compressibility component of flow depends upon the pressure change rate. Even in those cases, electrical circuit techniques can be used and Kirchoff's Current Law may be applied with insignificant error.

Perhaps the greatest reason for electrohydraulic specialists to study electrical circuit analysis is that:

● electrical theorems, laws, and procedures are firmly established
● these facts are widely proven, accepted, and documented, and
● they apply analogously to hydraulic-circuit analysis.

There is no better training for analysis of electrohydraulic circuits than a thorough command of electrical-circuit analysis. In this text, an understanding of hydraulic circuits has been assumed. That knowledge, used analogously, will help convey the concepts of electrical circuits.

Example Problems using Ohm's and Kirchoff's Laws:

Example 3.1. The current through a 20-Ω resistor is measured and found to be 2 A. What is the voltage drop across the resistor? (Refer to Figure 3.9).

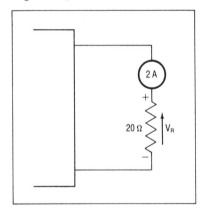

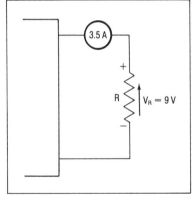

Fig. 3.9. Example for Problem 3.1.   *Fig. 3.10. Example for Problem 3.2.*

Solution 3.1. Because both the current and resistance are known, Ohm's Law can be applied directly:

$$Vr = (I)(R)$$
$$= (2)(20)$$
$$= 40\ V.$$

Example 3.2. An unknown resistor is known to be passing 3.5 A and the measured voltage drop is 9 V. What is the resistance of the resistor? (Refer to Figure 3.10).

Solution 3.2. In this case, solve Ohm's Law for the resistance:

$Vr = (I)(R)$ or,
$R = Vr/I$. So
$R = 9/3.5$
$\quad = 2.57\,\Omega.$

Example 3.3. What is the current through a 10-Ω resistor which is connected directly to a 24-V battery? (Refer to Figure 3.11).
Solution 3.3. Solve Ohm's Law for the current.

$Vr = (I)(R)$, or
$I = Vr/R$. So
$I = 24/10$
$\quad = 2.4\,A.$

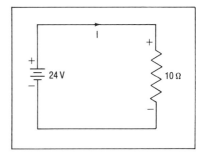

Fig. 3.11. Example for Problem 3.3.

Example 3.4. Three resistors, connected in series as shown in Figure 3.12, have measured voltage drops of 3, 6, and 5 V. What is the supply voltage, E?
Solution 3.4. Kirchoff's Voltage Law is applied directly, using the notations of Figure 3.12.

$E - 3 - 6 - 5 = 0.$

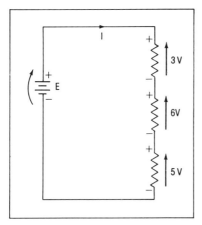

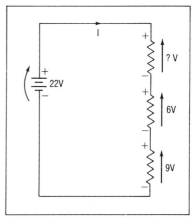

Fig. 3.12. Example for Problem 3.4.   *Fig. 3.13. Example for Problem 3.5.*

From which

$$E = 3 + 6 + 5$$
$$= 14 \; V.$$

Example 3.5. The circuit shown in Figure 3.13 is known to have a supply of 22 V, and the voltage drops across two of three resistors are known to be 6 and 9 V. The drop across the third resistor is unknown. Find the unknown voltage drop.
Solution 3.5. Kirchoff's Voltage Law is applied using the values and notations of Figure 3.13:

$$22 - V - 6 - 9 = 0,$$

wherein V is the only unknown, so the equation can be solved:

$$V = 22 - 6 - 9$$
$$= 7 \; V.$$

Example 3.6. Two resistors are connected to an unspecified source as shown in Figure 3.14. What is the total source current, Ie?
Solution 3.6. Source current, Ie, can be found directly using Kirchoff's Current Law:

$$Ie - 3 - 2 = 0,$$

from which

$$Ie = 3 + 2$$
$$= 5 \; A.$$

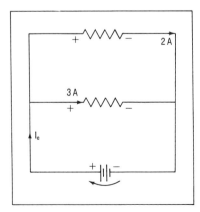

Fig. 3.14. Example for Problem 3.6.

Series circuits

Recognition that series circuits differ from parallel circuits can help simplify some circuit-analysis problems. The definition of a series circuit is: **A circuit in which the current is everywhere the same.** Flow continuity of a series circuit, Figure 3.15, demands that if an ammeter were placed in any one of the four positions indicated with an I, all current readings would be exactly the same.

It is important to recognize that in the general case, individual voltage drops V_1, V_2, and V_3 all differ from one another. Another way of defining a series circuit concept: **If all current leaving one circuit element passes through a second element, the two elements are said to be in series with one another.**

The idea of series electrical circuits again has direct analogy and interpretation in hydraulic circuits. That is, the six circuit elements of Figure 3.7 are all in series because the flow is everywhere the same, fluid compressibility notwithstanding. Furthermore, all the flow departing the outlet of one element must pass through the next element downstream. Because the criterion for series connections is met, this arrangement is a series circuit.

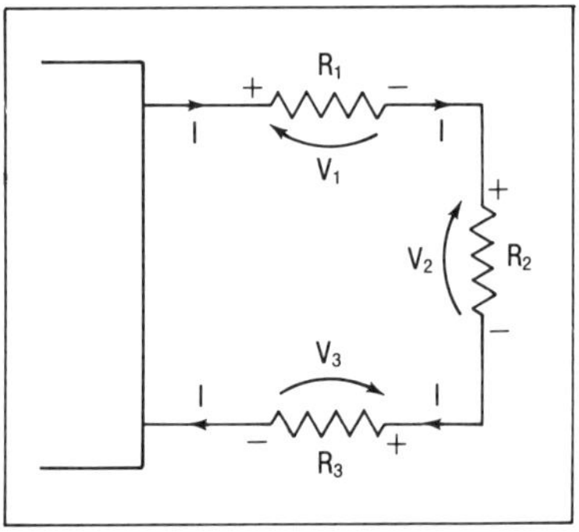

Fig. 3.15. R₁, R₂, and R₃ are in series with each other because they all carry the same current, I.

Parallel circuits

When flow departing the outlet of one element is presented with more than one downstream path, the flow will split into two or more paths which are said to be in parallel. The definition of a parallel electrical circuit: **A circuit in which the voltage is everywhere the same.** Note that if the conductor material used to connect the four resistors in a simple parallel circuit, Figure 3.16, is essentially resistance-free, the line voltage drop, V_C, is 0 V. That leads to the conclusion that

$$V_1 = V_2 = V_3 = V_4,$$

or all voltages are the same. In the general case, however, currents are all different. That is, Kirchoff's Current Law requires that

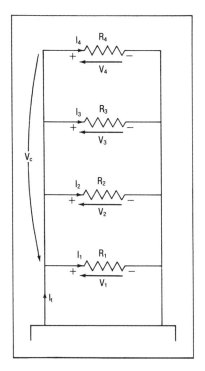

Fig. 3.16. R_1, R_2, R_3, and R_4 are in parallel with one another because they all have the same voltage drop.

$$I_t = I_1 + I_2 + I_3 + I_4.$$

Not surprisingly, there is another direct analogy between electrical and hydraulic circuits regarding parallel connections. A typical parallel hydraulic circuit, Figure 3.17, uses the familiar bleed-off flow control; pump flow must equal bleed-off flow plus load flow. With essentially constant pump flow, varying the amount of bleed-off flow controls motor speed.

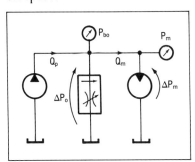

Fig. 3.17. Because pump output flow Q_p is offered two paths, the flow control valve and the motor are said to be in parallel with each other, but only if P_m is equal to P_{bo}. This further requires that there be no pressure loss in the connecting plumbing — not an unreasonable assumption.

45

Equivalent resistance

When analyzing electrical circuits, it is helpful to reduce complex circuits to simpler equivalents. Sometimes, a complex series-parallel circuit can be converted to an equivalent but simplified series circuit. Replacing resistance networks with their single-resistor equivalent is the beginning of circuit simplification. Basic resistor network configurations, of course, are series and parallel.

The equivalent — or as it is sometimes called, the *total* resistance — of a series resistor network is merely the sum of the individual series resistances. Application of Ohm's and Kirchoff's Laws provide quick proof of that statement. Consider the generalized series circuit, Figure 3.18, which has an arbitrary number of resistors connected in series. Kirchoff's Voltage Law requires that

$$E = V_1 + V_2 + V_3 + ... + V_n. \tag{3.24}$$

Ohm's Law further requires that

$$V_1 = (I)(R_1), \tag{3.25}$$
$$V_2 = (I)(R_2), \tag{3.26}$$
$$V_3 = (I)(R_3), \text{ and} \tag{3.27}$$
$$V_n = (I)(R_n). \tag{3.28}$$

Thus

$$E = (I)(R_1) + (I)(R_2) + (I)(R_3) + ... + (I)(R_n). \tag{3.29}$$

Because I is common to all terms on the right side, the Equation factors to:

$$E = (I)(R_1 + R_2 + R_3 + ... + R_n). \tag{3.30}$$

If supply voltage E and current I in the series circuit are measured, it seems reasonable that the measured voltage divided by the measured current would result in the effective resistance experienced by the source, and that is the case. The beauty of mathematical anlyses is that the same ends can be attained without making measurements every time a solution is desired. Just divide both sides of Equation (3.30) by current I, to solve for the effective, equivalent, or total circuit resistance:

$$E/I = Re = R_1 + R_2 + R_3 + ... + R_n. \tag{3.31}$$

which is the expected result.

This means, for example, that three resistors in series can be replaced by a single resistor which has a value equal to the sum of the three individual resistances. The currents in the original and the equivalent circuits will be the same as long as circuit supply voltages are the same.

A similar approach can be taken to find the equivalent resistance of a simple parallel circuit. In that case, though, first apply Kirchoff's Current Law as suggested in Figure 3.19. The current continuity law requires that

$$I_t = I_1 + I_2 + I_3 + \dots + I_n. \qquad (3.32)$$

Ohm's Law says that

$$I_1 = V/R_1, \qquad (3.33)$$
$$I_2 = V/R_2, \qquad (3.34)$$
$$I_3 = V/R_3, \text{ and} \qquad (3.35)$$

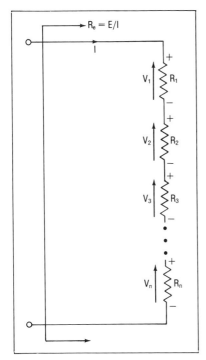

Fig. 3.18. Application of Ohm's and Kirchoff's Laws indicates that the equivalent resistance of n resistors in series is their sum, that is $R_e = R_1 + R_2 + R_3 + \dots + R_n$.

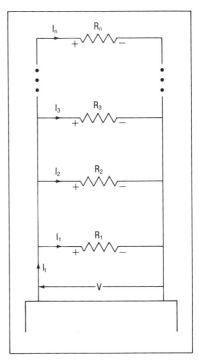

Fig. 3.19. With parallel resistances, $1/R_e = 1/R_1 + 1/R_2 + 1/R_3 + \dots + 1/R_n$. When there are only two resistors, $R_e = [(R_1)(R_2)]/R_1 + R_2$.

$$I_n = V/R_n. \tag{3.36}$$

Substituting Equations (3.33) through (3.36) into Equation (3.32) gives

$$I_t = V/R_1 + V/R_2 + V/R_3 + ... + V/R_n. \tag{3.37}$$

Dividing both sides of Equation (3.37) by V produces

$$I_t/V = 1/R_1 + 1/R_2 + 1/R_3 + ... + 1/R_n. \tag{3.38}$$

Note that in this Equation the left side is the *reciprocal* of the equivalent resistance rather than the equivalent resistance itself.

The form shown is convenient for a general formula which can be adapted to a specific circuit at the time of application. For example, when considering the special case of a parallel circuit with only resistors R_1 and R_2, Equation (3.38) can be simplified to the *product over sum* formula:

$$R_e = [(R_1)(R_2)]/(R_1 + R_2). \tag{3.39}$$

Two parallel resistances can be replaced by a single resistor and its value calculated using Equation (3.39). By successively and alternately applying Equations (3.31) and (3.38) or (3.39), many complex circuits can be reduced to simple series circuits.

Using the parallel idea of equivalent circuits in hydraulic circuit analysis is valid but is complicated by the fact that the simple, linear relationship given in Ohm's Law does not correlate with the nature of hydraulic circuits. Instead, pressure and flow through a restriction (orifice) are given by Merritt's formula:

$$Q = 100 (A) (P)^{1/2}, \tag{3.40}$$

where the orifice flow coefficient is defined as

$$K_v = 100 (A). \tag{3.41}$$

Now,

$$Q = (K_v)(P)^{1/2} \tag{3.42}$$

Solving for pressure gives

$$P = (Q/Kv)^2. \tag{3.43}$$

A series hydraulic circuit, Figure 3.20, which has only two orifices (an arbitrary number of series restrictors can be analyzed, but the algebra needed to make the point is not worth the effort), submits to Kirchoff's Pressure Law as follows:

$$P_s = P_1 + P_2. \tag{3.44}$$

Substituting Equation (3.43) into Equation (3.44), and allowing for the condition that the two orifices do not have the same K_v, provides

$$P_s = (Q/K_{v1})^2 + (Q/K_{v2})^2. \tag{3.45}$$

Dividing both sides of Equation (3.45) by Q, yields

$$P_s/Q^2 = 1/(K/_{v1})^2 + 1/(K_{v2})^2. \tag{3.46}$$

But the left hand side of Equation (3.46) is the square of the reciprocal of the equivalent flow coefficient, $Kveq$, so now

$$P_s/Q^2 = 1/(K_{veq})^2 + 1/(K_{veq})^2. \tag{3.47}$$

Simplifying to solve for the equivalent flow coefficient gives

$$(K_{veq})^2 = [(K_{v1})^2 (K_{v2})^2]/[(K_{v1})^2 + (K_{v2})^2], \tag{3.48}$$

which indicates that two orifices in series produce an equivalent single orifice whose square is found from the *product of the individual squares divided by the sum of the individual squares*. After calculating the right side of Equation (3.48), be aware that value of the K_{veq} is unknown until the square root is extracted.

Understand that orifices in a series combine *approximately* using the product-over-sum formula, but electrical resistances can combine directly as the sum of the individual resistances. This curiosity arises be-

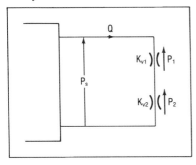

Q

K_{v1})(P_1

P_s

K_{v2})(P_2

Fig. 3.20. *The equivalent flow coefficient is* $K_{veq2} = [(K_{v1})^2(K_{v2})^2]/K_{v1}^2 + K_{v2}^2.$

cause of the differences between the definitions of the flow coefficient compared with the electrical resistance. Resistance in an electrical circuit is a measure of the resistor's opposition to electrical current. As the resistance increases, the electrical flow (current) decreases with constant voltage. Valve coefficient K_v of a hydraulic circuit, however, is a function of the orifice area; therefore, as K_v increases, the orifice area must also increase permitting an increase in hydraulic flow with constant pressure drop. **Thus, K_v is a measure of hydraulic conductivity or permissivity of the orifice, while resistance, as its name correctly implies, is a measure of restrictiveness.**

In a parallel hydraulic circuit, expect that the equivalent flow coefficient of orifices is related to the simple sum, which indeed is the case. This fact can be developed by considering a parallel hydraulic circuit, Figure 3.21. Note that Kirchoff's Hydraulic Flow Law or flow continuity equation requires that

$$Q_t = Q_1 + Q_2 + ... + Q_n. \tag{3.49}$$

The orifice pressure-flow relationship says that

$$Q_1 = Kv_1 (P)^{1/2}. \tag{3.50}$$

Fig. 3.21. The equivalent coefficient for orifices in parallel is $K_{veq} = K_{v1} + K_{v2} + ... + K_{vn}$.

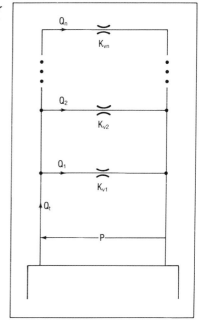

$$Q_2 = K_{v2}(P)^{1/2}, \text{and} \tag{3.51}$$
$$Q_n = K_{vn}(P)^{1/2}. \tag{3.52}$$

Substituting Equations (3.50) through (3.52) into Equation (3.49) gives

$$Q_t = K_{v1}(P)^{1/2} + K_{v2}(P)^{1/2} + ... + K_{vn}(P)^{1/2}. \tag{3.53}$$

Because there is an $(P)^{1/2}$ common to each term on the right side of Equation (3.53), dividing both sides by that factor defines the K_{veg} for n orifices in parallel:

$$Q_t/P^{1/2} = K_{veq} = K_{v1} + K_{v2} + ... + K_{vn}. \tag{3.54}$$

the expected result.

In some hydraulic circuits there can simultaneously exist both square-law flow (as covered above and in Merritt's formula) as well as laminar flow where the pressure and flow are related linearly as in Ohm's Law. A typical example of this occurs when a pump and motor are connected to a square-law valve, not an uncommon situation. Internal leakage of the pump and motor tends to be laminar and thus related linearly to the pressure, while pressure drop through the valve is related to the square of the flow.

Such circuit combinations lead to equations so complex, except in the simplest cases, that a computer solution is the only practical method. Analogous situations occur in electrical circuits when non-linear devices such as diodes are used with linear resistors. Just because equations pertain to electrical rather than hydraulic circuits does not speed their solution. A complex non-linear equation is still a complex non-linear equation that needs a computer to ease the mathematical pain. Such circuits are beyond the scope of this text, except in a qualitative sense.

Voltage-divider equation

Electrohydraulic application engineers often are required to match the voltage from a command source such as a programmable controller to the voltage developed by a feedback transducer. A handy formula that helps make the match is the *voltage-divider* equation, also known as the *voltage-attenuator* equation. There are a number of other instances where this equation can be put to good use and so it is given a special place in this text.

When a voltage is too high for an application and must be reduced or attenuated, a simple voltage-divider circuit can sometimes be used; the sizing of its components can be solved very easily. But when a voltage is too low and must be boosted, the necessary circuit is not so simple. In that considerably more complex circuit, amplifiers are needed.

The generalized voltage divider circuit, Figure 3.22, has a source or input voltage connected to several series resistances. Ohm's and Kirchoff's Laws are used to derive the equation to calculate the output voltage, V_o.

Fig. 3.22. The voltage divider. $V_o = [(V_i)(R_o)]/\Sigma R_{series}$.

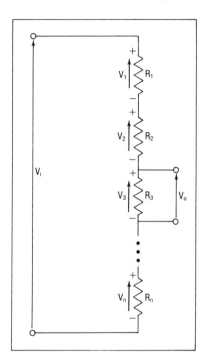

The voltage law requires that

$$V_i = V_1 + V_2 + \ldots + V_o + \ldots + V_n. \tag{3.55}$$

Ohm's Law requires that

$$V_1 = (I)(R_1), \tag{3.56}$$
$$V_2 = (I)(R_2), \tag{3.57}$$
$$V_o = (I)(R_o), \text{ and} \tag{3.58}$$
$$V_n = (I)(R_n). \tag{3.59}$$

After substitution,

$$V_i = I(R_1 + R_2 + \ldots + R_o + \ldots + R_n). \tag{3.60}$$

Solving Equation (3.60) for current I provides

$$I = V_i / (R_1 + R_2 + ... + R_o + ... + R_n). \qquad (3.61)$$

It can be seen that substituting Equation (3.61) into Equation (3.58) will give the desired result:

$$V_t = [(V_i)(R_o)] / (R_1 + R_2 + ... + R_o + ... + R_n), \qquad (3.62)$$

which says that the output voltage across any one of several series resistors can be calculated when all resistances and input voltage V_i are known. The voltage-divider equation: **To calculate the voltage divider output voltage, multiply the applied (input) voltage times the resistance whose voltage is desired and divide that result by the total sum of all resistances in series.**

Output voltage of the voltage-divider circuit must always be less than the input voltage and so it is an attenuator circuit. There is no real combination of resistances which will yield a higher output than input voltage. An analogous equation can be developed for hydraulic circuits, but its derivation is left to the interested student.

Circuit loading

One of the most important electrical phenomena for the systems integrator is circuit loading. Circuit loading occurs any time a source, such as a transducer, is connected to any receiver and so becomes loaded. Typical receivers are amplifiers, or voltage-measuring instruments such as voltmeters or oscilloscopes.

Because the loading device (receiver) necessarily draws some current from the source, the voltage at the common connector terminals will be less because of the connected load than the voltage would be if the load were not connected. That is, as the current demanded by the load increases, the voltage at the terminals of the source must decrease. This is because of the finite source resistance, R_S, Figure 3.23.

The ideal interfacing situation for circuit loading should now be obvi-

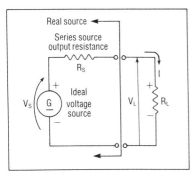

Fig. 3.23. A real voltage source can be represented as an ideal voltage source, V_S, with a series source (output) resistance, R_S, (impedance). R_L is an arbitrary load resistance.

ous, when one of the purposes of the design is to trasmit information from one circuit point to another:

● the ideal source should have zero source resistance, and
● the ideal load should have infinite input resistance.

As there are no ideal loads or sources, some loading effect is inevitable; it merely is a matter of degree. In a great many instances, electronic devices can be interconnected without significant loading effects. This is because transducer signal-conditioning equipment designers try to keep their source output resistances as low as practical, while receiving-device designers try to keep input resistances as high as possible.

But systems engineers must understand that some pieces of commercially available hardware have unduly high output resistances. Neglect of the loading effects of this hardware can produce disastrous results. Three approaches to alleviate this loading problem are to:

● maintain a sufficiently high input-to-output resistance ratio to create negligible loading effects
● determine the input and output resistances and compensate for them, and
● design an interfacing amplifier, such as a unity-gain amplifier, to artificially create low output resistance and high input resistance (see Chapter 7).

This second approach requires a knowledge of the specific input and output resistances along with some simple calculation. Consider Figure 3.23, in which connection of load resistance R_L results in current I. The current through source resistance R_S causes a voltage drop assumed to be internal to the source. Output voltage V_L must, then, be less than source voltage V_S by the amount of that internal voltage drop. That is,

$$V_L = V_S - (I)(R_S). \tag{3.63}$$

Figure 3.24 shows the nominal graph of Equation (3.63).

It is easy to see from Equation (3.63) that if the voltage source were ideal, ie if R_S were zero, there would be no drop in terminal voltage re-

Fig. 3.24. Graph of output voltage as a function of output current. Another name for the output voltage and current is load voltage and load current. Voltage axis intercept point V_S is also referred to as the open circuit voltage.

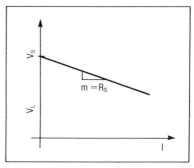

gardless of the current. Two examples will help develop an understanding of this and the values that can be encountered.

Terminal voltage problems

Example 3.7. A certain strain-gage pressure transducer generates 10-mV full-scale output (FSO), and has a known output resistance of 300 Ω. Three amplifiers being considered have the same gain (each amplifies the transducer voltage by a like factor) of 500 output V/V input. They differ in their input resistances: $R_{in1} = 100$ KΩ, $R_{in2} = 10$ KΩ, and $R_{in3} = 1$ KΩ. What will be the percent of loading if each amplifier were connected to the transducer?

Solution 3.7. From the transducer-amplifier circuit, Figure 3.25, and the description of the transducer, we know that source voltage V_S is 0.01 V (10 mV), R_S is 300 Ω and each amplifier will be represented with its specific input resistance. We could calculate the current for each R_{in}, but it is faster to use the voltage divider Equation (3.62) derived earlier. Adapting that generalized equation to this example tells us that

$$V_x = (V_S)(R_{in})/(R_{in} + R_S).$$

Using the given values,

$$V_x(100K) = (0.01)(100,000)/(100,000 + 300)$$
$$= (1000)/100,300$$
$$= 0.00997 \text{ V}.$$

We know that the unloaded transducer output voltage ($R_{in} = \infty$) is 0.01 V, so the loading is the difference, or

$$Loading \ loss = V_S - V_{x\text{-loaded}}$$

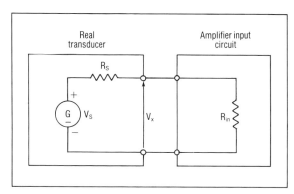

Fig. 3.25. A real transducer can be represented as an *ideal voltage source*, V$_s$, and output (source) resistance, R$_s$. The receiving amplifier has an input resistance, R$_{in}$, which acts as a load on the transducer.

Real transducer

Amplifier input circuit

R$_S$

G V$_S$

V$_x$

R$_{in}$

$$= 0.01 - 0.00997$$
$$= 0.00003 \text{ V}$$
$$= 30 \text{ } \mu\text{V}.$$

The percent of loading can be found by comparing the ratio of the unloaded source voltage to the loaded output voltage:

$$\% \text{ loading} = (100)(V_S - V_{x\text{-loaded}})/V_S$$
$$= (100)(0.00003)/0.01$$
$$= 0.3\%.$$

For the second amplifier,

$$V_x(10\text{K}) = (0.01)(10,000)/(10,000 + 300)$$
$$= (100)/10,300$$
$$= 0.00971 \text{ V}.$$

The loading loss is:

$$Loading \text{ } loss = V_S - V_{x\text{-loaded}}$$
$$= 0.01 - 0.00971$$
$$= 0.00029 \text{ V}$$
$$= 290 \text{ } \mu\text{V}.$$

$$\% \text{ loading} = (100)(V_S - V_{x\text{-loaded}})/V_S$$
$$= (100)(0.00029/0.01)$$
$$= 2.9\%.$$

Using an identical analysis for the 1-KΩ amplifier, the loading effect is about 23.1%. The calculations are left to the interested reader.

From this example, two things should be obvious:
- the lower the load resistance (input resistance of the receiving device) when compared to the output resistance of the source, the more pronounced the loading effect, and
- the amount of the loading effect can be approximated from

$$\% \text{ loading loss (approx)} = R_{source}/R_L.$$

(Note: This approximation is reasonably valid when the load resistance is about 10 times or more greater than the source resistance.)

Example 3.8. A certain 12-V wet-cell automotive battery is being tested. The no-load voltage is 13.47 V. Under a load current of 100 A, the battery terminal voltage is 10.82 V. What is the source resistance of the battery?

56

Solution 3.8. Use Equation (3.63) and directly substitute known values:

$$10.82 = 13.47 - (100)(R_S).$$
$$R_S = (13.47 - 10.82)/100$$
$$= 0.0265 \, \Omega.$$

The loading effect phenomenon is universal in that it occurs with all types of machinery, not just electrical sources. When increasing the load torque of an internal combustion engine, its speed decreases if not accompanied by an increased throttle setting. This explains why we must press on the accelerator of our car when approaching a hill if speed is to remain constant.

Hydraulic pumps are not immune to the effects of loading. It is well known that as pump outlet pressure increases, flow delivered to the load decreases. This flow loss is attributed to the increased internal leakage at the higher pump differential pressure.

$$Q_p = Q_i - Q_L \tag{3.64}$$

describes pump output flow, where Q_p is output flow, Q_i is the ideal flow of the internal-displacement members, and Q_L is internal leakage. Equation (3.64) suggests the equivalent circuit of Figure 3.26.

Note here that the pump has an ideal displacement element, shown as an industrial pump symbol with an I within its envelope to signify that it is ideal, ie it has no losses. The actual losses of a real pump are indicated by addition of an internal leakage path, R_L. When analyzing test results of real-world pumps, it becomes apparent that internal leakage largely is a laminar phenomenon. This gives rise to a linear pressure-flow relationship with the typical constant speed pump P-Q characteristic curve, Figure 3.27.

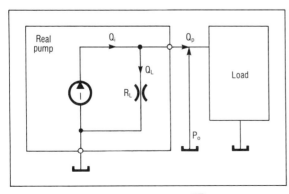

Fig. 3.26. A real hydraulic pump can be represented as an ideal flow source in parallel with an internal leakage resistance, R_L. The internal leakage path, caused by clearances within the pump, accounts for a drop in output flow, Q_p as the pump's output pressure, P_o, increases.

Fig. 3.27. Actual pump output flow drops as pressure increases due to internal pump leakage. Leakage is sometimes called slippage. The horizontal dashed line is flow from an ideal pump. The difference between the ideal-flow dashed line and the pump's actual flow, Q_p, is a measure of the pump's internal leakage. Slope m of the output flow line is the inverse of R_L. Note then, that R_L has units of pressure/flow, that is psi/in^3/sec.

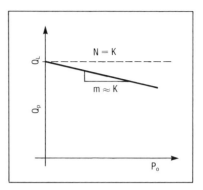

With some basic knowledge of pumps and judicious approximations, the circuit of Figure 3.26 can be used to develop a suitable linear model of a positive-displacement pump operating at constant temperature. That is, the ideal flow is well-known:

$$Q_i = (D)(N)/60, \tag{3.65}$$

where D is the displaced volume in in^3/rev of the pump shaft, N is the shaft speed in rpm, and Q_i is the ideal flow in in^3/sec. Now, knowing that the leakage is essentially laminar,

$$Q_p = (D)(N)/60 - P_o/R_L. \tag{3.66}$$

This equation is valid for any speed, and gives a reasonably good estimate of the actual pump output flow for any pressure and any displacement of a variable-displacement pump. The problem is that pump manufacturers normally do not publish the laminar leakage parameter, R_L. Note that its units must be psi/in^3/sec, the reciprocal of the slope of the pump's P-Q characteristic.

Pump manufacturers prefer to provide a graph of the performance data or, optionally, to publish volumetric and mechanical efficiencies. When pump efficiencies and the pressure, speed, and displacement corresponding to those efficiencies are known, the leakage parameter can be calculated. For an essentially linear, positive-displacement pump operating in its non-pressure-compensated region, it can be shown that

$$R_L = 60(P_r)/[(D_r)(N_r)(1 - E_{vr})], \tag{3.67}$$

where R_L is the pump's leakage parameter in psi/in^3/sec, P_r is the pump's rated pressure or alternatively, the pressure at which the volumetric efficiency is known, D_r is the rated displacement or alternatively, the displacement at which the volumetric efficiency is known, N_r is rated speed or alternatively, the speed at which the volumetric efficiency is known, and E_{vr} is the volumetric efficiency that was determined when the pump was operated at P_r, N_r, and D_r.

The hydraulic machinery industry has placed itself in an unfortunate position by emphasizing efficiency parameters rather than the more universal leakage-coefficient parameter. It is well known that efficiencies vary with operating point. Efficiency can be anywhere between 0% and 99% depending on the immediate operating level.

On the other hand, the leakage coefficient tends to be constant regardless of operating level. Internal leakage path R_L is a characteristic of the pump even when it is sitting on a shelf. It makes good sense to evaluate the leakage coefficient and then use it to calculate the efficiency rather than the other way around.

Of course, the leakage coefficient is dependent upon oil viscosity and therefore is valid only for one temperature. Nonetheless, the leakage path is a useful parameter to use when designing electrohydraulic control systems and it will be used here to assess loading effects on hydraulic pumps.

Leakage coefficient problem
Example 3.9. The published operating parameters of a certain variable-displacement pump are: E_{vr} of 89.7%, P_r of 2500 psi, N_r of 3000 rpm, and D_r of 2.56 in^3/rev. What is leakage coefficient R_L, and what is the expected flow when operated at full displacement, 2250 psi and 1750 rpm? What is the volumetric efficiency under these conditions?

Solution 3.9. The leakage coefficient can be found directly from the given data using Equation (3.67):

$$R_L = (60)(2500)/[(2.56)(3000)(1 - 0.897)]$$
$$= 189.6 \text{ psi/in}^3/\text{sec}.$$

Estimation of the output flow at the non-rated operating point can be made using Equation (3.66):

$$Q_p = [(2.56)(1750)/60] - (2250/189.6)$$
$$= 74.66 - 11.86$$
$$= 62.8 \text{ in}^3/\text{sec}.$$

The volumetric efficiency at the non-rated operating point can best be evaluated by observing that the first term in Equation (3.66) is the ideal flow at that operating speed and that the second term is the leakage flow. Volumetric efficiency is defined as the actual flow divided by the ideal flow (often called the theoretical flow in the industry, but that does not tell users how many *theories* are to be applied to arrive at a value):

$$E_v = Q_p/Q_i. \tag{3.68}$$

For the problem at hand,

$$E_v = (62.8)/(74.67)$$
$$= 0.841,$$

or 84.1%. Leakage flow is about 11.96 in^3/sec at the operating point.

Power

When dealing with electrical circuits, power is the product of current and voltage:

$$P = (V)(I). \tag{3.69}$$

Of course V is in volts, I is in amperes, and power, P, is in watts. The algebraic sign convention is such that if the current is **leaving** the positive terminal of a device, it is a **power source**, and power is **delivered by** the device. Conversely, when current **enters** the positive terminal, that device is a **load** and a **power consumer**, Figure 3.28.

Resistors, being consumers of power, offer a frictional path to current. Charges passing along the frictional path convert their electrical potential energy into heat energy. Thus, resistors get hot when carrying current. The energy converted to heat is irretrievably lost to the electrical circuit, so resistors can never store energy; they only irretrievably convert it to heat.

Fig. 3.28. Sign convention has current leaving the positive terminal of a source and entering the positive terminal of the load. Power, then, leaves source E and enters load R. Note that if R were to be replaced by a source with voltage higher than E, then E would become the consumer. This is the way battery chargers work.

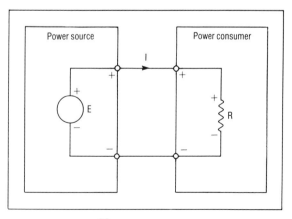

The temperature of a resistor is a complex function of its geometry, heat transfer characteristics, and environment. Not all operating resistors are hot to the touch because heating is a matter of degree. A given resistor in a servo amplifier may never vary from ambient temperature by a significant amount but, in contrast, the filament of an incandescent bulb gets so hot that it literally glows.

When dealing quantitatively with resistive power consumption, Equation (3.69) can be revised into two other equivalent forms using Ohm's Law:

$$V = (I)(R). \tag{3.70}$$

This can be substituted into Equation (3.69) to give:

$$P = (I)^2(R), \tag{3.71}$$

which is a handy form when current and resistance are known. Or, solving Equation (3.70) for I and then substituting into Equation (3.69) gives:

$$P = V^2/R. \tag{3.72}$$

Here is the interpretation of Equations (3.69), (3.70), and (3.71): when V is the voltage with reference to a common point, such as ground or circuit board common, then $(V)(I)$ is the total power passing that point in the circuit; when I is the current **through** resistor R, then P is the power consumed by that resistor; and when V is the differential voltage drop **across** resistor R, then P is the power consumed by that resistor.

Example 3.10. A DC generator powers a DC motor, Figure 3.29. E_g is the ideal source voltage produced by the generator, R_g is the generator's armature resistance (source resistance), R_m is the motor's armature resistance, and E_m is the *counter-emf* voltage generated because of the motor's armature rotation in its magnetic field.

(The exact electro-magnetic phenomena resulting in counter emf in a motor are exactly the same as those in a generator, but is not necessary at this time to know the details. It is only necessary to understand that a motor generates the counter-emf; it is vital in the energy conversion process. The analogous situation in hydraulic systems is that a hydraulic motor, through its internal pumping [displacement] elements, also happens to be pumping in a *flow absorbing* manner. The electrical system shown is a simplification of the so-called Ward-Leonard drive, which is almost perfectly analgous to a closed-loop hydrostatic transmission).

The motor and generator are electrically similar — they both have an armature resistance of 0.372 Ω. The current is 17.4 A while the terminal

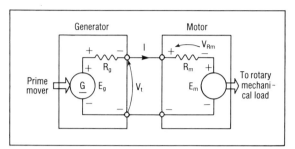

Fig. 3.29. A DC motor-generator set (Ward-Leonard drive) is used to control power to a rotary load described in Example 3.10. The Ward-Leonard drive is the electrical analog to the closed-loop hydrostatic transmission. See Example 3.10 for explanation of the symbols.

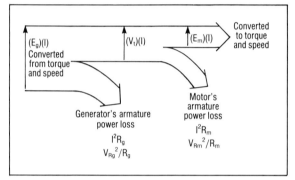

Fig. 3.30. Power accounting diagram for Example 3.10.

voltage, V_t, is found to be 204.5 V. How much power is delivered by the generator, how much power is consumed by the motor, and how much power is consumed by each of the armature resistances? Do a complete power accounting, Figure 3.30, for the m-g (motor-generator) set.

Solution 3.10. Because the terminal current and voltage are given, the power can be found directly:

$$P_g = (V_t)(I)$$
$$= (204.5)(17.4)$$
$$= 3558.3 \text{ W}$$
$$= 3.5583 \text{ kW}$$
$$= 4.77 \text{ hp.}$$

It should be apparent that power delivered by the generator equals power consumed by motor. Therefore,

$$P_m = P_g$$
$$= 3558.3 \text{ W.}$$

The resistive power can be found from

$$P_{rg} = (I)^2(R_g)$$
$$= (17.4)^2(0.372)$$
$$= 112.6 \text{ W.}$$

Because the motor and generator have identical armature resistances,

$$P_{rm} = P_{rg}$$
$$= 112.6 \text{ W.}$$

Power accounting requires the calculation of all power consumptions in the circuit and then checking that they balance. That is,

$$Power\ delivered = Power\ consumed \qquad\qquad (3.73)$$

First it is necessary to determine the voltage generated in the ideal portion of generator E_g. A loop equation provides the approach:

$$V_t = E_g - (I)(R_g).$$

The only unknown is E_g, so

$$E_g = V_t + (I)(R_g)$$
$$= 204.5 + (17.4)(0.372)$$
$$= 210.97 \text{ V.}$$

A similar approach is used to find the motor's counter emf:

$$V_t = (I)(R_m) + E_m,$$

in which only E_m is unknown. So

$$E_m = V_t - (I)(R_m)$$
$$= 204.5 - (17.4)(0.372)$$
$$= 198.03 \text{ V.}$$

The total electrical power delivered to the electrical circuit is

$$P_{total} = (E_g)(I)$$
$$= (210.97)(17.4)$$
$$= 3670.9 \text{ W.}$$

The power converted into torque and speed by the motor is:

$$P_{mech} = (E_m)(I)$$
$$= (198.03)(17.4)$$

$$= 3445.7 \text{ W}.$$

It is necessary that

$$P_{total} = P_{rg} + P_{rm} + P_{mech}$$
$$3670.9 \doteq 112.6 + 112.6 + 3445.7$$
$$3670.9 = 3670.9 . \checkmark$$

This provides a check on the accuracy and correctness of the individual calculations. The power consumptions must balance. The analysis could be further checked by finding the voltage drops across each of the armature resistances, and then calculating the power consumptions using Equation (3.72). Details are left to the interested reader.

Example 3.11. A certain servovalve has two coils, each with a resistance of 27 Ω at 75° F. The coils can be connected in series or in parallel at the user's discretion and each coil has a rated current of 60 μA. (When rated current is applied to both coils of a servovalve, the main spool of the valve will be fully shifted.) For both the series and parallel connections, determine the applied voltage required to achieve rated current in each coil and the power consumed by both coils.

Solution 3.11. Figure 3.31 shows the two connecting schemes. It

Fig. 3.31. Schematic of series and parallel connection of servovalve coils, Example 3.11.

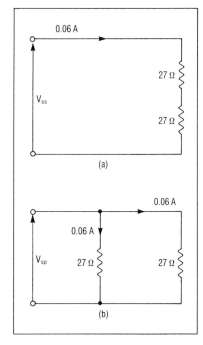

64

should be apparent from these schematics that for the series connection, Figure 3.31(a),

$$V_{ss} = (I_r)(R_s)$$
$$= (0.06)(54)$$
$$= 3.24 \text{ V.}$$

For the parallel connection, Figure 3.31(b),

$$I_t = 0.06 + 0.06$$

$$= 0.12 \text{ A.}$$

For parallel resistances,

$$R_{eq} = (R_1)(R_2)/[(R_1 + R_2)]$$
$$= (27)(27)/[(27 + 27)]$$
$$= 13.5 \text{ Ω.}$$

Therefore,

$$V_{sp} = (I_t)(R_{eq})$$
$$= (0.120)(13.5)$$
$$= 1.62 \text{ V.}$$

Now, all the power consumptions can be found. For the series connection,

$$P = (E)(I)$$
$$= (3.24)(0.06)$$
$$= 0.1944 \text{ W}$$
$$= 194.4 \text{ μW.}$$

For the parallel connection,

$$P = (E)(I)$$
$$= (1.62)(0.120)$$
$$= 0.1944 \text{ W}$$
$$= 194.4 \text{ μW.}$$

It is gratifying to note that when the valve coils are operated at their rated currents, the power required to drive them is independent of the connection method. Any other result would imply that energy could be created by one method, but not the other.

In hydraulic circuits, power is the product of pressure and flow:

$$W = (P)(Q). \qquad (3.74)$$

Immediately, two problems are apparent. The first deals with symbols, because in the hydraulic technology, P always indicates pressure, but in electrical circuits, P always denotes power. Therefore, in Equation (3.74), P is pressure in psi, and flow Q is in in^3/sec; a new symbol, W, will signify hydraulic power. This author has no solution for this dilemma, except to urge the reader to remain aware of the context in which a certain symbol is used and to comprehend the meaning of a particular discussion, rather than blindly accepting equations and symbols.

The second problem arises because of the units of measure. Using the suggested US units, Equation (3.74) uses P in psi and Q in in^3/sec to provide an answer in in-lb/sec, a unit of power. Unfortunately, no one uses the equation this way, instead preferring to convert the answer to horsepower or watts. Knowing that there are 6600 in-lb/sec/hp, we can modify Equation (3.74) to provide horsepower:

$$W = (P)(Q)/6600. \qquad (3.75)$$

Or, knowing that there are 746 watts per horsepower, Equation (3.74) may be modified to give watts:

$$\begin{aligned} W &= 746(P)(Q)/6600 \\ &= (P)(Q)/8.847. \end{aligned} \qquad (3.76)$$

Therefore, the formulae for power in hydraulic systems always contain a constant of proportionality which modifies the $(P)(Q)$ product into the practical units of power. By way of contrast, the practical units of voltage and current always yield a practical unit of power, namely the watt, without the need for a proportionality constant. A generalized form for the power equation has the form

$$W = (P)(Q)/K_u, \qquad (3.77)$$

where the desired units of W can be selected for the situation at hand and K_u will be the constant of proportionality needed to convert the in-lb/sec units of $(P)(Q)$ into the desired power units. That is

$$K_u = 6600$$

when horsepower is the desired result, and

$$K_u = 8.847$$

when power is to be expressed in watts. From now on when using Equation (3.77), it will be understood that the units of P will be psi, Q will be in in^3/sec, and the units of W must be negotiated for the investigation at hand. This should be contrasted with the electrical power formula, Equation (3.69).

When the power in question is that being absorbed or consumed by a restriction or orifice in which the flow is turbulent, we know that

$$Q = (K_c)(P)^{1/2}, \tag{3.78}$$

which can be substituted into Equation (3.77), so that

$$W = (K_c)(P)^{3/2}/K_u. \tag{3.79}$$

Or, by solving Equation (3.78) for pressure,

$$P = Q^2/K_c^2. \tag{3.80}$$

Substituting that into Equation (3.77),

$$W = Q^3/(K_c^2)(K_u). \tag{3.81}$$

We see then that resistive power in a hydraulic circuit varies with the three-halves power of pressure, or the cube of the flow. The student should contrast all of these hydraulic forms with their electrical counterparts. But after citing those differences, it can happily be reported that the concept of power in hydraulic circuits is perfectly analogous to that of electrical circuits.

When P is pressure with reference to a common point, such as tank or ambient, then $(P)(Q)/K_u$ is the total power passing that point in the circuit. However, when P is the differential pressure across an element, W is then the power consumed or delivered by that element provided that

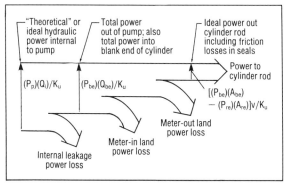

Fig. 3.32. Power accounting diagram for Example 3.12.

67

MOTION CONTROL

the flow entering the component equals the flow that leaves.
When Q is the flow **through** orifice K_c, W is the power consumed by
that orifice. When P is the differential pressure **across** orifice K_c, W is the
power consumed by that orifice.

Example 3.12. Perform a complete power accounting, Figure 3.32,
on the circuit of Figure 3.33, and determine the pressures indicated by the

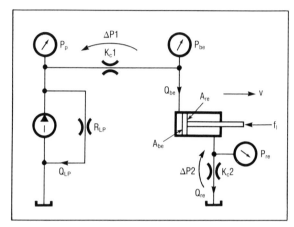

three pressure gages given the following: the load force is 14,800
pounds; the cylinder propels the load at 18.6 in/sec; the cylinder bore is
5 in; the diameter of the rod is 2.5 in; the 4-way directional control valve
is considered to be two orifices, K_{c1} and K_{c2}, which represent the meter-
in and meter-out lands, respectively, while the valve is shifted to the cyl-
inder-extend position. The values for the orifices are 14.79 and 10.33
in³/sec/(psi)$^{1/2}$, respectively; and the pump has an ideal displacement
element in parallel with an internal leakage coefficient of 101.4 psi/in³/
sec.

Solution 3.12. It first will be helpful to calculate the cylinder areas:

$A_{bore} = (3.14159)(bore)^2/(4)$
   $= (3.14159)(5)^2/(4)$
   $= 19.63 \text{ in}^2.$

$A_{rod\ end} = (3.14159)[(5)^2 - (2.5)^2]/(4)$
   $= 14.73 \text{ in}^2.$

$Q_{re} = (v)(A_{re})$
   $= (18.6)(14.73)$
   $= 273.9 \text{ in}^3/\text{sec}.$

$$Q_{be} = (v)(A_{be})$$
$$= (18.6)(19.63)$$
$$= 365.1 \text{ in}^3/\text{sec.}$$

A free-body diagram of the piston indicates that

$$(P_{be})(A_{be}) - (P_{re})(A_{re}) - f_l = 0. \tag{3.82}$$

Pressures P_{be} and P_{re} are **gage** pressures, but notice in Figure 3.33 that the pressure drop across the meter-out land, ΔP_2, is the same as gage pressure P_{re}. Because flow coefficient K_{c2} is given, the rod end pressure is:

$$P_{re(gage)} = \Delta P_{2(differential)} = Q_{re}^2/K_{c2}^2$$
$$= (273.9)^2/(10.33)^2$$
$$= 703 \text{ psig.}$$

Now, the only unknown in Equation (3.82) is the cap-end gage pressure, P_{be}. This can be calculated:

$$P_{be} = [(P_{re})(A_{re}) + f_l]/A_{be}$$
$$= [(703)(14.73) + 14800]/19.63$$
$$= 1281 \text{ psig.}$$

With knowledge of the flow and valve coefficient K_{c1}, the differential pressure drop across the meter-in land, ΔP_1 is:

$$\Delta P_1 = Q_{be}^2/K_{c1}^2$$
$$= (365.1)^2/(14.79)^2$$
$$= 609.38 \text{ psid.}$$

Now, pressure summation tells us that

$$P_p = \Delta P_1 + P_{be}$$
$$= 609.38 + 1281$$
$$= 1890.4 \text{ psig.}$$

Knowing the pump outlet pressure and the pump's leakage parameter, leakage flow can be calculated.

$$Q_L = P_p/R_{LP}$$
$$= (1890.4)/(101.4)$$
$$= 18.64 \text{ in}^3/\text{sec.}$$

The ideal pump output flow can be determined:

$$Q_I = Q_{be} + Q_L$$
$$= 365.1 + 18.64$$
$$= 383.7 \text{ in}^3/\text{sec.}$$

All pressures and flows are known, so power consumptions can be calculated:

$$W_{total} = (P_p)(Q_I)/K_u.$$

In this case we want horsepower, so

$$W_{total} = (1890.4)(383.7)/6600$$
$$= 109.91 \text{ hp, and}$$
$$WK_{c1} = Q_{be}^3/(K_{c1})^2(K_u)$$
$$= (365.1)^3/(14.79)^2(6600)$$
$$= 33.71 \text{ hp.}$$

The total power passing downstream of the meter-in land is given by

$$W_{into\,cyl} = (P_{be\text{-}gage})(Q_{be})/K_u$$
$$= (1281)(365.1)/6600$$
$$= 70.86 \text{ hp.}$$

Of the total power going past the meter-in land, some will move the 14,800-pound load at 18.6 in/sec, while some of it will push the meter-out oil through the meter-out land. The power out to the load is

$$W_{load} = (f_l)(v)/6600$$
$$= (14,800)(18.6)/6600$$
$$= 41.71 \text{ hp.}$$

The power consumed by the meter-out land must be

$$W_{meter\text{-}out} = (P_{re})(Q_{re})/6600$$
$$= (703)(273.9)/6600$$
$$= 29.17 \text{ hp.}$$

As a check,

$$W_{into\,cyl} = W_{load} + W_{meter\text{-}out}$$
$$70.86 \overset{?}{=} 41.71 + 29.17$$
$$70.86 = 70.88, \checkmark$$

which checks (round-off error notwithstanding).

It is interesting to calculate the efficiency of this system. Efficiency is defined, in general, as the output power divided by the total input power. Both required values are known; that is,

$$E_o = Output\ power/Input\ power$$
$$= 41.71/109.91$$
$$= 37.95\%.$$

That answer takes into account the leakage inefficiency of the pump but not its mechanical inefficiency.

Maximum power transfer

One function of an electric system as well as a hydraulic system is to deliver power to a load. It is well known that the power delivered to the load depends upon the specific characteristics of the load as well as of the source. We shall investigate the phenomenon of power transfer from the source to the load and determine the conditions necessary to maximize power. For both hydraulic and electrical power amplifier design, these conditions which provide maximum power transfer are useful goals.

First consider the power transfer of an electrical DC source which has a finite (non-zero) source resistance. It is expressed mathematically in Equation (3.63), and graphically in Figure 3.34. Note in Figure 3.34 that the short circuit condition, ie the point where output voltage V_L goes to zero is I-axis intercept point I_N. That notation is used because the short circuit current happens to be called the *Norton current* when using Norton's theorem for equivalent circuits.

Consider this discussion about short-circuit conditions along with real hardware; **in fact, an actual test under short circuit conditions may be dangerous to man and/or machine.** Short circuit current is the current that would result if an ammeter were connected to the output terminals of a source. Imagine the sparks if the source were the power company's line that leads into a home! Analytically, there is no danger; short circuit conditions can be imposed with impunity.

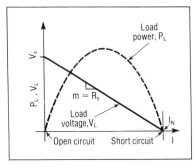

Fig. 3.34. For a voltage source with a finite source resistance, load power is zero at both shorted and open-circuit loads, but maximizes at the mid-load point, the point of maximum power transfer. It also is true that $R_L = R_s$ at the point of maximum power transfer, leading to the statement that the load impedance is matched to the source impedance.

The analogous situation for a hydraulic system would be to deadhead a positive-displacement pump. This rarely is done because when deadheaded, most pumps can develop destructive pressures. Nonetheless, we will deal with deadhead conditions analytically even though **a real test may be impractical, dangerous, or destructive.**

Note the dashed curve in Figure 3.34 labeled *Load power, P_L*. An intuitive sense can be gained by considering the nature of power. Recall that power is the product of current times voltage. First consider the open circuit condition, ie $R_L = \infty$, wherein the voltage is at its highest value, but the current is zero. Clearly, the power delivered to the load is zero.

At the other extreme, the short circuit condition, $R_L = 0$, current is at a maximum but the voltage across the load is zero. Again, the volt-ampere product is zero and so the power is zero. On the other hand, at R_L values between zero and infinity, current through and voltage across the load cannot be zero; therefore, the power cannot be zero. The load power, beginning at zero and ending at zero, must maximize somewhere in between.

It is useful to determine the exact conditions that define maximum load power, that is, the conditions for transfer of maximum power from the source to the load. By now, it should be intuitively obvious that maximum power transfer occurs when the load resistance is adjusted to produce a load voltage which is half the open-circuit voltage. This is exactly the case.

The development begins with Equation 3.63, multiplying both sides by the current to form a power equation. That is

$$(I)(V_L) = (I)(V_s) - (I)^2(R_s).\qquad(3.83)$$

Recognizing that the left hand side is the power delivered to the load, Equation (3.83) becomes

$$P_L = (I)(V_s) - (I)^2(R_s).\qquad(3.84)$$

The plot of Equation (3.84) is a parabola; for example, the dashed curve of Figure 3.34. The calculus teaches that to find the point of maximum power, find the derivative and then set it equal to zero. In this case, differentiating load power with respect to current derives the point of maximum load power:

$$dP_L/dI = V_s - 2(I)(R_s) = 0.\qquad(3.85)$$
Now, solving for I,

$$I = V_s/2R_s,\qquad(3.86)$$

because

$V_s/R_s = I$, a short circuit, $= I_N$. (3.87)

So for maximum power transfer,

$I = I_N/2$. (3.88)

Substituting Equation (3.85) into Equation (3.63) provides the load voltage that maximizes power:

$V_L = V_s - (V_s/2R_s)R_s$, (3.89)

or

$V_L = V_s/2$. (3.90)

Using voltage divider Equation (3.62) for the load voltage, the load resistance that maximizes power is:

$V_L = V_s/2 = V_s R_L/(R_s + R_L)$. (3.91)

Solving for R_L,

$R_L = R_s$. (3.92)

Not surprisingly, power to the load is maximized when the load resistance equals the source resistance.

Impedance matching

The process of designing electronic circuits for maximum power transfer also is referred to as the process of *impedance matching*. Impedance refers to the opposition offered to alternating current in circuits. Impedance has a resistive element identical to the resistance discussed so far, as well as reactive components caused by the other two circuit elements, inductance and capacitance. They will be addressed later.

When the conditions of Equation (3.92) are met, the source has been matched to the load or the *impedances have been matched*. Strictly speaking, meeting Equation (3.92) results only in a resistive match. Even so, the more general term *matching impedance* permeates industrial jargon.

Thus, when a design matches impedances, maximum power transfer is automatically achieved. It can be shown similarly that the more general case of AC circuits achieve maximum power transfer under matched impedance conditions even though inductance and/or capacitance may be present in either the load or the source. That subject is beyond the scope of this text.

Example 3.13 Teenage Freddie, with hearing already impaired by overexposure to loud rock music, concludes that his 120-W stereo amplifier has lost some of its "oomph". Having just completed a brief introduction to some DC circuit analysis in his high school physics class, he decides that he needs additional speakers to again enjoy the pleasures of rapturous noise.

He concludes that if he adds one speaker in parallel with each of the two speakers (one on each stereo channel), the additional current resulting from the reduced resistance of two speakers in parallel will boost the sound level by the desired amount.

He purchases two new speakers identical to the originals and makes his set up. But, instead of getting more sound out, he senses there is less. Furthermore, his amplifier now smells as if it is overheating. In desperation, Freddie comes to you, his beneficent uncle, for consultation. Please explain to Freddie what is wrong, why his approach will not work, and advise him on future actions.

Solution 3.13. A look at the amplifier specifications indicates a total continuous output power of 120 W, or 60 W per channel into an 8-Ω speaker on each channel. Because high-powered audio amplifiers are always designed for maximum power transfer, you conclude that the output impedance of the amplifier is 8 Ω as well. At full power out,

$$V^2/8 = 60, \text{ that is,}$$
$$V = [(8)(60)]^{1/2}$$
$$= 21.9 \text{ V,}$$

the voltage across the speaker at full output power, Figure 3.35. Because you know that the amplifier is impedance matched, you immediately conclude that the open-circuit voltage of the amplifier is 43.8 V. This is because with equal source and speaker resistance, the voltage drop

Fig. 3.35. Simplified schematic and values for the audio amplifier of Example 3.13 when operated at maximum power.

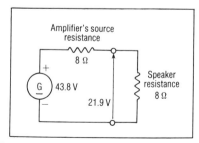

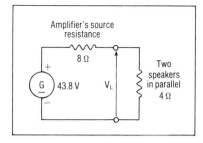

Fig. 3.36. When two 8-Ω speakers are connected in parallel, the net load is only 4 Ω.

across the load (speaker) must equal the voltage drop across the source resistance, or 43.8 V at the source. Redrawing the circuit with one 8-Ω speaker replaced by the 4-Ω equivalent of two speakers in parallel, Figure 3.36, the new current can be calculated.

$$I = 43.8/(8 + 4)$$
$$= 3.65 \text{ A.}$$

You inform Freddie that his conclusion about more current was correct because the current with the original 8-Ω speaker would have been

$$I = 43.8/(8 + 8)$$
$$= 2.74 \text{ A.}$$

However, a power calculation reveals the reason for reduced sound with the higher current. With the single 8-Ω speaker,

$$P = (I)^2 (R_L)$$
$$= (2.74)^2(8)$$
$$= 60 \text{ watts,}$$

which we knew all along. However, when the 4-Ω system is evaluated,

$$P = (I)^2 (R_L)$$
$$= (3.65)^2(4)$$
$$= 53.3 \text{ W,}$$

so the power level is lower even though the current is higher. As for the overheating of the amplifier, you now turn your attention to the power consumed by the amplifier's source resistance. It was originally designed to dissipate exactly the same amount of power that the load was to consume, namely, 60 watts. Under the 4-Ω load, however

$$P = (I)^2(R_s)$$
$$= (3.65)^2(8)$$
$$= 106.6 \text{ W}.$$

The output transistor(s) must consume nearly twice the power for which they were designed, leading to excessive self-heating and accounting for the burning odor. Having made these calculations, you now explain to your nephew that the problem lies in the music itself, that rock music is incapable of generating more than 60 watts, and therefore, his goal of boosted output is not achievable no matter how many speakers he connects to his stereo amplifier. Instead you counsel him to pursue a career as a librarian — advice he heeds. The ensuing years of quietude allow restoration of a good portion of his hearing.

Maximum power transfer is a useful design goal for audio power amplifiers but it is not the goal of all electronic devices. For example, a high-performance, regulated-DC power supply may carry specifications of 15-V regulated, with a source resistance of 0.01 Ω. Quick calculation shows that a load resistance of 0.01 Ω connected across the power supply results in a current of 750 A. While the rated output current may be only 10 A, this power supply clearly will be damaged if operated at its maximum power-transfer point.

Likewise, hydraulic systems do not always operate at the point of maximum power transfer. This is generally the case in pump-controlled circuits in which pump displacement and speed regulate the flow. Just as in electrical circuits, the point of maximum power transfer will occur when the delivered flow is one-half the fully unloaded flow. The internal leakage path under that condition has to absorb one-half the pump's output. For a tight pump, ie, one with high volumetric efficiency, the resulting pressure will probably be so high that it will lead to the pump's destruction well short of the maximum power point.

When using proportional or servovalves to control flow, the hydraulic power supply usually is configured to provide constant pressure, not positive displacement. This control scheme allows the variable restriction valve to control flow to the load. In such systems, maximum power transfer is achieved at viable pressures and flows and can be a system design goal.

Consider the conditions which transfer maximum power to a load when the hydraulic supply contains a throttling valve, Figure 3.37. This simplified equivalent circuit uses a constant pressure generator to develop fixed pressure P_s in psig. This pressure is connected through throttling orifice K_s to an arbitrary load. For analysis, begin with the assumption that the valve is fully open and it therefore can be represented by a fixed orifice. That is usually one of the design parameters of the system: the valve is sized and selected on the basis of its fully open capacity.

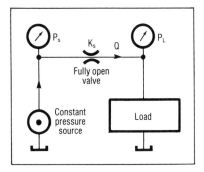

Fig. 3.37. This schematic, typical of the hydraulic essentials of servosystems, represents a valve-controlled load using a constant-pressure source, which is a well-regulated pressure-compensated pump.

That condition is assumed in this development. Begin with the pressure-drop loop equation for the circuit of Figure 3.37:

$$P_s = \Delta P_{across\,K_s} + P_L, \tag{3.93}$$

or

$$P_s = Q^2/K_s^2 + P_L. \tag{3.94}$$

To form a power equation, multiply both sides of Equation (3.94) by the flow, Q:

$$(Q)(P_s) = (Q^3/K_s^2) + (Q)(P_L), \tag{3.95}$$

from which we recognize that $(Q)(P_L)$ is the power delivered to the load. That is

$$W_L = (Q)(P_s) - Q^3/K_s^2, \tag{3.96}$$

which is the desired form. To find conditions for maximum load power, differentiate load power with respect to flow and set the result to zero:

$$d(W_L)/d(Q) = (P_s - 3)(Q)^2/(K_s)^2 = 0. \tag{3.97}$$

Understanding that

$$(Q)^2/(K_s)^2 = \Delta P_{across\,valve\,Ks}, \tag{3.98}$$

that is substituted into Equation (3.97) so that

$$(P_s - 3)(\Delta P_v) = 0, \tag{3.99}$$
$$\Delta P_v = P_s/3. \tag{3.100}$$

That is, the drop across the valve must be one-third the supply pressure so as to deliver maximum power to the load. Conversely, the load pressure must be two-thirds of the supply pressure in order to receive maximum power.

Electrical power transfer requires equal load and source resistances. An analogous statement would be possible for a hydraulic system except for two practical reasons:

• the hydraulics industry, lamentably, has never accepted the notion of resistance and/or impedance, although the adoption of standardized definitions would be beneficial, and

• the load on a hydraulic power unit is not usually a simple restrictive device such as an orifice. Instead, the load is an energy-conversion device such as a cylinder or motor which couples power to yet another device, the ultimate load. Therefore, conditions for maximum power transfer will remain in pressure terms, as in Equation (3.100).

Example 3.14. It is necessary to design a hydraulic power unit with valve control which will result in maximum power transfer to the load. The load is known only to require 1850 psi while absorbing a flow of 188 in³/sec. If the valve is a flow-rated 1000-psi servovalve what is the flow rating of the valve in gpm?

Solution 3.14. Because we desire to design for maximum power transfer,

$$P_s = 3(P_L)/2$$
$$= (3)(1850)/2$$
$$= 2775 \text{ psig.}$$

Valve coefficient K_s can now be found:

$$K_s = (Q_{\text{ at the design point}})/[P_s - (P_{L \text{ at the design point}})]^{1/2}$$
$$= 188/(2775 - 1850)^{1/2}$$
$$= 6.18 \text{ in}^3/\text{sec}/(\text{psi})^{1/2}.$$

The rated flow of this valve can be found from the orifice flow equation and evaluated using the conditions under which the valve is flow-rated, ie, 1000 psid:

$$Q_{vr} = K_v(1000)^{1/2}$$
$$= (6.18)(31.62)$$
$$= 195 \text{ in}^3/\text{sec}$$
$$= 50.76 \text{ gpm.}$$

Chapter Four
Capacitance and
Inductance

A capacitor is formed anytime two conductors (usually plates) are separated by an insulator. The insulation used in capacitors is called a dielectric, Figure 4.1. If one conductor accumulates electron or ion charges relative to the other, the charges cannot neutralize one another because of the insulated separation.

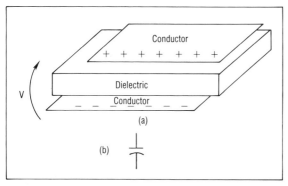

Fig. 4.1. Capacitors are comprised of two conductor plates separated by an insulating dielectric, (a). Capacitor symbol, (b).

A voltage difference therefore exists between the two conducting plates and the capacitor is said to have some degree of charge. Should a conductor be connected between them, the charges will move to neutralize one another and discharge the capacitor. The charge-holding ability of a capacitor is called its *capacitance*.

The hydraulic analogy to the capacitor is a volume or accumulator. Just as an accumulator is a mechanical bucket that holds molecules of oil, the capacitor is an electronic bucket that holds electrons. The analogy can continue: as additional molecules of oil are packed into the accumulator, it pushes back with increasing pressure because of its gas precharge; more effort is required to push the next batch of molecules into the accumulator. The accumulator becomes charged as the packing continues, Figure 4.2.

The electronic analogy: if an electron is stripped off the upper plate of a capacitor and deposited on its lower plate, the upper plate loses a net charge of one electron that is gained by the lower plate. When attempting to strip another electron from the upper plate, the positive

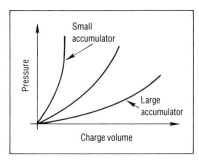

Fig. 4.2. Curves indicate how size of accumulator affects pressure as oil charge volume changes.

charge already existing there resists the stripping effort. Further, the lower, negatively charged plate tries to push the new electron away as it is deposited there. As this stripping or charging process continues, it requires more and more effort to strip and deposit each new charge. This effort is measured in volts.

Capacitance is a measure of the amount the voltage builds with each succeeding new charge transferred from one plate to the other. The unit of capacitance is the farad but because this unit is too large to be practical, capacitance usually is measured in microfarads and picofarads:

$$1 \text{ farad} = 1,000,000 \, \mu f = 10^6 \mu f,$$

and

$$1 \text{ farad} = 1,000,000,000,000 \text{ pf} = 10^{12} \text{pf}.$$

A large capacitor will hold a large number of charges for a given volt-

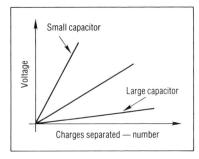

Fig. 4.3. Analagous to accumulator charges indicated in Figure 4.2, these curves indicate how voltage changes as number of separated charges vary in large and small capacitors.

age while a small capacitor requires only a small charge before it builds to the same voltage, Figure 4.3.

In a more practical situation, the charging of an accumulator is done with the aid of a pump, Figure 4.4. As the pump transfers molecules of oil from the reservoir to the accumulator, the pressure builds. The speed

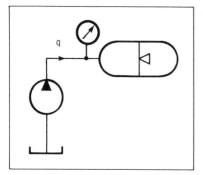

Fig. 4.4. Simplified hydraulic circuit with flow, q, which charges accumulator.

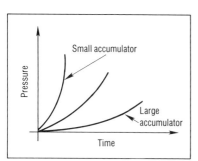

Fig. 4.5 Curves indicate time vs. pressure for various sizes of accumulators.

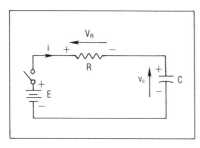

Fig. 4.6. Simple illustrative electrical circuit with capacitance C.

with which accumulator pressure builds depends upon the rate at which oil is pumped or charged into the accumulator and its size, that is, the volume or "capacitance" of the accumulator, Figure 4.5.

An analogous situation exists in an electrical circuit with a capacitor, Figure 4.6. When the switch is closed in this circuit, the energy present in the voltage source will begin stripping charges off the lower plate of the capacitor and simultaneously deposit them on the upper plate. The movement of charges constitutes current i.

Charges are transferred to the upper capacitor plate and the capacitor voltage increases until it equals battery voltage E. Then, because Kirchoff's Laws still apply, there will be no voltage across the resistor and hence no current, and the charging process stops.

The time required for the capacitor to reach full charge, E volts, depends upon the size of the capacitor and the rate at which the current deposits charges on the capacitor, Figure 4.7. But the amount of current depends upon the difference between applied voltage E and the voltage to which the capacitor is already charged. The difference between applied voltage E and capacitor voltage v_c is the drop across the resistor which produces the current:

$$i = V_R/R,$$

which causes capacitor voltage to rise.

Thus, the current deposits a charge on the capacitor to increase capacitor voltage. This reduces current so the rate at which voltage rises diminishes constantly. The representative curve is called *an exponential charging curve*, Figure 4.8. It is an electrical response to the child's puzzle: if

Fig. 4.7. Curves indicate how capacitor size affects the time it takes a capacitor to charge.

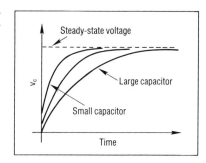

Fig. 4.8. Exponential charging curve indicates how capacitor voltage changes with respect to time to reach applied voltage E.

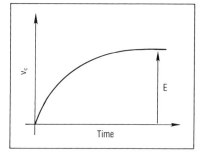

you are 3 feet from a wall and you make a series of steps, each one of which is half the distance remaining, how many steps are needed to reach the wall? The answer is that it will take an infinite number of steps because you will never reach the wall.

In reality, the capacitor charge never reaches applied voltage E because it charges 63% of the remaining voltage in each increment of time. The time increment for that 63% charge is the *time constant*, τ;

$$\tau = RC \tag{4.1}$$

where τ is in seconds, resistance R is in ohms, and capacitance C is in farads, Figure 4.9.

For all practical purposes, the capacitor reaches full charge in four time constants or 98.17%. But because many authors use five time constants, or 99.37% of full charge, we will use the more conservative five time constants as the definition of full charge.

Example 4.1. How long will it take to fully charge a 0.047 μf capacitor which is connected to a 560K resistor?

Solution 4.1. Because five time constants are needed to produce full charge, use Equation (4.1) to calculate time constant τ:

$$
\begin{aligned}
\tau &= RC \\
&= 560,000(0.047 \times 10^{-6}) \\
&= 26,320(10^{-6}) \\
&= 0.0263 \text{ s.}
\end{aligned}
$$

$$
\begin{aligned}
5\tau &= 5(0.0263) \\
&= 0.132 \text{ s, or} \\
&= 132 \text{ ms.}
\end{aligned}
$$

As one might expect, capacitors undergo discharge cycles, too. If a capacitor is connected to a voltage source and charged, it attempts to retain

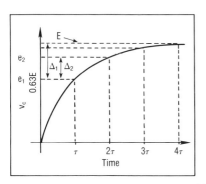

Fig. 4.9. Exponential charging curve uses time constant, τ, to indicate how long it takes to charge capacitor. The voltage changes by 63% of the difference remaining during each time constant. $e_1 = 0.63E$; $\Delta_1 = E - e_1$; $\Delta_2 = 0.63\Delta_1$; and $e_2 = e_1 + \Delta_2$.

83

the charge separation when the source voltage is removed. This is because there is no way for the charges to neutralize one another across the dielectric when the dielectric is a perfect insulator. But if a resistor is connected between the two capacitor plates, Figure 4.10, a current path is formed, however restrictive.

When the switch is closed, there will be current i as separated charges move to neutralize one another. Capacitor voltage decays exponentially, again 63% during each time constant, Figure 4.11.

The nature of the charge and discharge of the capacitor is called the *exponential rise* when related to charging, and the *exponential decay* when discharging. Exponential rises and decays occur frequently in nature.

For charging, the general form of the exponential rise equation is

$$v_c = V_{ss} + (V_{co} - V_{ss})\epsilon^{-t/\tau}, \tag{4.2}$$

where v_c is the instantaneous voltage across the capacitor, V_{co} is the intitial voltage at time $= 0$, τ is the time constant of the circuit, t is the amount of time that has elapsed since switch closure, and ϵ is the base of the natural logarithm system, a constant equal to 2.71828... . V_{ss} is the steady-state or final value the voltage reaches after a very long time has passed. When the initial voltage is 0, Equation (4.2) can be simplified to

$$v_c = V_{ss} - V_{ss}\epsilon^{-t/\tau}, \tag{4.3}$$

or in another form,

Fig. 4.10. Simple electrical circuit illustrates precharged capacitor discharge when switch is closed.

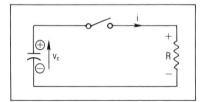

Fig. 4.11. Characteristic curve for capacitor discharge voltage vs. time when starting from full charge.

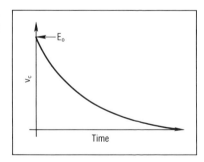

$$v_c = V_{ss}(1 - \epsilon)^{-t/\tau}. \tag{4.4}$$

For discharge, the general form of the exponential decay equation is

$$v_c = V_{co}\epsilon^{-t/\tau}, \tag{4.5}$$

where v_c, V_{co}, t, τ, and ϵ have the same interpretation as in Equation (4.2). More details on exponential functions are given in Appendix B.

Example 4.2. A 0.5 μf capacitor is initially charged to 185 V. What will be its voltage 1.5 s after starting its discharge through a 1 MΩ resistor, Figure 4.12?

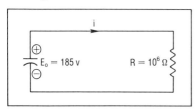

Fig. 4.12. Circuit for Example 4.2.

i

$E_o = 185$ v $R = 10^6 \Omega$

Solution 4.2. Use the exponential decay formula, Equation (4.5):

$$\begin{aligned}
v_c &= V_{co}\epsilon^{-t/RC} \\
&= 185(2.71828)(-1.5)/[(0.5 \times 10^{-6})(1 \times 10^6)] \\
&= (185)/(2.71828)^3 \\
&= 9.21v.
\end{aligned}$$

Summary of capacitance:

● capacitors introduce a time factor into circuit operation because of the time needed to transfer charges from one side of the capacitor to the other

● capacitors charge and discharge exponentially; Equation (4.2) describes charging and is the formula for the curve of Figure 4.8. For the discharge process, Equation (4.5) produces the curve of Figure 4.11

● the time to charge or discharge is affected by the time constant τ

● when a capacitor first starts charging it can be treated like a short circuit, but only for the very first instant. A moment later, its voltage is no longer zero

● when a capacitor first starts discharging it can be treated as a battery, but only for the first instant, and

● when a capacitor reaches its final steady-state charge, it acts like an open circuit.

Inductance

Inductance arises anytime the magnetic flux created by a current links with the wire conductor that carries the current. Inductance even exists in a straight piece of wire but because its value is so very small, it is inconsequential in slow systems such as electrohydraulics. When the wire is wrapped in a coil to form an inductor, the flux linkage is enhanced and the inductive properties become significant.

If the current through a coil is changing, the amount of flux linking with the coil also changes and during the change, a voltage is *induced* which opposes the current change. The ± signs in Figure 4.13 indicate the polarity of this induced voltage. Note that the polarity wants to *push back* against the incoming current and impede its growth.

Fig. 4.13. Inductor coil shows elements of inductance and polarity of subsequent induced voltage. Circular magnetic flux, Φ, is increasing.

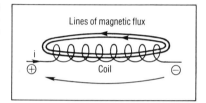

Fig. 4.14. Graph indicates accelerations of various sizes of mass with constant force applied to mass. Friction is ignored.

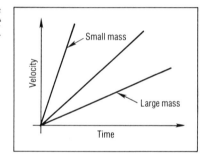

Fig. 4.15. Graph plots current increases vs. size of inductance with constant voltage applied to coil.

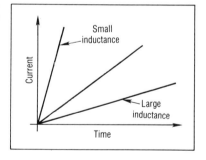

The mechanical analogy to inductance is mass or inertia. That is, inductance of an electrical coil resists changes in current similarly to the way mass and inertia resist changes in velocity. When a constant force is applied to a mass and no friction is present, such as in situations encountered in the weightlessness of space, there is uniform acceleration and velocity increases constantly, Figure 4.14. In analogous fashion, a constant voltage applied to a resistanceless coil (a practical impossibility even in space), will produce a continuously rising current, Figure 4.15.

In practice, a coil must have some resistance because, after all, it is wound with real wire. Furthermore, Ohm's Law cannot be violated; it says that maximum current i can never exceed E/R, where E is the applied voltage and R is the total series resistance, Figure 4.16. Therefore, in real coils, the current does not rise without limit. Instead, it rises and asymptotically approaches E/R, Figure 4.17.

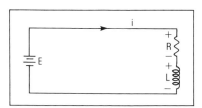

Fig. 4.16. Illustrative inductance circuit. Maximum current cannot exceed E/R.

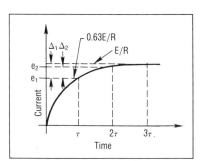

Fig. 4.17. Inductor current builds exponentially according to time constant.

The unit of inductance is the henry and its algebraic and schematic symbol is L. Note in Figure 4.17 that current build-up is exponential as is voltage build-up in a capacitor. The time constant in an inductive circuit is

$$\tau = L/R, \tag{4.6}$$

where τ remains in seconds when L is in henries and R is in ohms.

The exponential rise of inductance is brought about because of the voltage drop across resistance iR. When first excited there is no current, a state the inductor would like to maintain; consequently there is no iR drop and full source voltage E is felt across the coil. This results in a current rise however gradual. As the current rises, some voltage is lost across resistor iR; hence, less voltage is available at the inductor. The rate of current rise begins to decrease and the end result is an exponential current increase.

Actually, the coil current and the flux that it created represent energy stored in the flux field. When electric power is removed from a coil, flux field energy must decay and dissipate. As the magnetic field collapses, it induces a voltage in its parent coil that attempts to keep coil current going. The peak voltage depends upon the electrical resistance presented to the inductor at the instant the power source was disconnected. The peak instantaneous voltage can be calculated when the resistance is known.

Example 4.3. If the switch of Figure 4.18 is closed for a long time and then suddenly opened, what will be the voltage across dissipating resistor R_D?

Fig. 4.18. Circuit of concern in Example 4.3.

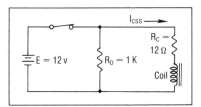

Fig. 4.19. State of circuit of Example 4.3 at instant switch is opened.

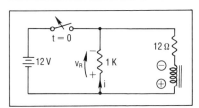

Solution 4.3. After the switch has been closed for a long time, the coil current will rise to its steady-state value:

$$i_{CSS} = E/R_C$$
$$= 12V/12$$
$$= 1A,$$

with circuit state at the instant the switch is opened indicated in Figure 4.19. At the instant the switch is opened, the inductor maintains the 1 A which must go through the 1000 Ω resistance because the switch opening killed the path through the battery. Now,

$$V_R = -IR_D$$
$$= -1(1000)$$

$$= -1000 \, V.$$

Summary of inductance:
- inductors introduce the time factor as a variable because there is a delay in *current* increase when the coil becomes engergized. This is in contrast with, but similar to, capacitors which cause delays in *voltage* increase
- charging and discharging of inductors is exponential, that is for charging

$$i = (E/R)(1 - \epsilon)^{-Rt/L}. \qquad (4.7)$$

For discharging,

$$i = Io\epsilon^{-Rt/L} \qquad (4.8)$$

- the inductive time constant is

$$\tau = L/R \qquad (4.9)$$

in seconds
- when an inductor first starts charging, it acts like an open circuit
- when an inductor reaches steady-state, it acts like a short circuit, and
- **disrupting or opening an inductive circuit which is carrying current can result in extremely high induced voltages.**

Chapter Five
Alternating Current Circuits

Alternating current (AC) has evolved as the electrical power transmission method of choice throughout the world. The main reasons for this are because:

● AC can be easily transformed (stepped up or down) with nearly 100% efficiency

● transformation efficiency leads to greater transmission line efficiency, and

● machines that produce alternating current are simpler and less costly than their direct current counterparts.

The basic AC generating machine is an alternator, Figure 5.1. It produces a voltage which is different at every instant of time and undergoes reversals in polarity twice each cycle. Output voltage, v_o, varies with time, and its amplitude depends on:

● the rotational frequency, f, or speed at which the alternator coils rotate

● the flux density, ϕ, or strength of the magnetic field, and

Fig. 5.1. Simplified cutaway drawing of an alternator indicates the magnets, the rotating coil at 0° position in the air gap, magnetic lines of flux, ϕ, and the brushes which deliver the generated voltage to the circuit.

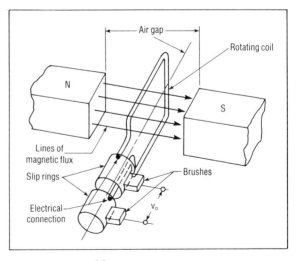

● the number of turns of wire used to make each rotating coil.

Because coil movement is parallel to the flux lines in Figure 5.1, output voltage is zero. When the coil has turned to the horizontal or 90° position, the coil then is passing through the maximum number of flux lines/unit of time, and the output voltage instantaneously is maximum. At the 180° position, voltage again is instantaneously zero. As rotation continues past 180°, output undergoes a sign reversal and begins increasing negatively.

The resulting voltage wave curve in a properly designed alternator is a sine wave, Figure 5.2, that follows the mathematical function from trigonometry, sin Θ. This wave has a maximum value of +1 and a minimum value of −1. Note that when the coil rotates at a constant

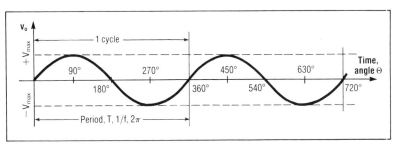

Fig. 5.2. *The sine wave shape delivered by an alternator indicates its time-de-pendence/time-angle relationship and the magnitude of its output voltages. In a sense, the wave shape represents the number of magnetic flux lines being cut at any particular instant.*

speed, angle theta, Θ, Figure 5.2, is a linear function of time. That is

$$\Theta° = Kt. \tag{5.1}$$

where constant K is the rotary speed in degrees/second when degrees are used as the measure of the angle. Because radians are a more mathematically pure angular measure, most literature prefers their use. Using radians, Equation (5.1) becomes

$$\Theta^r = 2\pi ft, \tag{5.2}$$

where f is the angular frequency or rotational speed in hertz, Hz, or cycles/second. For convenience, $2\pi f$ is called the angular frequency in radians/second, and usually is indicated with a lower case Greek omega, ω:

$$\omega = 2\pi f. \tag{5.3}$$

Continuing, the frequency in Hz is the reciprocal of the period of the wave shape, T:

$$T(seconds/cycle) = 1/[f(cycles/second)]. \qquad (5.4)$$

Now, it is possible to express one equation which describes the sinusoidal voltage, Figure 5.2, for all time and in terms that usually are known or very easily determined:

$$V = V_{max}\sin(2\pi ft), \qquad (5.5)$$

or

$$V = V_{max}\sin(2\pi t)/T, \qquad (5.6)$$

or

$$V = V_{max}\sin(\omega t). \qquad (5.7)$$

Degrees and radians are measures of rotational angles just as feet and yards are measures of distance; the last unit is just longer than the first. The degree divides a circle into 360 parts, while the radian divides it into 2π parts. This simple ratio converts radians to degrees and back:

$$\Theta'/\Theta° = (2\pi)^r/360° = (\pi)^r/180° \cong 0.0175 \cong 1^r/57.3°. \qquad (5.8)$$

To be sure, dealing with the instantaneous value of AC voltages is cumbersome. Fortunately, if only the *peak amplitude* and *frequency* of sinusoidal AC voltages are known, everything else can be determined immediately. When dealing with fixed or single-frequency systems, only the amplitude is important.

Happily, AC circuits can be engineered using methods similar to those used with DC circuits, although the mathematics admittedly are more complex. Actually, the branch of mathematics which applies to AC circuits is called *complex* algebra. This is not because the mathematics is so complicated, but because it deals with *complex numbers*, which have real and imaginary parts.

All AC circuits can be analyzed using the peak amplitude of the sine wave voltage, but a more convenient value, called the *Root Mean Square* or *RMS*, is used. It is derived from AC or DC voltages which will provide heating equivalence. Specifically, and by definition:

$$V_{RMS} = [average\ value\ (v)^2]^{1/2}.$$

This is based upon the equation:

$power = v^2/R.$

Look at the sinusoidal voltage and its squared value, Figure 5.3. Now

$$V_{RMS} = [average(v)^2]^{1/2} \tag{5.9}$$
$$= (V_{max}^2/2)^{1/2}$$
$$= V_{max}/(2)^{1/2} = V_{max}/1.414 = 0.707\ V_{max}.$$

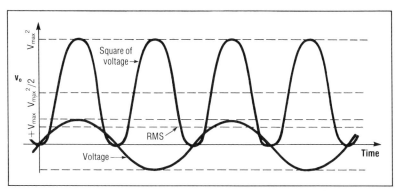

Fig. 5.3. Comparison of the maximum voltage, its square, and the RMS value.

When the voltage in a home is said to be 115 volts, this is really an RMS value. Understand that

$V_{max}\ line = (V_{RMS}\ line)/0.707 = 115/0.707 = 163\ V,$

the peak value of house voltage.

AC circuit analysis deals with current and voltage in circuits built from **R**esistors, **i**nductors, and **C**apacitors **(R/L/C)**. When a sinusoidal voltage is applied to an R/L/C circuit, the resulting current also is sinusoidal. The problem then becomes one of determining the current, given values for voltage and the R/L/C.

This concept can be extended to circuits of any required complexity. That is, sinusoidal voltages result in sinusoidal currents and sinusoidal currents result in sinusoidal voltages. In all remaining sections of this book, the following notations will be observed:

● **lower case letters will imply instantaneous, or time-varying values, and**

● **upper case letters will imply constant, DC, or RMS values.**

Current and voltage in resistive circuits

Ohm's Law applies to AC circuits as well as DC circuits.

$$i = e/R = (E_{max})[\sin(\omega t)]/R, \qquad (5.10)$$

and so, because we recognize that the maximum current is the coefficient on the $\sin(\omega t)$,

$$I_{max} = E_{max}/R. \qquad (5.11)$$

The current and voltage in a resistive circuit are said to be in phase with each other, because they both pass through their respective peaks and valleys at exactly the same time, Figure 5.4.

Current and voltage in capacitive circuits

The basic law governing current and voltage says that the current in a

Fig. 5.4. Curves indicate how AC voltage and current remain in phase with each other.

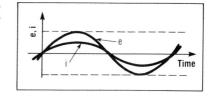

capacitor depends upon the rate at which its voltage changes. The faster the voltage changes, the higher the current; and the larger the capacitance, C, the higher the current.

Mathematically,

$i_c = C$ *times the rate of voltage change.*

$$i_c = C(\Delta V)/\Delta t. \qquad (5.12)$$

Understand that the actual voltage level does not affect the current, only the rate at which the voltage changes.

Example 5.1. Consider the following, non-sinusoidal, time-varying voltage being impressed across a capacitor, Figure 5.5(a). What will the current waveform be?

Solution 5.1. Because capacitive current depends on the time rate of change of voltage, the current waveshape tracks the steepness of the voltage waveshape, Figure 5.5(b).

Example 5.2. Now consider what happens when the voltage is sinusoidal, Figure 5.6(a). Again use the fact that current depends upon how fast the voltage changes.

Solution 5.2. Voltage across the capacitor is given as being a sine wave. Therefore the current through the capacitor is a cosine wave, Figure 5.6(b). Now,

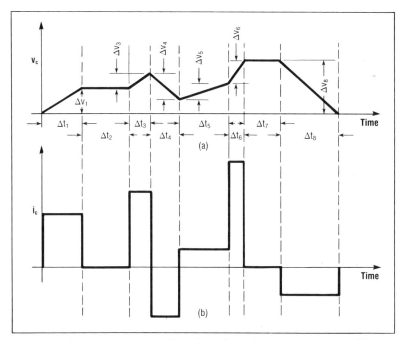

Fig. 5.5. In those time intervals where the voltage, (a), cnanges most rapidly, the current, (b), is greatest. Where the voltage decreases, the current is negative.

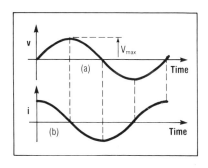

Fig. 5.6. The current is a sinusoidal cosine wave, (b), and as such, leads the voltage, (a), by 90°.

$$i = I_{max}\cos(\omega t)$$
$$= I_{max}\sin(\omega t - 90),$$

where it is necessary to determine I_{max} now that the phase shift has been found.

It can be shown that the rate of change of voltage from a sinusoidal source is directly proportional to the angular frequency and the peak value of voltage. That is:

$$I_{max} = 2\pi f V_{max} C. \qquad (5.13)$$

Capacitive reactance, X_C, is in ohms. This is a new term and is defined defined as:

$$X_C = 1/(2\pi f C). \qquad (5.14)$$

Now,

$$I_{max} = V_{max}/X_C. \qquad (5.15)$$

See how much this looks like Ohm's Law.

When both sides of Equation (5.15) are multiplied by 0.707, RMS current can be related to RMS voltage:

$$0.707 I_{max} = 0.707 V_{max}/X_C.$$

$$I_{RMS} = V_{RMS}/X_C. \qquad (5.16)$$

Example 5.3. A 0.01-μf capacitor is connected directly across a 120 V AC line. What will the RMS current be? Sketch the current and voltage waveforms.

Solution 5.3. Because the line voltage is 120 V_{RMS}, the peak voltage is 120(1.414) which rounds to 170 volts. Now, the instantaneous voltage is

$$v_c = 170\sin(377t),$$

where 377 is the angular frequency of the 60 Hz line in rad/sec.

$$I_{RMS} = E_{RMS}/X_C,$$
$$X_C = 1/2\pi f C$$
$$= 1/[(6.28)(0.01 \times 10^{-6})(60)]$$
$$= 265,000 \ \Omega.$$

$$I_{RMS} = 120/265,000$$

Fig. 5.7. Curves for Example 5.3. The curent appears to be ahead of the voltage in a capacitive circuit. Therefore, we say that the current leads the voltage.

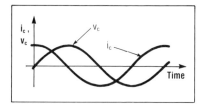

96

$= 452 \, \mu A.$

Therefore, the peak current is $1.414(452 \, \mu A)$, or 639×10^{-6} A. Thus, instantaneous current, i_C, is $639 \times 10^{-6} \sin(377t - 90°)$. Figure 5.7 shows the current and voltage waveforms.

Current and voltage in inductor circuits

The basic law governing current and voltage in an inductor should be compared to the law for current and voltage in capacitors. The voltage across an inductor depends on the rate at which its current changes. The faster the current changes, the higher the voltage.

Mathematically,

$$v_L = L(\Delta i / \Delta t), \tag{5.17}$$

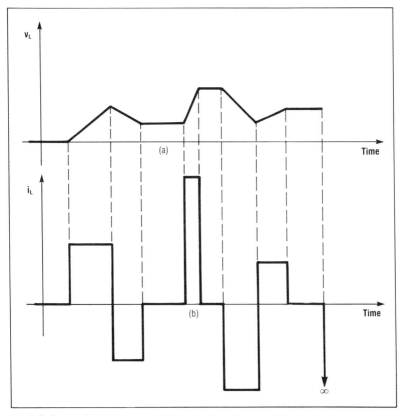

Fig. 5.8. Curves for Example 5.4. Inductor voltage is curve (b).

where inductance, L, is measured in henries. Understand that the magnitude of current i does not affect the voltage, but only the rate at which the current changes during the time interval.

Example 5.4. Consider the non-sinusoidal, time-varying current through an inductor, Figure 5.8(a). What will the voltage waveform be?

Solution 5.4. Voltage across an inductor depends upon the rate at which the current changes. Note, then, that a vertical (instantaneous) change in current requires an **infinite** voltage, an impossibility, Figure 5.8(b).

Example 5.5. Now consider the case where the current is a sine wave, Figure 5.9(a). Recall that $i_L = I_{max}\sin(\omega t)$.

Solution 5.5. Inductor voltage depends upon the rate at which its current changes. Therefore, when the current is a sine wave, the voltage must be a cosine wave and therefore **lead** the current by 90° as indicated by the curve in Figure 5.9(b). Now,

$$v_L = V_{max}\cos\omega t$$
$$= V_{max}\sin(\omega t - 90°).$$

It is now necessary to determine the peak voltage, V_{max}. The rate of change of current is directly proportional to the angular frequency at the maximum rate of change, and the maximum voltage is also directly proportional to the inductance, measured in henries. That is:

$$V_{max, inductor} = 2\pi f L I_{max}. \tag{5.18}$$

It now is convenient to introduce *inductive reactance*:

$$X_L = 2\pi f L, \tag{5.19}$$

and

$$V_{max} = X_L I_{max}. \tag{5.20}$$

Fig. 5.9. Curves for Example 5.5. As indicated, the voltage (cosine) function, (b), leads the current (sine) curve, (a), by 90°.

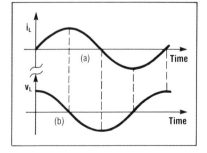

98

By multiplying both sides by 0.707, RMS values can be used:

$$V_{RMS} = X_L I_{RMS}. \tag{5.21}$$

Example 5.6. What RMS voltage is required to cause a 300-mA current in a 0.5 henry inductor at 250 Hz? Sketch the wave form.

Solution 5.6. Because the current is a sine wave of 250 Hz, $\omega = 1570$ rad/sec, and the frequency of the current and voltage must be the same, $\omega_I = \omega_V$.

$$\begin{aligned} X_L &= 2\pi f L \\ &= 6.28(250)0.5 \\ &= 785\ \Omega. \end{aligned}$$

$$\begin{aligned} V_{RMS} &= X_L I_{RMS} \\ &= 785(0.3) \\ &= 235.5\ \text{V}. \end{aligned}$$

$$\begin{aligned} i_L &= [0.3\sin(1570t)]/0.707 \\ &= 0.424\sin(1570t). \end{aligned}$$

By inspection, we see that

$$I_{L.\ max} = 0.424\ A.$$

$$\begin{aligned} v_L &= [235\cos(1570t)]/0.707 \\ &= 332.4\cos(1570t). \end{aligned}$$

Also by inspection, we see that

$$V_{L.\ max} = 332.4\ \text{V}.$$

The waveform can be sketched knowing the peak amplitude and frequency of the current and voltage, Figure 5.10.

Example 5.7. A 115 V AC voltage is connected to a 0.05 henry coil; the frequency is 2.5 kHz. What will the current be? Will the current lead or lag

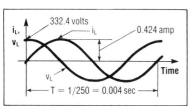

Fig. 5.10. Curves for Example 5.6. The voltage, dependent on the rate at which the current changes, leads the current by 90°. Therefore, the voltage is a cosine wave.

the voltage?

Solution 5.7. First, calculate the inductive reactance:

$$X_L = 2\pi f L$$
$$= 6.28(2500)0.05$$
$$= 78.5\ \Omega.$$

Now, calculate the RMS current:

$$I_L = V_L/X_L$$
$$= 115/78.5$$
$$= 1.46\ A.$$

The current will **lag** to the voltage, which is the same as saying the voltage will **lead** the current as shown in Figure 5.9.

The complex operator and impedance

Current and voltage in inductive and capacitive circuits are related by a variation of Ohm's Law for AC circuits:

$$I = V_C/X_C \qquad (5.22)$$

for capacitive circuits, and

$$I = V_L/X_L \qquad (5.23)$$

for inductive circuits.

Now, if the voltage or current and the inductive or capacitive reactance is known, the other parameter can be calculated. **But remember that there are 90° phase shifts between current and voltage and that the shift directions are opposite in inductive as opposed to capacitive circuits.**

A mnemonic crutch was created to help remember these phase shifts: **ELI THE ICE MAN.** This stands for:
- **E** (voltage) is before **I** in inductive circuits. (**E** leads **I** in **L** circuits), and
- **I** (current) is before **E** in capacitive circuits. (**I** leads **E** in **C** circuits).

It would be convenient if there was a way to handle the phase shift *automatically*, or in some way that it would take care of itself. Fortunately, there is a branch of algebra that deals with this problem with mathematical exactness. It is called *complex algebra* and deals with quantities which have real (resistors) and imaginary (reactive) parts.

The existence of a 90° phase shift will be denoted in formulas with j, the complex operator. That is, a 90° phase shift in the wave shapes can be handled by using imaginary numbers.

Complex operator $= j = (-1)^{1/2}.$ (5.24)

Math books use lower case i to symbolize complex numbers, but in electrical circuit analysis, i already is used for current, so j is preferred. Given this, **$-j$ indicates a phase lag of $90°$ and $+j$ denotes a phase lead of $90°$.**

The equations for current and voltage now can be expressed in their complex forms:

$$V_C = -j(X_C)I_C \qquad (5.25)$$

for capacitive circuits, and

$$V_L = +j(X_L)I_L, \qquad (5.26)$$

for inductive circuits.

The interpretation is that in capacitive circuits, voltage *lags* the current by $90°$. The $-jX_C$ in the capacitive Equation (5.25) is a reminder of this. Similarly, the $+jX_L$ in the inductive Equation (5.26) may be used as a reminder that voltage *leads* the current by $90°$.

The concept of *impedance* is helpful when developing a complete Ohm's Law for AC circuits. Impedance is an all-encompassing term which permits dealing with the most complicated combinations of R, L, and C in circuits. Impedance allows use of all the circuit theorems, because impedance in AC circuits is similar to resistance in DC circuits. That is, if resistance is a measure of the degree to which current meets opposition in DC circuits, then impedance is a measure of the degree to which R, L, and C impede current in AC circuits.

The rules of complex algebra govern how current, voltage, and impedance are quantified to keep track of phase shifts in AC circuits, phase shifts which nearly always are something other than $0°$ or $90°$. Commit the following definitions to memory for use with problems concerning AC circuits.

Impedance of a resistor:

$$\overline{Z}_R = R. \qquad (5.27)$$

Impedance of a capacitor:

$$\begin{aligned} \overline{Z}_C &= -jX_C = X_C \text{ at an angle of } -90° \\ &= -j1/2\pi fC \\ &= 1/2\pi fC \text{ at an angle of } -90°. \end{aligned} \qquad (5.28)$$

Impedance of an inductor:

$$\overline{Z}_L = +jX_L = X_L \text{ at an angle of } + 90° \qquad (5.29)$$
$$= +j2\pi fL$$
$$= 2\,\pi fL \text{ at an angle of } + 90°.$$

The bar above the Z is a reminder that it is a *complex* quantity and contains phase-angle information. Note that the phase angle associated with R is 0 and with capacitive impedance is 90°.

Here is Ohm's Law for AC circuits:

$$\overline{I} = \overline{E}/\overline{Z}, \qquad (5.30)$$

where the $\overline{Z}$ term, generally, is not confined to any specific R, L, or C element.

Basic concepts of complex algebra

Complex algebra deals with quantities which add together at right angles rather than in a straight line. The right angle addition is denoted by complex operator j, Figure 5.11. There are two equivalent mathematical forms using:

● rectangular coordinates,

$$R \pm jX, \qquad (5.31)$$

and

$$|\overline{Z}| \cos\phi \pm j|\overline{Z}| \sin\phi, \qquad (5.32)$$

and

● polar coordinates,

$$(R^2 + X^2)^{1/2} \text{ at an angle of } \phi = |\overline{Z}| \text{ at an angle of } \phi \qquad (5.33)$$

Fig. 5.11. *Complex operators, +jX and −jX, indicate the addition of quantities at right angles to each other rather than in staight lines. Since* tan ϕ = X/R, ϕ = tan⁻¹X/R *for triangle (a), and =* tan⁻¹−X/R *for triangle (b).*

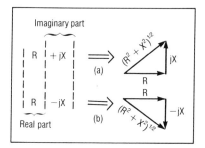

and

$$\phi = \tan^{-1} \pm X/R. \tag{5.34}$$

The addition of complex numbers is easier to carry out in rectangular form:

$$(R_1 + jX_1) + (R_2 + jX_2) + \ldots + (R_n + jX_n)$$
$$= (R_1 + R_2 + \ldots R_n) + j(X_1 + X_2 + \ldots + X_n).$$

Multiplication and division of complex numbers is easier to do in polar form:

A of angle $\phi \times B$ of angle $\theta = A \times B$ of angles $\phi + \theta$.

$(A$ of angle $\phi)/(B$ of angle$) \theta = A/B$ of angles $\phi - \theta$.

Current and voltage in R/L/C circuits

When resistive and reactive components are combined into a single circuit, the net phase angle between applied voltage and total current generally will not be 90°, but somewhere between 0° and 90°.

Example 5.8. Consider the series circuit, Figure 5.12, containing a resistance of 30 Ω, an inductive reactance of 40 Ω, and carrying a current of 1 A RMS.

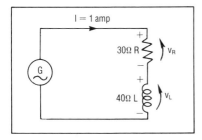

Fig. 5.12. Circuit illustrates Example 5.8.

Solution 5.8. To determine the value of applied voltage E, the impedance concept can be used. But first look at the problem from a sinusoidal wave shape point of view.

$$V_{R\,max} = I_{max}R$$
$$= I_{RMS}(R)/0.707$$
$$= (1)(30)/0.707$$
$$= 42.43 \text{ V}.$$

$$V_{L\,max} = I_{max}X_L$$
$$= I_{RMS}(X_L)/0.707$$
$$= 1(40)/0.707$$
$$= 56.58 \text{ V.}$$

It is known that the current and voltage are exactly in phase for the resistor and that the voltage across the inductor **leads** the current by 90°. Assuming that the current is a sine wave, the resistor voltage, v_R, is a sine wave as well, Figure 5.13.

Fig. 5.13. Wave-shapes for Example 5.8.

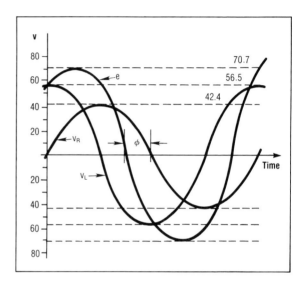

Kirchoff's Voltage Law applies at every instant of time, and so total voltage E must be the instantaneous sum of the resistor voltage and the inductor voltage, that is

$$\overline{E} = v_R + v_L. \tag{5.35}$$

The totally applied voltage curve, labeled e, Figure 5.13, was determined by graphically adding resistor voltage v_R to inductor voltage v_L. From this crude construction, it can be estimated that

$$\overline{E} = v_R + v_L,$$
$$\cong 70\sin(\omega t - 50°).$$

In more precise terms:

104

$$= 42.43\sin(\omega t) + 56.58\cos(\omega t).$$

There is a trigonometric identity of the form:

$$A\sin(X) + B\cos(X) = (A^2 + B^2)^{1/2}\sin(X - \phi), \qquad (5.36)$$

where

$$\phi = \tan^{-1}B/A \qquad (5.37)$$
$$= \tan^{-1}56.58/42.43$$
$$= 53.13°.$$

Now

$$42.43\sin(\omega t) + 56.58\cos(\omega t)$$
$$= [(42.43)^2 + (56.58)^2]^{1/2}\sin(\omega t - \phi),$$

so

$$e = 70.7\sin(\omega t - 53.13°),$$

the final results. Compare this with the graphical estimate reached earlier.

Note that the peak applied voltage is 70.7 volts, which means that the RMS voltage, $(0.707)E_{max}$, is 50 volts. Now, it can be said that the applied voltage of 50 volts RMS leads the current of 1 amp RMS by 53.13°.

Further understand that the same conclusion can be reached if the

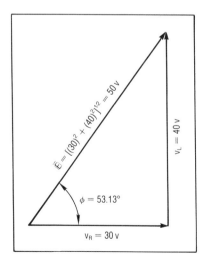

Fig. 5.14. The addition of complex voltages, that is 30 + j40, implies a right triangle with a hypotenuse of 50 volts at an angle of 53.13°. The angles in the triangular interpretation correspond exactly with the phase angles that would be seen if they were observed on an oscilloscope.

RMS values of resistor voltage and inductor voltage are treated as legs of a right triangle, Figure 5.14. This is much simpler than having to add sine and cosine waves and sketch complicated wave shapes.

In the general case, if we recognize that the resistor voltage is IR and the inductive voltage is IX_L, the two voltages add at right angles. Thus, a right triangle, Figure 5.15, can be sketched:

$$|\overline{E}| = [(IR)^2 + (IX_L)^2]^{1/2}, \tag{5.38}$$

and

$$\phi = \tan^{-1} X_L/R. \tag{5.39}$$

Observe that the hypotenuse of the voltage triangle, $\overline{E}$, contains a common current term that can be factored out:

$$|\overline{E}| = [(IR)^2 + (IX_L)^2]^{1/2}$$

Fig. 5.15. The voltage across the inductor, IX_L, and the voltage across the resistor, IR, add at right angles, that is, $E = IR + jIX_L$, which forms this right triangle.

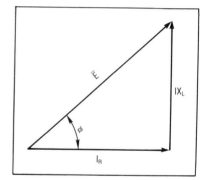

Fig. 5.16. The concept of impedance, $\overline{Z}$, develops when factoring the current out of Equation (5.37). The result is a right triangle formed by resistance R along the real axis and inductive reactance, X_L, in the imaginary direction.

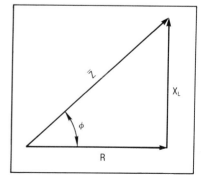

$$= [I^2(R^2 + X_L^2)]^{1/2}$$
$$= \overline{I}(R^2 + X_L^2)^{1/2}. \tag{5.40}$$

Now R and X_L are legs of the impedance right triangle, Figure 5.16, where the hypotenuse

$$|\overline{Z}| = (R^2 + X_L^2)^{1/2}, \tag{5.41}$$

and Equation (5.39) remains applicable.

Or given in the rectangular coordinates of complex algebra notation:

$$\overline{Z} = R + jX_L, \tag{5.42}$$

where R is the real part and jX_L is the imaginary part and the notation implies a right triangle. $\overline{Z}$ is called the complex impedance of an R/L circuit and this last equation contains the value of the impedance needed to solve R/L circuit problems including phase and magnitude.

Now for an R/L circuit, Ohm's Law is:

$$\overline{E} = \overline{IZ}$$
$$= \overline{I}(R + jX_L), \tag{5.43}$$

where it must be recalled that

$$X_L = 2\pi fL.$$

The circuit, of course, must have R in series with X_L, Figure 5.17, where

$$\overline{E} = \overline{I}(R + jX_L).$$

The idea can be extended to R/C circuits as well, remembering that the complex operator carries a negative sign, Figure 5.18. That is, R and $-jX_c$ are legs of a right triangle where the hypotenuse

$$|\overline{Z}| = (R^2 + X_c^2)^{1/2}, \tag{5.44}$$

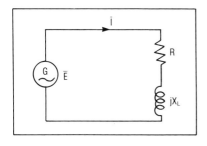

Fig. 5.17. Series R/L circuit.

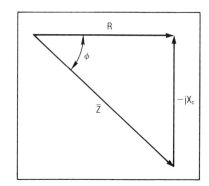

Fig. 5.18. Impedance triangle for a series R/C circuit.

Fig. 5.19 Simplified construction dia-gram of an iron-core transformer with a single winding pri-mary and a single winding secondary.

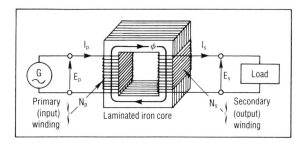

and

$$\phi = \tan^{-1} - X_C/R. \qquad (5.45)$$

Transformers

Transformers consist of two coils whose only linkage is the magnetic flux flowing through their common iron core, Figure 5.19. Primary voltage E_p, (RMS value of an alternating source) and its associated primary AC current I cause a flux ϕ in the iron core which links to the secondary winding. Because the flux is changing, there is a voltage induced into the secondary winding. If the secondary is connected to a load, secondary current I_p results. The voltage and current relationships (given without proof) are:

$$E_p = E_s(N_p)/N_s \qquad (5.46)$$

and

$$I_s = I_p(N_p)/N_s, \qquad (5.47)$$

where N_p is the number of turns in the primary winding and N_s is the

108

number of turns in the secondary winding. By controlling the number of primary and secondary turns, the transformer can step up or step down the voltage. But recognize that if there is a step up in voltage, there must be a step down in current; transformers do not create power, they only transform it.

Example 5.9. What *turns ratio*, N_p/N_s is needed to supply 24 V AC RMS from a 220 V AC RMS source?

Solution 5.7.

$$N_p = E_p(N_s)/E_s$$
$$= 220/24$$
$$= 9.17 \text{ turns/turn.}$$

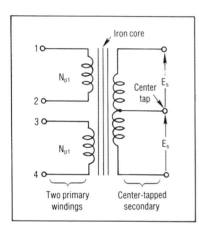

Fig. 5.20. Schematic diagram of a dual primary, center-tapped secondary transformer.

Commercial transformers come in a large variety of current and voltage ratings and in an equal variety of winding configurations and numbers. Two primary windings, Figure 5.20, are provided so the user can connect the windings in series for 230-V operation, or in parallel for 115-V operation. In either case the same secondary voltage is maintained.

This example is only for illustration. Each transformer must be approached individually. Some manufacturers print the required connection scheme on the transformer nameplate for quick reference.

Chapter Six
Diodes, Rectifiers, and Power Supplies

Semiconductor diodes consist of two mating layers of pure silicon (sand), each of which has been contaminated or doped with an impurity. The doping materials change the silicon layers so that they are no longer insulators but rather something in between an insulator and conductor, called a semiconductor. When one layer is doped with a *p*-type impurity such as arsenic, and the other is doped with an *n*-type impurity such as boron, a diode is formed which will conduct current in one direction but not the other, Figure 6.1.

When the silicon layer with the *p*-type impurity (the anode) is made positive with respect to the layer with the *n*-type impurity (the cathode), the diode is said to be *forward biased*, Figure 6.2. When the cathode silicon layer is made positive with respect to the anode, the diode is called *reverse biased* and will not conduct, Figure 6.3. The reason for this behavior is the subject of numerous books and is beyond the scope of this

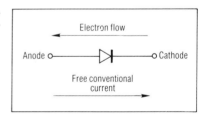

Fig. 6.1. Diode symbol indicates direction of electron flow and of free conventional current.

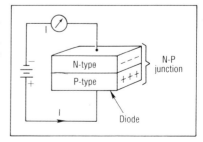

Fig. 6.2. A diode, consisting of an n-p *junction, will pass current when its* p-*terminal is made positive with respect to its* n-*terminal. With the* p-*terminal positively charged, the diode is termed forward biased.*

110

text. It is only important to note that a diode is the electrical equivalent of a check valve.

A diode's complete performance can be seen in its volt-ampere characteristic curve, Figure 6.4, obtained by measuring the current through the diode while the voltage varies. The complete test requires an adjustable power supply that must be capable of producing positive and negative output voltages. Otherwise, the supply leads would have to be reversed to get the curve for positive (forward bias) and negative (reverse bias) diode voltages.

Conversion function

A most important function of diodes is their ability to convert 115 volt, 60 Hz AC house current into another form that is suitable to power electronic devices. These devices include TV's, radios, stereos, computers, and microwave ovens. The section of the stereo or other device which

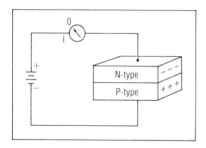

Fig. 6.3. When the n-terminal is made positive, little or no current passes; the diode then is termed reverse biased.

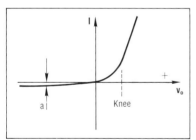

Fig. 6.4. Characteristic volt-ampere curve of a diode indicates the very low reverse leakage current, (a), when the supply voltage is negative and the rapidly increasing current once the voltage reaches 0.1 to 0.5 volts.

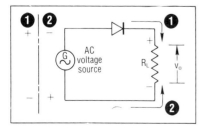

Fig. 6.5. AC current source in half-wave rectifier circuit provides current direction 1 or 2. Diode blocks or freely conducts current, produces load voltage when freely conducting.

111

makes the conversion from AC to DC is called the *power supply*, and this voltage conversion process is called *voltage rectification*.

With a positive AC voltage source, the forward-biased diode will permit current; with current, output voltage v_o will be across load resistor R_L, Figure 6.5. On the other hand, when the supply voltage is negative, the diode is reverse biased, there is no current, and output voltage is zero, Figure 6.6

A full-wave bridge rectifier, Figure 6.7, has four diodes arranged so there is a current through the load during the positive *and* negative half cycles of the AC supply voltage. When the supply voltage goes positive, D_1 and D_4 are forward biased so current passes through R_L from left to right; that is, the left side of R_L goes *high*, another term for positive.

But when the AC supply goes negative, the lower supply terminal is

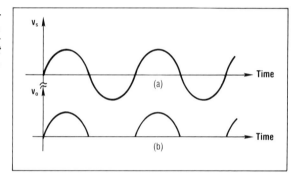

Fig. 6.6. Voltage-time source curve, (a), produces half-wave rectifier output voltage waveshape, (b).

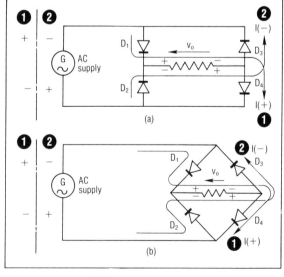

Fig. 6.7. Rectangular full-wave bridge rectifier circuit, (a), has four diodes arranged to provide current through both positive and negative halves of the sinusoidal input. Diamond configuration of bridge rectifier circuit, (b), provides the same electrical function.

112

positive. Then, diodes D_2 and D_3 become forward biased so current again passes through R_L from left to right. Thus, the output voltage is said to be *full-wave rectified* because it is positive during both half-cycles of the supply, Figure 6.8. Because there is a direct relationship between the amount of output voltage from any rectifier circuit and the amplitude of the AC voltage supplied to it, it becomes necessary to understand how AC voltage ratings are given to correlate them with rectifier output.

Heating values

AC line voltages are always expressed in terms of their Root Mean Square value, or RMS. An RMS value expresses the equivalent heating value of AC voltage: an AC voltage of 100-volts RMS has the same heating capacity as a constant 100-volt DC voltage. While the DC voltage is constant and the AC voltage varies continually, the *charges in both systems encounter equal friction in a resistance* and convert their volt-ampere (power in watts) products into equivalent heat energy. It is necessary to set some constant parameters for time-varying AC voltage, Figure 6.9.

When speaking about the voltage in a home, say 115 volts, that is the RMS value. Line voltage at the wall outlet is nominally 115 volts; it varies between about 110 volts and 125 volts depending on the power company's total load at the time. Therefore, the voltage's peak value is

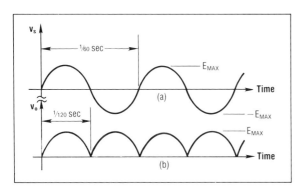

Fig. 6.8. Voltage-time source curve, (a), produces full-wave rectifier output voltage, (b).

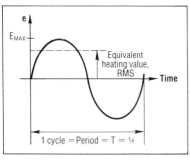

Fig. 6.9. Constant parameters for time-varying AC voltage. RMS value = equivalent heating value = $E_{MAX}/(2)^{1/2}$.

$$E_{MAX} = (2)^{1/2}E_{RMS} \qquad (6.1)$$
$$= 1.414(115)$$
$$= 162.2 \text{ V.}$$

A typical AC voltmeter reads the RMS value when connected to an alternating voltage source. **A word of caution:** most AC voltmeters and ammeters will indicate the RMS value **only** if the waveshape is sinusoidal. When waveshapes are square, triangular, or exponential, for example, significant errors will occur. Here, the discussion is confined to sinusoids.

Consider the full-wave rectifier circuit and accompanying measurements, Figure 6.10. The 115-V RMS AC supply, the same as 162.2-V maximum, produces a measured 103-V DC output voltage from the bridge because the DC voltmeter responds to the *average* voltage that it measures. The 103-V average, Figure 6.11, shows that area 1 = area 2.

It turns out that the average value of a full-wave rectified sinusoidal voltage is 0.636 times the peak or maximum AC value.

$$E_{AVERAGE\,DC} = 0.636E_{MAX} \qquad (6.2)$$

So now, using the E_{MAX} previously calculated from Equation (6.1), the analysis can be completed:

$$= 0.636(162.6)$$
$$= 103.4 \text{ V.}$$

Fig. 6.10. *Full-wave rectifier circuit with AC voltmeter a measuring 115 RMS supply and DC voltmeter b indicating 103 V DC load.*

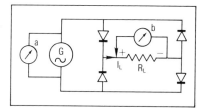

Fig. 6.11. *Curves of supply voltage, (a), and full-wave rectified output, (b), indicate average output.*

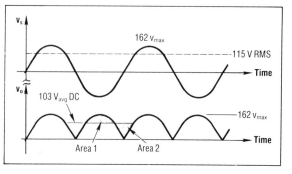

Note: although the average DC full-wave output is only 103 volts, its RMS value is still 115 volts. It is necessary **to use extreme care** in interpreting pulsating DC voltages, because the AC and DC components have their own heating ability. Using only DC values (which is typical) can be in error.

Circuit overpowered

One of the most common uses of rectifiers is to supply a DC voltage to operate electronic circuits contained in radios, stereos, and amplifiers, for example. Rectifiers convert AC voltage in the line from the power company to DC voltage. Most solid-state electronic circuits, however, need supply voltages that range from about 5 V DC to 18 or 20 V DC. Thus, to simply rectify the raw AC line voltage would result in a DC voltage so high that it would immediately destroy the circuit it was meant to service.

Raw line voltage has to be reduced to a more useable level, say 5 to 20 V. AC voltages are most efficiently changed (generally, the change can be up or down, but in this case it is down) with transformers. When raw line voltage is transformed to be used as input to a DC power supply, the line voltage is reduced to the more useable level of, say, 15 to 25 volts instead of 115 volts. There also are other benefits that may not be obvious which arise from use of a transformer:

● the earth-ground conductor, which is necessarily a part of the AC power line to the DC power supply (one line or the other is connected to mother earth), is removed from the solid-state circuit. This gives the electronic designer the option of placing the ground wherever it is best for the application

● a full-wave recitifier can be built with two diodes instead of four, if the transformer has a secondary is that is center-tapped (CT). When the secondary voltage is such that its upper terminal is positive, combination $1(+)$, Figure 6.12, D_1 is forward biased and current passes through R_L from top to bottom and then through the center tap of the transformer. Conversely, when the opposite voltage exists, combination $2(-)$, D_2 is forward biased, again making current go through R_L from top to bottom.

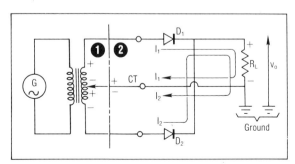

Fig. 6.12. Center-tapped transformer with two-diode rectifier can produce full-wave rectification.

The result is always a positive voltage at the transformer center-tap although it pulsates wildly. Except for a small forward voltage drop across the diodes, the peak output voltage will be equal to the peak voltage that appears on either side of the secondary winding.

Example 6.1. A certain power-supply transformer has a 115-V AC primary and a 36-V CT secondary. Sketch the full-wave rectified output voltage and show the maximum, average, and RMS values of the output voltage.

Solution 6.1. The 36-V CT designation for the secondary winding means 36-V RMS and the CT indicates that the transformer has a center tap. There will be 18-V RMS on each side of the CT. Now the peak voltage, E_{1MAX}, supplied to each one of the two diodes can be calculated:

$$E_{1MAX} = (2)^{1/2}E_{RMS}$$
$$= 1.414(18)$$
$$= 25.45 \text{ V.}$$

That is the peak voltage at the transformer secondary as well, Figure 6.13, ignoring the small forward voltage drop across the conducting diode. Using Equation (6.2):

$$E_{AVG\,DC} = 0.636E_{MAX}$$
$$= 0.636(25.45)$$
$$= 16.2 \text{ V.}$$

Critical electronic circuits that received DC voltages generated by rectifiers are highly sensitive to the pulsating DC described so far. Indeed, a practical power supply must be free of ripple and pulsations as far as is practical, usually a small fraction of a percent.

The ripple is reduced and perhaps eliminated with filters which take

Fig. 6.13. Curves illustrate solution to Example 6.1. With full-wave rectification, the peak rectified (DC) value is approximately the same as peak AC voltage. The average value can be calculated, or measured with a DC (averaging) voltmeter.

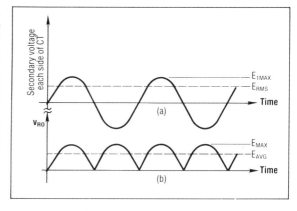

advantage of the charge-storage capabity of capacitors, Figure 6.14. The idea is to charge the capacitor while the diodes are on and passing current and then allow it to discharge into the load while the diodes are off. This fills in the valleys in the output waveform, Figure 6.15.

When the filter capacitor is properly sized, the resulting DC output voltage is almost ripple free. Additional smoothing can be obtained using a voltage regulator at the output of the power supply, Figure 6.16.

Voltage regulators are available commercially as integrated circuits and have outstanding capability for a very small cost. They are electronic amplifiers with large amounts of negative feedback so that they supress pulsations that appear at the input supply terminals, as well as adjust their output to compensate for changing load demands of the electronic circuits they supply.

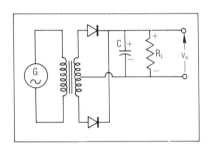

Fig. 6.14. Full-wave rectifier circuit now includes filter capacitor C installed to smooth current ripple.

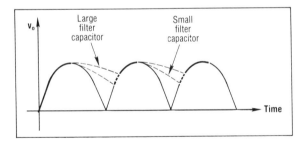

Fig. 6.15. With filter capacitor installed, output voltage smooths as indicated, depending on size of capacitor.

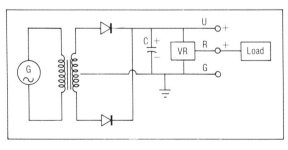

Fig. 6.16. Power supply circuit now has voltage regulator to further smooth voltage ripple; line U conducts unregulated DC while R conducts regulated DC.

Voltage regulator characteristics

Voltage regulators do wonderful things. They can:
● compensate for line voltage variations
● remove remnants of ripple the filter capacitor does not take out
● maintain constant output voltage
● compensate for changes in their own output current, and
● maintain their own output voltage in spite of load variations.
Some voltage regulators can be made to:
● be adjustable. Others have fixed, specific output voltage, and
● shut themselves off if the load tries to take more current than they can handle, providing overload protection; these automatically reset themselves after cooling.

As with all component design, there is a price to be paid for the good things that voltage regulators do, even though in this case, it is small:
● there is a voltage overhead; that is, the supply voltage must be greater than the regulated voltage level, usually 5 to 10 volts. For example, a 12-volt regulator will function well with 18 unregulated volts supplied to its input terminal, and
● because all the current demanded by all the loads, such as proportional valves for example, must pass through the regulator, it is a consumer of power. This is in large part, because of the overhead voltage. Heat sinks are necessary to help cool the regulator.

The center-tapped transformer also allows the generation of both negative and positive DC voltages, simply by adding two more diodes, another filter capacitor, and another regulator, Figure 6.17.

Fig. 6.17. Additional diodes provide power supply with bipolar capability. It produces regulated, R, and unregulated, U DC.

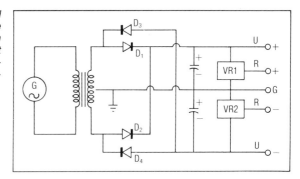

Chapter Seven
Transistors, Amplifiers, and Other Signal Processing

The electronic circuit designer uses these five components when creating new circuits:
- resistors
- capacitors
- inductors
- rectifiers, and
- amplifiers.

By judiciously interconnecting different combinations of these components, literally millions of different digital and analog electronic gadgets have been invented to enhance our lives. We have already considered the first four components; before looking at amplifiers, first consider some generalizations about amplification or gain.

Our everchanging and increasingly ingenious machinery makes great use of amplification. Amplification or gain occurs any time an input element such as a handle or a voltage terminal, for example, is activated with information and that information, in a proportionate way, controls the flow of energy, Figure 7.1. You may never have thought of an automobile engine as an amplifier, but it is and has some formidable specifications. Thus, if the information input is the accelerator setting of an automobile, and the power input is the flow of fuel into the engine, and the output is the speed of the automobile's driveshaft, it is clear that the power delivered to the driveshaft is far greater than the input power of the driver's foot on the accelerator. There is an enormous power gain when driveshaft output power is related to the power needed to activate the throttle.

Does this mean that the engine has more than 100% efficiency? Indeed not, because efficiency encompasses *all* sources of power including the

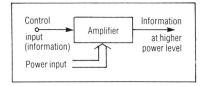

Fig. 7.1. Amplifiers receive control input (information) and elevate the power level of that information by modulating the flow of energy from the power input port to the output port.

119

fuel, whereas the amplification need not consider the fuel source; it is taken for granted.

In contrast to amplifying devices, there are a number of power-transforming machines which appear to be amplifiers but are not. For instance, it may be tempting to view a fixed-ratio gear box with a speed step-up as an amplifier. It is not, because there is only one input port for both information and power; all power delivered to the output must come from the same source that supplies the information. This definition means that a motorcycle is an amplifier while a bicycle is not.

The input or information port of an *ideal amplifier*:

● consumes no power from the information source. This is rarely true but can be approximated at times, and

● is completely unilateral; that is, changes in the command input cause the power output to follow proportionately, but changes in the load are not felt at the input.

Again considering the automobile engine, it is indeed unilateral. Whether the car travels on a level surface or goes up or down hill, there is no feel propagated back to the throttle. Some mechanically governed engines are not unilateral because the speed signal is coupled back to the throttle through a spring. Electronic amplifiers are not unilateral but can be designed to be with a reasonable degree of approximation.

Transistors

Electronic amplification or gain first deals with transistors. When a P-N

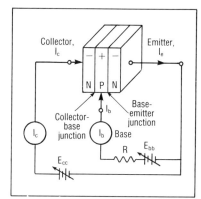

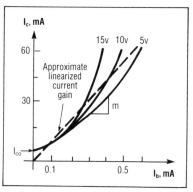

Fig. 7.2. Common emitter test circuit for an NPN transistor. Test results show that for a small input, I_b, there is a large output, I_c. The transistor leads are the emitter, base, and collector.

Fig. 7.3. Base-to-collector current transfer (input/output) characteristic of the common emitter circuit of Figure 7.2. m represents the slope of the curve and equals current gain and also equals $\Delta I_c / \Delta I_b$, both measured in mA. I_{co} represents collector cut-off current and 15, 10, and 5 v are different collector voltages, E_{cc}.

junction like that used to make a diode is outfitted with another semi-conductor layer, say of the N-type, to form a three-layered sandwich, the result is an NPN transistor, Figure 7.2, with the accompanying base-to-collector current transfer or input/output characteristic, Figure 7.3. Amplification takes place because the change in output current I_c is substantially greater than the base current, I_b, which caused it. The fictitious (but realistic) curves of Figure 7.3 indicate that linearized current gain is about 100: only 0.6 mA input is required to get 60 mA output. This gain value is commonly referred to in the literature as β or h_{fe}; typical h_{fe} values are from 30 or 40 to as high as 400.

The amplification takes place because of the differences in the energy levels of the electrons in the regions near the boundaries or junctions between the N- and P-type materials, Figure 7.2. The base-to-emitter junction forms a diode, and if it is to conduct like its two larger diode brethren, the P-type base material must be positive with respect to the emitter. The presence of the moving charges in the base-emitter junction causes the collector-base junction to break down and conduct profusely, even though the N-type collector is back biased — that is the positive terminal of the collector source voltage, E_{cc}, is connected to the N-type material of the collector. The collector does not want to conduct this way and is said to be back biased or reverse biased. Why this conduction takes place in the back-biased state is less important than accepting that profuse conduction takes place.

It is entirely correct to view the transistor as an *electric valve*. In normal operation, when the base current is zero, the collector is off, or not conducting. On the other hand, presence of a base current causes the collector current to increase. It is exactly like a proportional valve; as the base current increases, collector current increases proportionally as Figure 7.3 indicates.

When considering amplifiers, designers always are interested in the amplifier's *gain*. By definition,

$$Gain = \Delta output/\Delta input = G = A, \tag{7.1}$$

where the units of output and input are based on the device under consideration and the choice of output. In the case of a basic current-amplifying transistor, the input is base current I_b, and the output is collector current I_c. Therefore current gain G_I of a transistor by definition is

$$G_I = \Delta I_c/\Delta I_b. \tag{7.2}$$

Considering the transistor's transfer or input/output characteristic, Figure 7.3, the value of the instantaneous gain, $\Delta I_c/\Delta I_b$, depends upon the point chosen to find slope m. Selecting a spot in the more linear region leads to the conclusion that the gain is about 100. That is, a change in control input current ΔI_b of 0.1 mA causes a change in output current ΔI_c of about 100 times that amount or 10 mA.

Voltage amplifier conversion

A transistor can become a voltage amplifier by placing resistor R_c in the collector circuit, Figure 7.4, to *convert* the collector current into a voltage. Similarly, base input resistor R_b converts input voltage v_{in} into base current I_b. R_b also limits base current to a safe value. Note that when v_{in} in the circuit in Figure 7.4 is increased, base current I_b also increases in accordance with Ohm's law:

$$I_b \cong v_{in}/R_b . \tag{7.3}$$

When I_b increases, collector current I_c also increases substantially more than the increase in I_b because of the current-amplification properties of the transistor. Note that when the collector current increases, the voltage *loss* across collector resistor R_c also increases. This means that there is less voltage available at the collector. Consequently, collector voltage *drops* with an increase in base current.

Conversely, when v_{in} is low, say zero volts for example,

- there is no input base current
- the transistor is nearly cut off
- there is little collector current
- there is correspondingly little voltage loss across collector resistor R_c,

and so

- the collector voltage is close to supply voltage E_{cc}.

Figure 7.5 indicates a generalized voltage transfer characteristic.

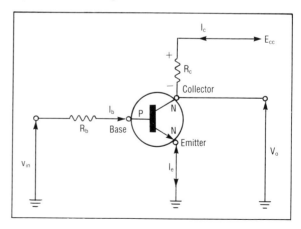

Fig. 7.4. Common and basic emitter amplifier has resistors added to the base and collector to convert current to voltage, so it becomes a voltage amplifier. Resistors R_c and R_b are external to the transistor, not an an integral part of it.

Voltage gain calculation

The definition of gain, Equation (7.1), suggests the existence of an experimental method based upon the transfer characteristic of Figure 7.3. To be sure, the large signal current gain, β, is determined from transistor data. When designing a voltage amplifier, predicting gain and other performance data can be facilitated by using a simple mathematical model of the transistor. That model makes use of only the large signal-gain parameter, β.

The approach can be seen by looking at the circuit in Figure 7.4 and the transfer (input/output) characteristic of Figure 7.3. In this Figure, note that the current gain or slope of the curve is relatively unaffected by collector voltage E_{cc}. This observation justifies the model; that is, collector current I_c depends primarily upon base current I_b, not upon collector voltage. It also simplifies transistor analysis. From these facts and the circuit in Figure 7.4, understand that:

$$I_c = \beta I_b . \tag{7.4}$$

Applying Kirchoff's voltage law to the output loop,

$$v_o = E_{cc} - I_c R_c . \tag{7.5}$$

Substituting Equation (7.4) into Equation (7.5) gives

$$v_o = E_{cc} - \beta I_b R_c . \tag{7.6}$$

The change in output voltage, Δv_o, is the quantity needed to determine voltage gain. Understand that the change in output is caused by a change in the input, ΔI_b. E_{cc} contributes nothing to the change in output because the power supply was deliberately designed to be very stable. So now,

$$\Delta v_o = -\beta \Delta I_b R_c . \tag{7.7}$$

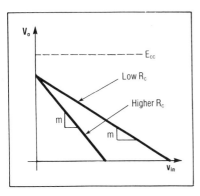

Fig. 7.5. Increasing input voltage v_{in} causes output voltage v_o to fall, leading to a negative value for voltage gain m. Increasing load resistor R_c gives a steeper curve and consequently, a higher voltage gain.

From Equation (7.3), see that the change in I_b is caused by a change in v_{in}, that is

$$\Delta I_b = \Delta v_{in}/R_b . \tag{7.8}$$

which can be substituted into Equation (7.7):

$$\Delta v_o = -\beta(\Delta v_{in}/R_b)R_c . \tag{7.9}$$

The voltage gain is formed by dividing both sides by Δv_{in} and noting that by definition,

$$G_v = \Delta v_o/\Delta v_{in} . \tag{7.10}$$

or,

$$G_v = \Delta v_o/\Delta v_{in} = -\beta R_c/R_b . \tag{7.11}$$

Note that the voltage gain depends, not surprisingly, on the current gain, β, of the transistor, modified by the ratio of the collector resistance-to-base resistance. Proper selection of R_c and R_b permits the designer to control amplifier gain.

Example 7.1. A MPS6566 transistor, with $\beta = 282$ is used in the circuit shown in Figure 7.4. (a.) When the base current is 0.2 mA, what will the collector current be? (b.) If $R_c = 150\ \Omega$, what will v_o be when $I_b = 0.2$ A? (c.) If $R_b = 2$ KΩ, what v_{in} is needed to cause $I_b = 0.2$mA? (d.) Calculate the voltage gain when $R_b = 1$ KΩ and $R_c = 15$ KΩ.

Solution 7.1. (a.) We know that the collector current is β times greater than the base current, so using Equation (7.4),

$$I_c = \beta I_b$$
$$= 282(0.2)$$
$$= 56.4\ \text{mA}.$$

(b). Using Equation (7.5),

$$v_o = V_{cc} - I_c R_c$$
$$= 12 - [(282)(0.0002)(150)]$$
$$= 3.54\ \text{v}.$$

(c). Using transposed Equation (7.3),

$$v_{in} \approx I_b R_b$$
$$= 0.0002(2000)$$
$$= 0.400\ \text{v, and}$$

(d). using Equation (7.11),

$$A_v = \Delta v_o / \Delta v_{in}$$
$$= \beta I_b R_c / I_b R_b$$
$$= \beta R_c / R_b$$
$$= [(282)(150)]/2000$$
$$= 21.15.$$

Unfortunately, the current gain from one particular transistor to another can vary by an order of magnitude. Consider the data published in the Texas Instruments "Master Selection Guide" for three different transistors:

- Type 2N5223: $80 \le h_{fe} \le 800$
- Type 2N2904: $100 \le h_{fe} \le 300$
- Type TIS150: $20,000 \le h_{fe} \le 70,000$.

The large variation in current gain makes overall gain prediction a perilous process when attempting to build the simple (and impractical) circuit of Figure 7.4. The large variations in current gain require that feedback be used to make the gain predictable at design time. Various feedback methods have been used. Only one is considered here to introduce the concept of voltage amplification so there is less agony accepting the characteristics of that special integrated circuit, the operational amplifier (op-amp). The circuit in Figure 7.6 shows a method of implementing feedback in a single-transistor amplifier.

Feedback resistor R_f:

- couples output voltage v_o to the input (base) to produce feedback
- couples some of the positive collector voltage into the base to overcome the 0.5 volt or so of base voltage needed to get the base-emitter diode junction into its conducting range.

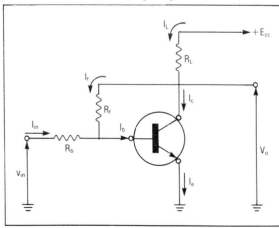

Fig. 7.6. Single-stage transistor amplifier with feedback.

• gives a forward bias current so that a small positive input voltage, v_{in}, will immediately cause the transistor to start conducting. This forward bias eliminates the input threshold because any positive value for v_{in} adds current to the already-conducting base.

An expression for the gain of this circuit can be derived with the aid of the simple linear transistor model. The circuit analysis is more complex with R_f in place. It can be seen from Figure 7.6 that

$$I_L = I_C + I_f, \tag{7.12}$$

and from the transistor model, Figure 7.2, recall that

$$I_c = \beta I_b. \tag{7.4}$$

Further, the circuit in Figure 7.6 tells us that

$$I_b = I_{in} + I_f, \tag{7.13}$$

and that

$$I_b = v_{in}/R_b, \tag{7.14}$$

and

$$I_f = v_o/R_f. \tag{7.15}$$

The output loop equation is

$$v_o = E_{cc} - I_L R_L. \tag{7.16}$$

but taking advantage of Equations (7.12) and (7.4),

$$v_o = E_{cc} - R_L(\beta I_b + I_f). \tag{7.17}$$

Now, using Equation (7.13),

$$v_o = E_{cc} - R_L(\beta I_{in} + \beta I_f + I_f). \tag{7.18}$$

Equations (7.14) and (7.15) will now eliminate the two currents in favor of input and output voltages so that gain can be formed. Now

$$v_o = E_{cc} - (\beta v_{in} R_L)/R_b - (\beta v_o R_L)/R_f - (v_o R_L)/R_f. \tag{7.19}$$

By collecting the v_o terms on the left side,

$$v_o[1 + (\beta R_L)/R_f + R_L/R_f] = E_{cc} - (\beta R_L v_{in})/R_b. \qquad (7.20)$$

Solving for v_o,

$$v_o = [E_{cc} - (\beta R_L v_{in})/R_b]/[1 + R_L(\beta + 1)/R_f]. \qquad (7.21)$$

Again, the change in output comes from only a change in v_{in}. Therefore,

$$G_v = \Delta v_o/\Delta v_{in} = (-\beta R_L/R_b)/[1 + R_L(\beta + 1)/R_f]. \qquad (7.22)$$

This equation gives a reasonable estimate of the gain for the circuit in Figure 7.6. Technically we need go no further, but there is an interesting characteristic regarding feedback that now can be introduced, if some assumptions or *what ifs* are made.

Suppose that the designer selects a large value for R_L, the load resistor in the collector circuit. Suppose further, that this value is considerably larger than feedback resistance R_f. Consider additionally that the transistor has a fairly large current gain, β. It now follows that

$$R_L(\beta + 1)/R_f \gg 1. \qquad (7.23)$$

So now, Equation (7.22) can be approximated by

$$G_v \cong (-\beta R_L/R_b)/[R_L(\beta + 1)]/R_f. \qquad (7.24)$$

Upon cancelling factors common to numerator and denominator,

$$G_v \cong (-\beta R_f)/[(\beta + 1)R_b]. \qquad (7.25)$$

If the designer selects a transistor with a very high β, further simplification is possible, that is

$$G_v = -R_f/R_b. \qquad (7.26)$$

Equation (7.26) teaches a profound lesson in feedback: *the final gain in this equation is completely independent of transistor performance parameter β*. Remember that the circuit designer has no control over β because its value varies widely during transistor manufacture. Instead, the gain depends *only on external resistors R_f and R_b*. Because the circuit designer chooses these external resistors, he can accept the large variation in transistor parameters. The designer can predict circuit gain not by regulating β of the transistor but rather by being assured that it is always greater than some minimum value.

Transistor characteristics

A review of transistor characteristics in any manufacturers' catalogs reveals a diverse set of specifications and data. A thorough examination of these data is a proper subject of a genuine electrical engineering course and far beyond the intent of this text. However, a review of several of the more prominent parameters is appropriate. The testing of a transistor suggests an equivalent circuit, Figure 7.7, which shows the popular h

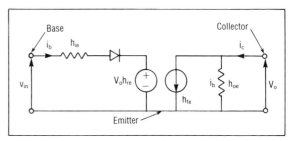

Fig. 7.7. Small signal model of a transistor has four h parameters.

parameters. These h for *hybrid* parameters come from analyzing the circuit using an input loop equation and an output node equation. The four hybrid parameters are:

• h_{ie}, the equivalent input resistance that can be seen or measured by looking into the base when conducting in the forward direction; h_{ie} units are ohms

• h_{re}, a small voltage generator which takes into account the fact that the transistor can propagate information bidirectionally. That is, if the output voltage varies, the change can be felt at the base as a much smaller voltage. Because it is so small, h_{re} usually can be ignored; it has no units

• h_{fe}, the current gain of the transistor. Gain is the only reason for the transistor's existence. Current in the base circuit controls current in the collector circuit. Thus, output of the current generator is $h_{fe}i_b$, a dimensionless number, and

• h_{oe}, the output *admittance* or resistance. Admittance is the reciprocal of impedance, and accounts for the small amount of current that leaks through the collector even when the controlling base current is zero. Admittance units are 1/ohms or *mhos*, as they are called in the industrial nomenclature.

Table 7.1 — 2N3904 specifications			
Symbol	Minimum	Maximum	Units
h_{ie}	1000	10,000	ohms
h_{re}	0.5×10^{-4}	8×10^{-4}	none
h_{fe}	100	400	none
h_{oe}	1.0	40	mhos

The Motorola *Small Signal Transistor Data* book on the 2N3904 transistor shows its specifications, reproduced in Table 7.1. The parameters of the Table range as much as 40:1 for h_{oe} and 4:1 for h_{fe}. That is, the company could only guarantee those values would be within those limits, (a specific value being only coincidence), when testing two Motorola 2N3904 specimens. The imprecision and lack of uniformity of these parameters leads to design concepts which circumvent the variability problem:

• a circuit designer can only be assured that the parameters fall above a minimum and below a maximum, and that

• use of feedback around this imprecision takes advantage of the inherent gain but makes the final gain depend on well-controlled externals such as resistors and capacitors.

Hydraulic transistor

To further appreciate amplification or gain, consider the hydraulic pressure amplifier, Figure 7.8, whose characteristics may be more under-

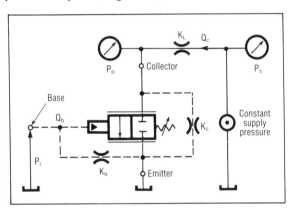

Fig. 7.8. Hydraulic transistor uses a proportioning valve to make a pressure amplifier. The circuit is only useful to illustrate pressure gain.

standable to fluid power specialists. This circuit clearly is a contrivance intended to illustrate pressure gain and that it has a negative value at the same time flow gain is positive.

K_L, Figure 7.8, is an external load orifice which converts flow to a differential pressure drop; K_c characterizes the internal leakage path through the valve, and K_b is a small leakage path in the pilot section of the valve. Pilot pressure acting against the spool-end area causes the spool to shift against the adjustable return spring.

When pilot pressure P_o is low, the spool is in the position shown and collector flow is blocked except for the small leakage through K_c. This small flow, Q_c, also results in a small differential pressure drop across K_L. Therefore, collector output pressure P_o is nearly equal to supply pressure

MOTION CONTROL

P_s. As pilot (base) pressure P_i increases, the spool begins to shift. Opening the valve results in an increase in flow Q_c which, in turn, creates an increasing pressure differential across K_L. Thus, an increase in pilot pressure P_i results in a drop in output pressure P_O.

The generalized transfer characteristic curves, Figure 7.9, indicate two

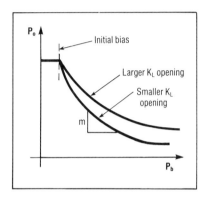

Fig. 7.9. Input-to-output pressure transfer characteristic for the hydraulic transistor shown in Figure 7.8.

different load-orifice sizes. The pressure gain of the circuit is slope m of the output pressure vs. input pressure curve. If orifice K_L has a smaller hole, a small increase or decrease in pilot pressure P_i results in a larger increase or decrease (gain) in output pressure P_o compared with use of a load orifice with a larger hole. So, the size of the load restrictor affects pressure gain. These key valve parameters also affect the pressure gain:
- area of the end of the spool
- return spring's spring rate, and
- maximum opening of the valve, especially when compared to the size of the load restrictor.

The pre-compression of the return spring controls location of the point labelled *initial bias* in Figure 7.9; adjusting spring compression does not affect gain. Spring compression only changes the pilot pressure needed to start metering. As pilot pressure increases and opens the valve, the flow *also increases* to result in an unsurprising *positive* flow gain. Simultaneously, outlet pressure *decreases*, to give a *negative* pressure gain. The analogy to a transistor is profound.

Pump amplifier

Variable-displacement hydraulic pumps are excellent high-powered, high-gain amplifiers. On the other hand, fixed-displacement pumps do not amplify; their general nature is that of a fixed gear box, a bicycle, or a fixed transformer because the control input, the shaft, also is the power input, Figure 7.10(a). Contrast the variable-displacement pump, Figure

130

7.10(b); it has the three I/O points necessary for amplification:
● power input through the shaft
● control input to vary the displacement, and
● power output at the pump outlet ports.

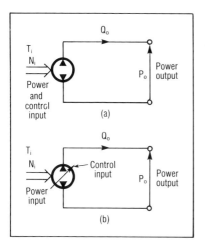

(a)

(b)

Fig. 7.10. Operation of (a) fixed-displacement and (b) variable-displacement pumps results in power output, but the fixed-displacement variety does not have a separate control-input port. Thus the fixed pump is not an amplifier.

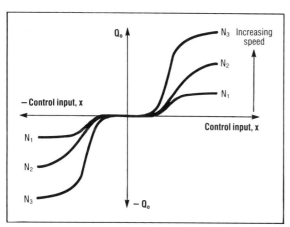

Fig. 7.11. Generic variable-displacement pump transfer characteristic at several shaft speeds, N.

A complicating factor when considering pumps as amplifiers is the variety of control schemes; each scheme must be taken individually. Here, for example, is a partial list of ways to change pump displacement:
● lever or handle to change cam position
● hydraulic pilot pressure acting on stroking piston(s), and
● servo or proportional valve metering flow and pressure to drive stroking piston(s).

Add to that complication other internal pump characteristics, such as feedback from the cam to the stroking mechanism, load-sensing flow-control and limits, and pressure compensation, and the result is a proliferation of control schemes and an almost bewildering range of system-performance characteristics. Regardless, the most basic pump-amplifier produces hydraulic flow as an output when one of these control variables causes a displacement change:

- lever or handle position
- hydraulic pilot pressure
- electrical current, or
- electrical voltage.

The result is the generic transfer curve, Figure 7.11, with the generic schematic for a variable-displacement pump, Figure 7.12. The exact shape of the transfer characteristic depends on the specific pump, but generally, displacement varies as some function of control input, Figure 7.13.

The linear control curve of a zero dead-zone pump, Figure 7.13(a), is desirable when using automatic feedback control in a null-seeking system such as a positional servo. When humans manually control displacement of a pump with this characteristic, it is difficult for them to find the null.

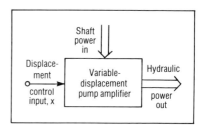

Fig. 7.12. Schematic indicates generic diagram of variable-displacement hydraulic pump as an amplifier.

The continuity through the origin of the curve makes it almost impossible to stop the actuator. So, when humans are part of the control loop, the pump transfer characteristic should have a deliberate dead zone, Figure 7.13(b). This allows some latitude in input positioning and still provides zero output flow and a stopped actuator. On the other hand, an automatic controller can have great difficulty dealing with a non-linear dead zone such as this.

The curve in Figure 7.13(c) represents all other forms of the transfer characteristic and, in one way or another, more realistically represents the curves of Figures 7.13(a) and (b). That is, the curves of Figures 7.13(a) and (b) are quite idealized; they share many of the characteristics of the curve in Figure 7.13(c).

The equations which describe pump output of a linearized machine are relatively simple except for the specific pump's transfer characteristic.

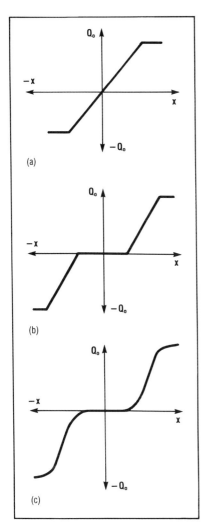

(a)

(b)

(c)

Fig. 7.13. Examples of hydraulic pump transfer characteristic; (a), linear control with saturation; (b), linear control with central region dead zone and saturation; and (c), non-linear control with dead zone and saturation.

That is,

$$Q_o = [D(x)N/60] - (P_o/R_L), \qquad (7.27)$$

where $D(x)$ is the function which describes how the pump's displacement varies with control parameter (x). Displacement is measured in in^3/rev of the shaft, but the actual control parameter must remain generic until the pump is identified; N is the shaft speed in rpm; P_o is the pump outlet pressure in psid, and R_L is the pump's internal leakage resistance in psi/in^3/sec.

The control system designer's challenge is to make $D(x)$ vary to achieve one or more of these performance goals:

- pressure regulation, as in pressure-compensated operation
- flow regulation as in load-sensing operation
- horsepower limiting to minimize the risk of prime mover stall
- actuator speed control
- actuator position control, and
- others that inventive minds can and will create.

The first three of these goals usually are implemented at the pump using hydromechanical methods and are most often thought of as part of the pump. That is, pressure-compensated, horsepower-limiting, and load-sensing pumps are widely available as standard products. Current practice closes control loops mechanically or uses fluid porting within the pump's housing to close the loop. With increased use of electrical control parameters as (x), that need not be the case.

The last three goals are thought of as being external to the pump, belonging to the *system* of the user or applications engineer. If the concept of control-loop closure is extended beyond the pump case, any mode of control can be implemented through software. A system can be operated at one instant as a speed control and at the next instant as a torque control; similar changes presently are made in hydraulic presses.

One basic, electrically controlled variable-displacement pump plus a computer with a variety of control algorithms is all that is needed. A single configuration of an electrically controlled pump provides all the hydromechanical variability required. Hydromechanical control and feedback schemes are out of date and soon will be replaced by the more generic, more flexible electrohydraulic system.

Transistor amplifier summary

Most analog circuit designers today make more extensive use of *integrated circuits* (ICs) made up of several transistors and resistors on a single IC chip rather than discrete components. Discreet transistors can be seen on electrohydraulic control amplifiers but the transistors mostly provide the final output power to a coil. The common IC chip for analog functions is the operational amplifier or op-amp. It offers the circuit designer limitless flexibility and yet is easy to use.

The basic element of an op-amp is the transistor. In fact, any given op-amp chip will have from several to dozens of transistors. The compactness of an IC is a clear advantage over a discreet circuit. Not so clear at this time, perhaps, is the degree of difficulty involved when designing circuits around transistors. Analysis of the circuit often becomes complex when more than one transistor is used. Furthermore, the simple single-

transistor amplifier discussed earlier has some undesirable characteristics:
• the voltage gain is negative. This is not always a disadvantage, but there are instances when positive gain is desirable
• there is a discontinuity in the input-output voltage-transfer characteristic caused by the need to overcome the 0.5 volt or so required to forward bias the base-emitter junction, and
• when the input voltage is zero, output voltage is high and proceeds toward zero as input voltage increases.

The negative gain problem can be overcome using multiple transistor stages; that is, when the first stage has negative gain and its output is coupled to a second stage also with negative gain. The resulting double negative provides a positive.

The second and third problems are solved using a bipolar power supply (a power supply that produces both positive *and* negative voltages), Figure 7.14, to bias the operating points so that bipolar input voltages do not cause rectification at the transistor bases. R_{L1} and R_{E1} are selected so that with zero input, the voltage at the collector of Q_1 is positive but not saturated. R_{A1} and R_{B1} form a voltage divider so that the base resistor of Q_2, R_b, couples a positive current into the base of Q_2. R_{L2} and R_{E2} are chosen to have the collector of Q_2 at a positive value below saturation. R_{A2} and R_{B2} are another voltage divider whose values are selected so that output voltage v_o is zero when v_{in} equals 0. The methods of selection are beyond the scope of this book. Instead, the circuit is shown to provide insight into how resistors and power supply voltages are chosen to achieve

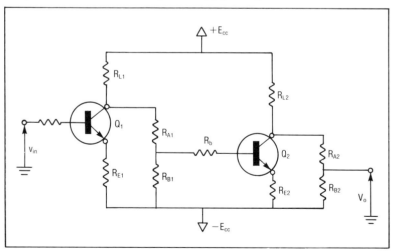

Fig. 7.14. By staging two transistors, positive gain can be achieved. Output can be at zero with zero input, and positive and negative inputs and outputs are possible using both positive and negative sides of a bipolar power supply.

the desired ends.

But there are still drawbacks to this circuit which render it unsuitable for commercial use. For example, the zero input condition is meant to be a short circuit at the v_{in} terminal. This creates a problem if the circuit input represents only one of many inputs. The unused input terminals must be shorted to circuit common. It is much more convenient if the user can let the unused terminals be open.

On the other hand, an advantage of this circuit is the control the designer has over its input impedance. The existence of resistor R_{E1} in the Q_1 emitter provides an emitter-follower effect (see the discussion on the emitter-follower circuit in the section on *Special circuits*). The actual input impedance is much higher than the value of R_{E1}. This minimizes the loading effect that occurs when a sending device is connected to the v_{in} terminal.

Operational amplifiers

The simple transistor/voltage amplifier discussed earlier is the nucleus of a more practical device. Since the early 1920s when de Forrest invented the first triode amplifier, supporting circuits have been the focus of considerable engineering development. Today, integrated-circuit amplifiers are developed to such an advanced state that they approach the ideal. The one-transistor amplifier was nonlinear and its output was not zero when its input was zero.

Today's op-amps are about the size of a thumbnail and are linear because of their reliance upon massive amounts of negative feedback through external linear resistors. Op-amps form a very practical starting point for understanding commercial, industrial control amplifiers. They

Fig. 7.15. Complete IC op-amp symbol, (a), has two inputs. Designer selects which to use, depending on desired output. Simplified and more commonly used op-amp symbol, (b), does not show the power input or optional balance terminal indicated in the complete version.

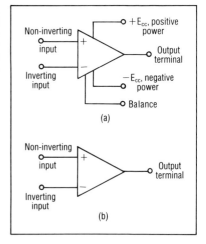

136

may contain as many as 35 transistors and have an open loop voltage gain approaching 10^6 and cost less than $1.00 in small quantities, Figure 7.15.

Today's commercial op-amps are about as near to being ideal as any device could be with one additional characteristic: their gain is so high that it usually is correct to treat them as having infinite gain. The gain is so high as to preclude use without external feedback in many applications. This external feedback serves two critical, practical purposes:

• gain is reduced to practical levels, and
• resulting gain depends on the feedback network, not the op-amp.

Op-amp characteristics

Looking at the technical data sheets for a particular op-amp, there is a plethora of information; it is important here to consider just a few of the data. The input-output voltage transfer characteristic, Figure 7.16, shows that there are two sets of curves, one for each of the two possible inputs. If the user selects the inverting input in Figure 7.15 (and it is strictly the user's choice), the other terminal must be connected to circuit common. The simplified test schematic, Figure 7.17(a) and (b), shows the different connections made to obtain the two curves of Figure 7.16.

As v_{in} is varied from some negative value and becomes positive, output voltage v_o swings from positive to negative. This leads to the inverting input curve, Figure 7.16. Recall that gain is defined as the change in output divided by the change in input which caused the output change. In this test, the change produces a negative value and is the reason for the name of the inverting input terminal. **Voltages applied to the inverting**

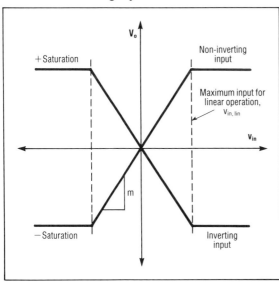

Fig. 7.16. Curves indicate input/output voltage characteristic for op-amp with slope G_{OL}.

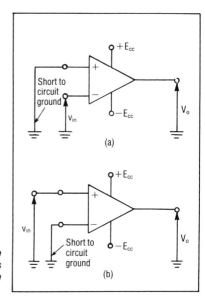

Fig. 7.17. Schematics (a) and (b) indicate the different test-circuit connections used to determine open-loop gain of the op-amp.

input result in an inverse output. For varying inputs, which is *always* the case, there is a 180° phase shift or phase inversion when a signal passes from the inverting input to the output.

But this is not so when using the non-inverting input terminal. There, the gain is positive so that positive-going inputs yield positive-going outputs. Also understand that zero input to this terminal gives zero output, a very desirable characteristic.

Inspecting the voltage transfer characteristic of the op-amp makes it possible to determine its gain. In the tests suggested in Figure 7.17, the slope of the transfer characteristic is the gain and is called the open-loop voltage gain, G_{OL} of the op-amp. Open-loop voltage gains can range from a minimum of about 100,000 to a maximum of several million. That is to say $\Delta v_o / \Delta v_{in}$ for a commercial op-amp, routinely is greater than 100,000 and typically is over 200,000. In fact, 200,000 is a reasonable value to assume if there are no technical data sheets handy for reference.

If the amplifier were unlimitedly linear, an input of 1 volt would, for example, produce an output of 200,000 volts, quite a feat for a 79-cent piece of sand. But this is not the case. Instead, the output reaches saturation when the input exceeds several microvolts. The number of microvolts can be estimated with knowledge of the open-loop gain and the supply voltage.

Except in rare cases of inductive loads, amplifier output cannot exceed its $\pm E_{cc}$ supply. Typical saturation voltages are from about 80% to about 97% of supply voltage of the polarity that is saturated. The actual percentage depends upon the type of op-amp and whether the saturation is on the plus or minus side. Op-amp technical-data sheets must be consulted to establish the exact value. It always is true that saturation output depends on the power supply voltage in a linear manner.

When estimating the limits of linear operation, a good first estimate would assume that the saturation output is approximately equal to the plus and/or minus supply voltage. That assumption is very much like the practice of saying that the relief valve setting or pressure-compensator setting is the same as the maximum operating pressure of a hydraulic system. So now,

$$+v_{o, sat} \cong +E_{cc}, \tag{7.28}$$

and

$$-v_{o, sat} \cong -E_{cc}. \tag{7.29}$$

Looking at Figure 7.16, we see that

$$+v_{in, lin} = +v_{o, sat}/G_{OL}, \tag{7.30}$$

or

$$v_{in, lin} \cong E_{cc}/G_{OL}, \tag{7.31}$$

where v_{in} is the limit of the linear range of input beyond which output saturation will occur. It is only an estimate, and the actual value could be as much as 20% less, depending upon the transistor.

Example 7.2. Suppose an op-amp has an open-loop gain of 200,000 and it is powered by a ± 10 V power supply. What is the linear limit of input voltage.

Solution 7.2. Use Equation (7.31):

$$
\begin{aligned}
v_{in, lin} &= E_{cc}/G_{OL} \\
&= 10/200{,}000 \\
&= 0.00005 \text{ Volts} \\
&= 0.05 \text{ millivolts (mV)} \\
&= 50 \text{ microvolts } (\mu V).
\end{aligned}
$$

This result shows that the normal range of input is very low; 50 microvolts is approximately the voltage that is induced in the antenna of your AM radio due to the radiation of Radio Moscow on a good day. That same 50 microvolts causes an op-amp output of 10 volts. That is amplification! We'll see later that except for the op-amp comparator circuit, the open-loop gain is too high and will be reduced to more usable levels with feedback.

Equivalent circuit

It is useful to look at the equivalent op-amp circuit as fabricated by specialists in the field. For our purposes a simple model, Figure 7.18, will

Fig. 7.18. Simplified equivalent circuit of an op-amp. A is a virtual ground within the op-amp envelope.

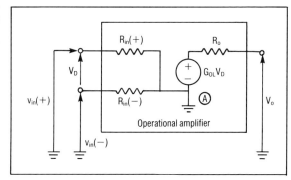

suffice. A subtle feature is the *virtual ground, A*, within the op-amp chip. Physically it does not exist, but it explains that output voltage v_o is to be measured with respect to circuit-board common which is not to be confused with mother earth. Recall that circuit-board common is taken as the center top of the power supply transformer.

$R_{in}(+)$ and $R_{in}(-)$ are the effective internal input resistances, respectively, which couple input signals $v_{in}(+)$ and $v_{in}(-)$, respectively, to the non-inverting and inverting pins. The small generator, called a dependent generator, tells us that its voltage is a dependent, linear function of the *differential* voltage, V_D, between the two inputs. Note then, that if $v_{in}(+)$ is greater than $v_{in}(-)$, the dependent generator voltage has a positive value. When $v_{in}(-)$ is higher than $v_{in}(+)$, the opposite output sign appears. Resistor R_o is the op-amp's output impedance (resistance) and accounts for the fact that when we connect a load to the output pin, the internal voltage drop across R_o results in a smaller output voltage than if there were no load. This is obviously a loading effect. Output impedances of the basic op-amp range from a few hundred to a few thousand ohms. However, feedback incorporated around the op-amp reduces effective output impedance to a fraction of an ohm, eliminating loading effects in all but the most unusual applications.

Now the circuit designer has several options:

● short the non-inverting terminal to ground and use the inverting terminal as the single input. Now, output undergoes a 180° phase shift
● short the inverting terminal to ground, and use the non-inverting terminal as a single input. In this case, output is not inverted , and

● use both inputs as two independent inputs, so that output is a function of the difference between the two, that is

$$v_o = G_{OL}[v_{in}(+) - v_{in}(-)].\qquad(7.32)$$

Literally hundreds of different operational amplifier application circuits have been developed and put to useful tasks. A compendium of them would be huge. Fortunately for the electrohydraulic practitioner, there are fewer than a dozen encountered in the work-a-day world. Next is a summary of the most common op-amp circuits along with a brief explanation and the key formulas for calculating gains, etc. They are important for fluid power practitioners because they lurk behind the user terminals of transducers, servo amplifiers, and proportional-valve amplifiers. Each has its own peculiarities. Especially important is the input impedance because that directly affects the degree to which a connection will result in loading error.

The ideal amplifier

The amplification process is vital to typical electrohydraulic hardware. When examining an operational amplifier, it is helpful to consider an *ideal amplifier* for a moment. Although we know there is no such thing as an ideal amplifier, the concept is useful because it presents a hypothetical goal. Furthermore, it is much easier to predict circuit performance if its amplifier is treated as though it were ideal.

Thinking of an amplifier as ideal is akin to treating a pump as ideal when estimating hydraulic circuit performance. Hydraulic circuit designers frequently ignore internal leakage when initially estimating pump capacity — they consider volumetric efficiency to be 100%. Later, when selecting actual hardware, the same designers will oversize the pump to allow room for error because they understand the pump is not ideal.

When examining the following operational amplifier circuits, a distinction must be made between the individual op-amp and its implementation in a complete circuit. *Amplifier* refers to a generic circuit on a circuit board or card of which the op-amp is a component. Clearly the operational amplifier is an amplifier, but there is need to distinguish between a servo amplifier or a hi-fi amplifier for example, and the operational-amplifier integrated-circuit chip. *Amplifier circuit* will be used occasionally to distinguish between the op-amp and a circuit made up of the op-amp and other circuit elements (most of which are resistors).

The ideal voltage amplifier has a number of desirable characteristics; it
● has infinite input impedance, R_r
● has zero output impedance, R_s
● is linear

141

● does not saturate, and
● has zero output with zero input.

On this incomplete list, the first two items are the most important to practitioners of the electrohydraulic art.

It is essential that one understands that an amplifier is an interface device which always links some signal source or sending device to some load, Figure 7.19. Electronic engineers call an amplifier a *two-port device*, because it has an input side or port and an output side or port. This name is appropriate if the power port is taken for granted, which most often is the case.

Fig. 7.19 An amplifier is an interface device which links some sending device to some load or receiving device. The fictitious ideal amplifier does not cause a loading error at the sending device and the load does not cause a loading error at the amplifier output.

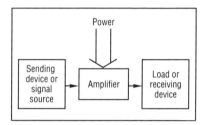

Note that the terms *sending* and *receiving* are relative. The amplifier is a receiver at its input terminals and a sender at its output terminal(s). Indeed, design and construction of electrohydraulic systems is nothing more than interconnecting a variety of sending and receiving devices in a way that achieves desired system performance.

It should be apparent that the amplifier, having been connected to the sending device, has the potential for loading the output of the sending device. That is, if we measure voltage output of the sending device without the amplifier connected, the sender's output voltage would be higher than that measured when the amplifier is connected. **This voltage loss or loading error occurs because the finite input impedance (the load) of the amplifier results in a current draw into the amplifier terminals. This current draw, in turn, results in a voltage drop within the sending device due to its finite output impedance.**

We learned from Teenage Freddie in Chapter Three that the amount of loading error, E_l, can be calculated from the output and input impedances of the sending and receiving devices, respectively:

$$E_{l(in \%)} = (100)R_s/R_r, \qquad (7.33)$$

where R_s is the output impedance (resistance) of the sending device and R_r is the input impedance (resistance) of the receiving device.   Inspection of Equation (7.33) and consideration of the action that takes place with the interconnection shows that loading error can be reduced to zero if:
● output impedance R_s of the sending device is zero, **or**

● input impedance R_r of the receiving device is infinite.

Only one of these conditions must be met. Also note that these conditions are the first two characteristics of an ideal amplifier.

Of course, ideal amplifiers do not exist any more than do ideal pumps. However, many practical amplifiers are designed so they can be considered ideal at certain times. That is, amplifier designers are well aware of loading effects and strive to design for the highest input impedance and the lowest output impedance consistent with other design goals.

Amplifier users should never take idealism for granted, however, because there always are application-specific issues which amplifier designers cannot possibly know. Amplifier users have control over application-specific constraints and must be fully aware of the input and output impedances for the equipment they use.

Thus, it becomes useful to study the characteristics of common amplifier circuits used in electrohydraulic design so one can make the interconnections among the several components in the most knowledgeable way. The following circuit-analysis summaries are presented for that purpose.

Operational amplifier comparator circuit

The most basic operational amplifier circuit is called a *comparator* and is used to compare one voltage with another. Fluid power designers, for example, use this circuit to detect when a cylinder reaches a preset position. The comparator circuit is properly called a *programable limit switch*. The circuit produces a sudden change in output voltage and algebraic sign whenever the preset voltage is crossed. The circuit functions without external feedback and contains only the op-amp, its two input terminals, and a power supply.

But first consider the conventional limit-switch arrangement often used in hydraulic cylinder applications. A cylinder and mechanical limit switch , Figure 7.20(a), are mounted so the cylinder rod reaches the trip arm of limit switch $LS1$. Sufficient deflection of the trip arm causes $LS1$ to change state from, say, open to closed. The cylinder cycles so that a trace of its position is a trianglar wave, Figure 7.20(b).

If the cylinder starts in its retracted position, it moves toward $LS1$ as it extends. Eventually, the cylinder-rod cam depresses $LS1$ so that it changes state, Figure 7.20(b). What happens next after this change of state is unimportant here, but there are many possibilities: the signal generated by the change of state may stop the cylinder, may start another portion of a machine cycle, or trigger some other events.

Now, however, an important factor is whether the state of $LS1$ is monitored. If it is, the passage of the cylinder cam over $LS1$ (a special event) can be detected. This circuit has been used in countless fluid power applications, but recognize that there are important disadvantages to this system.

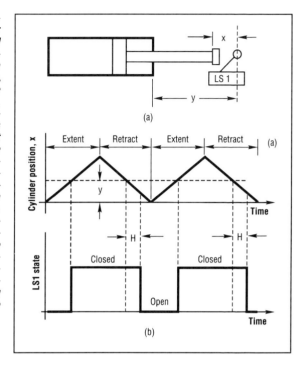

Fig. 7.20. (a) Conventional cylinder and mechanical limit switch arranged so switch LS1 changes states, that is open to close or close to open, when cylinder extension x crosses switch placement position y. (b) As the cylinder cycles, a triangular wave describes cylinder position. When cylinder position x crosses LS1 placement y, LS1 changes from open to closed. Upon retraction, switch hysteresis causes delay H when going from closed to open.

One notable disadvantage is that $LS1$ must be physically moved if the position where it changes state must be altered. This move requires set-up time and downtime of production machinery. Another disadvantage is that mechanical limit switches have hysteresis. To change $LS1$ from closed to open, for example, requires the trip arm to be displaced a specific distance. When returning from open to closed, the cylinder rod releases the trip arm at a place significantly different from the closed to open trip point. This change of trip-point position is an intractable problem of automation when it becomes necessary to detect trip-point crossing in extending and retracting directions. Sometimes, two limit switches must be used to overcome these hysteresis effects.

Use of an op-amp and a linear position transducer, Figure 7.21(a), to similarly indicate cylinder position can alleviate set-up delays and hysteresis problems. In this case, the cyclically operating cylinder moves the wiper arm of a linear position transducer. The two end terminals of the potentiometer are connected electrically to $+V_{cc}$ and $-V_{cc}$ so that as the cylinder cycles, output voltage at the transducer wiper arm similarly cycles with respect to circuit common but between $\pm V_{cc}$. Thus, the wiper signal also is a triangular wave carrying cylinder position information.

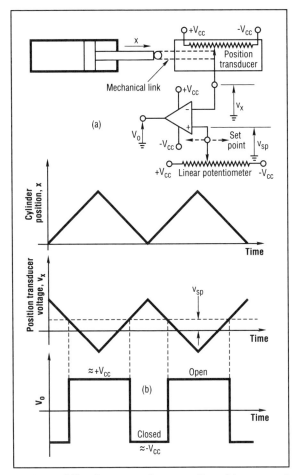

Fig. 7.21. (a) A programmable limit switch can be implemented by mounting a linear position transducer on the cylinder rod while using an op-amp to monitor position transducer output. State of op-amp output V_o will switch from a large negative value, say, to a large positive value as the set point of the potentiometer is passed. (b) Cyclical cylinder motion produces triangular voltage V_x at the wiper arm of the position transducer. Output of the op-amp comparator switches rapidly from positive to negative as transducer output crosses potentiometer set-point voltage v_{sp}.

Meanwhile, for example, an adjustable manual potentiometer has been preset to a position where its wiper voltage signals set point v_{sp}. The value of v_{sp} can be superimposed directly on top of the position transducer output voltage as in the center trace, Figure 7.21(b). That voltage represents the transition point of op-amp output V_o.

Recall that the open-loop gain of an op-amp is extremely large, usually more than 200,000 volts/volt. Recall also that the op-amp amplifies the difference in voltage between its two input terminals. This means that any time transducer voltage v_x differs from set point voltage v_{sp} by more than about 50 microvolts, op-amp output voltage V_o will be either positively or negatively saturated.

The sign of V_o depends upon whether v_x is greater or smaller than v_{sp}. In the circuit shown, anytime v_x is greater than or more positive than v_{sp}, op-amp output voltage V_o is at its negative saturation limit, approximately the same as the negative DC power supply voltage, $-V_{cc}$. Thus for this circuit, op-amp output is negative with the cylinder fully retracted and positive with the cylinder fully extended. Swapping input terminals of the op-amp only reverses the phase relationship.

Note that the output of this circuit is similar to that of the limit-switch circuit of Figure 7.20. That is, a sudden change in output state signals the crossing of the transition point. The difference between the two systems lies in the versatility of the op-amp circuit. Specifically, to change the position of the cylinder where the output transistion occurs, one need only change the setting of the set-point potentiometer in the op-amp circuit. Sometimes this change may be made without system shut-down.

A second difference is the lack of appreciable hysteresis in the op-amp system. The transition point remains essentially the same regardless of the direction of cylinder movement although the op-amp system has a small *zone of ambiguity*. The active cross-over region of the op-amp causes this zone but the ambiguity-induced open-loop gain is easily estimated and dealt with when the op-amp error is known.

Suppose that an op-amp has an open-loop gain of 200,000 volts/volt and that cylinder travel is 48 inches. Further suppose that the bipolar DC power supply delivers ± 15 volts. The zone of ambiguity for this case is approximately ± 15 volts/200,000 or about ± 75 microvolts.

Transducer sensitivity is the full power supply range over cylinder stroke, that is 30/48 or 0.625 volts/inch; (75 microvolts)/(0.625 volts/inch) indicates that there is a zone of ambiguity which is only ± 120-microinches wide. The circuit can detect the crossing point only within ± 120 microinches. Whether that uncertainty is tolerable is an application-specific question that cannot be answered here. The important point is that the uncertainty can be estimated before the circuit is built, so decisions then can be made on an informed basis.

Basic inverting amplifier

The most common configuration of an op-amp is the basic inverting amplifier, Figure 7.22, where the designer controls the value of circuit gain by using feedback. Note that the inverting input terminal receives the input signal while the non-inverting terminal is connected to circuit common through bleed resistor R_b. Output is coupled to the input through feedback resistor R_f while input voltage v_{in} is coupled to the op-amp through input resistor R_i.

Suppose the input voltage were to go positive and cause the op-amp's inverting terminal to go positive as well. This small positive input results in amplified, negative-going output voltage V_o. But because part of the output returns to the input through R_f, the output negative tends to pull the inverting input terminal farther in the negative direction tending to negate the effects of the positive input.

The net result is that the output voltage is negative but only slightly more negative than the input that causes it. Voltage at the inverting terminal of the op-amp is only a few microvolts above circuit common. In normal operation, this voltage is so small that it cannot be measured with the typical troubleshooting voltmeters used by most fluid power technicians.

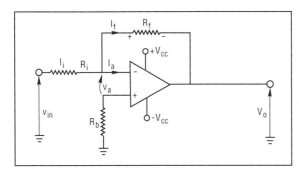

Fig. 7.22. Basic inverting amplifier circuit uses external feedback resistance R_f to control circuit gain. Bleed resistor R_b helps zero the circuit by cancelling effects of small leakage currents that issue from input terminals.

Feedback through R_f always causes the circuit to attempt to keep the inverting terminal at circuit common voltage. Therefore, the inverting terminal is called a *virtual ground* because its value is so close to circuit-common ground in normal linear operation.

It helps to view the inverting terminal as being at ground voltage when evaluating the input impedance of the circuit. Recall that the input impedance affects the amount of loading error (voltage loss) that results when the output of a signal generator such as a transducer is connected to the input of the op-amp.

Circuit designers and users of this circuit are interested in the gain of the inverting op-amp. The designer's need should be obvious. Knowing the gain helps users understand how the circuit can be used correctly and also helps when troubleshooting. Fortunately, gain can be easily calculated when the resistances are known. The gain equation can be derived considering the circuit of Figure 7.22.

To begin with, we know that input impedance to the inverting terminal of the op-amp is extremely large, typically in the tens of megaohms. For most normal applications then, we can assume that op-amp input current I_a, Figure 7.22, is zero. Therefore

$$I_i = I_f. \tag{7.34}$$

Or, in terms of voltage drops across the R_i and R_f resistors,

$$(v_{in} - v_a)/R_i = (v_a - V_o)/R_f. \tag{7.35}$$

Recall that it is the *difference* in voltage between the inverting and the non-inverting terminals that is amplified by the open-loop gain of the op-amp. Therefore,

$$V_o = -v_a A_{OL}, \tag{7.36}$$

where the minus sign accounts for the sign inversion that occurs when using the inverting terminal and A_{OL} is the open-loop gain of the raw op-amp. When using this circuit in a control system, the sign change results in a $180°$ phase shift, a very important factor when assuring proper servo loop phasing. Now, solving for the op-amp input voltage,

$$v_a = -V_o/A_{OL}. \tag{7.37}$$

This can be substituted into Equation (7.35), so that

$$v_{in}/R_i + V_o/R_i A_{OL} = V_o/R_f A_{OL} - V_o/R_f. \tag{7.38}$$

It is helpful to consider the range of op-amp open loop gain A_{OL}. Recall that it nearly always exceeds 200,000 volts/volt and often is >one million volts/volt. Note then that when A_{OL} is very large, the second term on the left hand side and the first term on the right hand side of Equation (7.38) are extremely small. They can be ignored because of this, so Equation (7.38) can be reduced to

$$v_{in}/R_i \approx -V_o/R_f. \tag{7.39}$$

Gain is defined as the ratio of the change in output divided by the corresponding change in input. Here, the gain can be found mathematically by solving the ratio of V_o to v_{in}, that is

$$V_o/v_{in} = G_{CL} = G = -R_f/R_i, \tag{7.40}$$

where G_{CL} is the closed-loop gain, ie, the gain of the entire circuit including op-amp and resistors. We refer to this as circuit gain and henceforth drop the *closed loop* notation.

The fundamental significance of Equation (7.40) is that there is no op-amp parameter in it, thus **the final gain of the circuit is a function only of external resistances** R_i **and** R_f. The lesson at hand is that equations are helpful in designing and understanding circuits but considerable and knowledgeable interpretation always is vital to real world applications.

Equation (7.40) is important because it explains why circuit designers can live with the vast variations in op-amp gains that issue from typical manufacturing processes of solid state devices. It is only necessary at design time that open-loop gain of an op-amp be greater than some minimum. Quality control procedures during manufacture ensure that minimum gains are maintained and published in technical manuals for all operational amplifiers. Many times, maximum gain values are not controlled or published, but high values are not usually the problem. It is only important that the gain of all production op-amps be above a minimum value. Then, circuit designers control circuit gain by using external resistors.

The importance of the inverting amplifier to the electrohydraulic practitioner cannot be overstated. Sometimes, usually when trying to get a critical system up and running during an emergency, it may be necessary for the fluid power engineer to design an amplifier circuit as a temporary, patchwork solution. This may be a situation where sign inversion in the feedback branch can not be achieved another way, or perhaps excessive loading error occurs when the transducer is connected to the servo amplifier; the number of scenarios is endless.

More likely, however, is the simple interconnection of the commer-cially packaged electronic devices. All major manufacturers of servo and proportional electrohydraulic electronics supply amplifiers where the interconnection with the command and feedback devices is made through an inverting amplifier. Knowing the gain and the input impedance of this amplifier allows the practitioner to understand the consequences of this interconnection.

Inverting amplifier circuit input, output impedances

The input impedance of an electronic device controls the size of the load the driven device places on the driving device. In Chapter 3, we saw that when a load was connected to a source that had a non-zero output impedance, the voltage at the source output would be reduced merely for having connected the load. The amount of voltage decrease is the loading error and can be approximated by Equation (7.33), where E_l is the loading error in percent (the percentage by which the voltage drops), R_s is the output impedance of the sending or driving device, and R_r is the input impedance of the receiving device. In this case, the receiving device is the inverting amplifier circuit.

Note that the input and output impedances of the receiving and sending devices are necessary to estimate the loading error in Equation (7.33). **Input impedance of an inverting amplifier is easy to remember: it is the value of input resistor R_i.** In most instances, the value given on the circuit schematic is sufficient; it is not necessary to have the exact value of the specific resistor on a specific amplifier-circuit card.

Input resistance also is the value of the input resistor. This can be seen because the op-amp's inverting terminal is virtually a ground. Assuming that input voltage is always limited to less than saturation, the inverting terminal will be hundreds of thousands of times smaller — in the micro-volt range. When inputs and outputs are in the range of a few volts, it is clear that the inverting terminal is nearly a million times closer to circuit common than they. For all practical purposes, inverting terminal voltage constitutes a ground. It is called a *virtual ground.*

Therefore, any input voltage v_{in} totally drops across input resistor R_i and any connected sending device simply sees that value of input resistance. **It is important for users of that amplifier card to recognize input impedance so they will not inadvertently introduce intolerable loading errors.** This may seem like a trivial assessment, but it is not always possible to tell input or output impedances of electronic amplifier circuits simply by inspecting the circuit. Instead, complex circuit analysis or direct measurement must be used to determine these impedances.

Such is the case with the output impedance of the inverting op-amp circuit. Suffice to say that including external negative feedback reduces the output impedance to make the circuit output impedance substantially less than the output impedance of the raw op-amp. Output impedance of this circuit normally is less than one ohm, allowing it to be ignored in most situations the electrohydraulic practitioner will likely encounter. It is usually correct to consider the output impedance of a basic inverting amplifier to be zero ohms. Proof of this goes beyond the scope and intent of this text.

Example 7.3. What is the gain of an inverting amplifier circuit which uses an input resistance of 5.6 KΩ and a feedback resistance of 47 KΩ? What is the input impedance of the circuit?

Solution 7.3. Calculate the closed loop gain using Equation (7.40):

$$G = A = -R_f/R_i$$
$$= -47,000/5600$$
$$= -8.39 \text{ volts/volt.}$$

Input impedance is the value of the input resistor, that is

$$R_{in} = R_i$$
$$= 5.6 \text{ KΩ.}$$

Example 7.4. Full scale output of a certain strain-gage transducer is known to be ±0.05 volts. What amplifier gain is required if the circuit output voltage is to be ±5 volts FSO, and what feedback resistance is needed if the input resistor has been selected as 22 KΩ and the amplifier is connected in the basic inverting configuration?

150

Solution 7.4. The required gain can be found from the definition of gain:

A_r = *output volts/input volts*
    = 5/0.05
    = 100 volts/volt;

$R_f/R_i = 100$,

therefore

$R_f = 100(R_i)$
    = 100(22,000)
    = 2.2 MΩ.

Basic non-inverting operational amplifier circuit

The basic non-inverting operational amplifier circuit, Figure 7.23, has similarities and dissimiliarities when compared with the inverting amplifier circuit. For the non-inverting circuit to be stable, it is *always* necessary for the output to be coupled through the feedback resistor to the op-amp's inverting terminal. If the feedback is connected to the non-inverting terminal, the circuit has positive feedback which causes the positive input on the non-inverting terminal to regenerate and send the output to positive saturation. The non-inverting terminal is used to couple a feedback signal from the output only in special circuits.

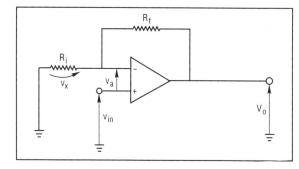

Fig. 7.23. Like the inverting amplifier, this basic non-inverting amplifier circuit has feedback from the output terminal to the inverting input, and input resistor R_i is connected to the inverting terminal. The left side of R_i is connected to circuit common. Note that the significant difference between this circuit and the inverting amplifier circuit in Figure 7.22 is that here, the user connects input voltage to the non-inverting input terminal.

Also note input resistance R_i; similar to the inverting amplifier circuit, it is connected to the inverting terminal, but its opposite end is connected directly to circuit common. Users will connect their input signal directly to the non-inverting terminal for the desired result. That is, a positive-going input voltage will result in a positive-going output voltage. Due to feedback resistor R_f and the voltage divider formed by R_f and R_i, some fraction of the output voltage appears at the inverting terminal. With positive v_{in}, the output voltage will rise until voltage at the inverting input, v_x, Figure 7.23, is just enough to sustain tiny differential voltage v_a, commensurate with the op-amp's open-loop gain.

The major advantage of this circuit over the inverting configuration is its high input impedance. Note that because the user's input signal connects directly to the non-inverting input terminal of the op-amp, the input terminal experiences the raw input impedance of the op-amp itself which could be on the order of several megaohms. Lack of a reversal in algebraic sign may or may not be an advantage. Humans usually perceive it as an advantage because a sign change can become a logical challenge.

Gain of the basic non-inverting amplifier circuit

Gain of the basic non-inverting amplifier circuit can be derived assuming knowledge of the feedback and input resistances. This solution can be approached by summing input current at the inverting terminal as in the case of the inverting amplifier. But now, we will use the voltage divider approach just for variety.

We see that voltage drop v_x, Figure 7.23, across input resistance R_i can be calculated from output voltage V_o, and the voltage divider formed by R_f and R_i. Recall that current into the inverting terminal of the op-amp is very small due to the high input impedance. Now,

$$v_x = V_o R_i / (R_f + R_i). \tag{7.41}$$

The voltage amplified by the op-amp, v_a, can be evaluated by writing a loop equation around the input side of the op-amp. That is,

$$v_{in} + v_a - v_x = 0. \tag{7.42}$$

We also know that because v_a is amplified,

$$V_o = -v_a A_{OL}. \tag{7.36}$$

Solving Equation (7.36) for op-amp input voltage v_a, and then substituting it and Equation (7.41) into Equation (7.42) eliminates both v_a and v_x, leaving one equation in desired variables v_{in} and V_o:

$$v_{in} - V_o / A_{OL} - V_o R_i / (R_f + R_i) = 0. \tag{7.43}$$

Because A_{OL} is always very large, the middle term in Equation (7.43) effectively vanishes. Solving for the ratio of V_o to v_{in} yields the circuit gain:

$$V_o / v_{in} = (R_f + R_i) / R_i. \tag{7.44}$$

Note that this is the inverse of the R_f/R_i voltage divider. It is many times written as

$$V_o/v_{in} = A = (1 + R_f)/R_i. \qquad (7.45)$$

Basic non-inverting amplifier circuit input, output impedances

Earlier we saw that input impedance of the basic non-inverting amplifier is extremely high because the user connects the input signal directly to the non-inverting terminal of the op-amp. This permits the user to take advantage of the inherently high input impedance of the raw op-amp. For most operational amplifiers, this input impedance is on the order of several megaohms.

Like its inverting brother, output impedance of the non-inverting amplifier is very low, usually under one ohm. This is not unexpected considering that the non-inverting circuit is basically an inverting circuit that uses a different input terminal. Because of their high input impedance and their low output impedance, non-inverting amplifiers many times are used as impedance-matching devices. In this context, **impedance matching refers to the process of minimizing loading error rather than maximizing power transfer.**

Loading error can be reduced by using a non-inverting amplifier because of its very high impedance. For example, we know that output impedance of a potentiometer is high. If we can connect the pot directly to input resistor R_i of, say, an inverting amplifier, the pot wiper arm would undergo a loading error because of the finite input R_i impedance offered by the inverting amplifier.

On the other hand, when the pot wiper arm is connected to the non-inverting terminal of a non-inverting amplifier as configured in Figure 7.23, high input impedance of the op-amp non-inverting input terminal results in negligible loading error. At the same time, this arrangement provides amplification of a desired and controlled degree by virtue of resistor selection, as well as low output impedance.

Example 7.5. What is the gain of a non-inverting amplifier circuit if the feedback resistance is 47 KΩ and the inverting input resistance is 6.8 KΩ?

Solution 7.5. The gain can be found using Equation (7.45):

$A = (1 + R_f)/R_i$
   $= 1 + 47,000/6800$
   $= 7.91$ volts/volt.

Non-inverting amplifier with input attenuator

A non-inverting amplifier with an input attenuator, Figure 7.24, is basically the same as the non-inverting amplifier of Figure 7.23. The

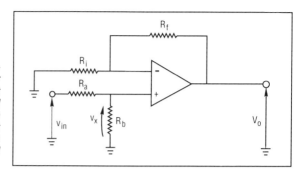

Fig. 7.24. The non-inverting amplifier circuit has an input attenuator formed by the R_a, R_b voltage divider. This circuit is a stepping stone to the differential amplifier.

difference is that instead of inputting directly to the op-amp + input terminal, input voltage v_{in} is coupled to the op-amp through the voltage divider formed by resistors R_a and R_b.

Gain of this circuit can be calculated by first taking advantage of the work done with the basic non-inverting amplifier. Note that the gain from the non-inverting terminal, ie, from v_x to V_o, is the same as given in Equation (7.44). Also note that v_{in} rather than v_x is the input to the circuit, so the desired gain will be the ratio of V_o to v_{in}. Calculate v_x from v_{in} recognizing that v_x is an attenuated version of v_{in} through the voltage divider. Thus

$$v_x = v_{in}R_b/(R_a + R_b). \tag{7.46}$$

Substituting Equation (7.46) into Equation (7.45), eliminates v_x and thus can form the V_o-to-v_{in} ratio, the desired gain:

$$V_o/v_{in} = [(1 + R_f)/R_i][R_b/(R_a + R_b)]. \tag{7.47}$$

In this equation, the quantity $[(1 + R_f)/R_i]$ is the *amplifier part* while $[R_a/(R_a + R_b)]$ is the *attenuator part*.

It may seem curious to start attenuating the signal first and then amplifying it in the very next step. The circuit of Figure 7.24 probably will not be found in commercial hardware, but it forms the basis for the two-input differential amplifier which has found practical application. That circuit will be discussed later.

Attenuated non-inverting amplifier input, output impedances

It must be emphasized that the addition of the input attenuator circuit, R_a and R_b, Figure 7.24, has destroyed the very high input impedance that the basic non-inverting amplifier enjoyed. Observe that these two resistors form a path from input signal source v_{in} to circuit common. Essentially no current will go into the op-amp's non-inverting input terminal because its impedance remains very high. All input current will go through the series circuit formed by R_a and R_b. That current will have a loading effect upon the v_x signal source and, depending upon values, will cause some degree of loading error.

It should be obvious that the input impedance to the circuit consists of the series combination of resistors R_a and R_b. Circuit designers have some control over circuit input impedance through manipulation of these resistor values and the designers want to make them as large as possible. While this is the case, there are other problems with operational amplifier circuits when external resistances begin to exceed a few hundred thousand ohms.

The final result is that input impedance of the attenuated non-inverting amplifier, Figure 7.24, is substantially less than the input impedance of the basic non-inverting circuit, Figure 7.23, due to the $R_a + R_b$ current path to common. The output impedance of the attenuated non-inverting amplifier remains at its desirable low level. This is because the attenuated non-inverting amplifier circuit remains a negative feedback-stabilized amplifier.

Two-input differential amplifier

A two-input differential amplifier circuit, Figure 7.25, accepts two different input signals and delivers a voltage dependent upon their algebraic difference. A very slight modification to the attenuated non-inverting amplifier, Figure 7.24, forms this circuit. The modification is the removal of the grounded side of R_i and use of its free end as a second input terminal.

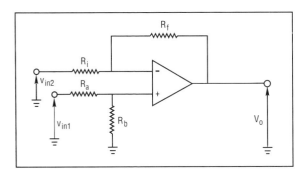

Fig. 7.25. This two-input differential amplifier circuit is used to calculate and scale the difference between input voltages v_{in1} and v_{in2}. Output voltage V_o carries that difference.

This circuit is best understood when seeing two different amplifiers, ie, an inverting and an attenuated non-inverting amplifier in the same circuit. We can consider each of the inputs separately: if the effect of v_{in2} is all that is considered, the circuit is just a basic inverting amplifier and the output is given by

$$V_{o(due\ to\ vin2\ only)} = -R_f v_{in2}/R_i .$$ (7.48)

Equation (7.49) can be used to calculate the output due to v_{in1} only:

$$V_{o(due\ to\ vin1\ only)} = [(1 + R_f)/R_i][R_b/(R_a + R_b)]v_{in1} .$$ (7.49)

The total output is the sum of the outputs from the individual inputs. That is, we can use Equations (7.48) and (7.49) and obtain the total output.

$$V_o = [(1 + R_f)/R_i][R_b/(R_a + R_b)]v_{in1} - (R_f/R_i)v_{in2} .$$ (7.50)

Equation (7.50) shows that the output contains a minus sign between the first and second terms and that the first term contains input voltage v_{in1} and the second term contains input voltage v_{in2}. Because of the two inputs, it is not possible to form a gain as such, except that each input voltage has its own gain. That is, the coefficients preceding the voltages are the respective gain factors. Circuit designers can control input impedances and scaling through appropriate selection of the four resistance values.

One practical application for this circuit is its use as an error-detection circuit for a servo system. Used in this way, one input voltage will be the commmand while the other will be the feedback. In stable, steady-state operation, the command and feedback voltages will be equal. When that happens, the valve should center to stop the hydraulic actuator. The two-input differential amplifier circuit can generate an error voltage, but the resistances must be properly selected to give the true difference.

Imagine an application where it is desirable to have a command voltage, v_{in1}, of say, 5 volts offset by an equal feedback voltage, v_{in2}. The error in this 1:1 case is obviously $v_{in1} - v_{in2}$. If we want the circuit of Figure 7.25 to perform this 1:1 subtraction, then the coefficients of both v_{in1} and v_{in2} in Equation (7.51) must be unity. Then, when command voltage is 5 volts, a feedback voltage of 5 volts will result in zero output voltage from the differential amplifier. One circuit configuration which produces an equal coefficient for each input is one in which all four resistances are equal. This design ploy produces the desired result:

$$V_o = (1)v_{in1} - (1)v_{in2} ,$$ (7.51)

where v_{in1} would carry the command voltage and v_{in2} would carry the feedback voltage.

It is unlikely that electrohydraulic practitioners will be selecting resistors for the amplifier circuit. It is much more likely they will encounter this circuit configuration as a part of an existing circuit card and must put it to use in an application. Several major electrohydraulic component manufacturers use this circuit; it forms an interface to which users connect external signals. Users must have a basic understanding of the circuit and its idiosyncrasies.

In the electrohydraulic world, a two-input differential amplifier has at least two uses. It can:

● generate a difference between command and feedback voltage in a closed loop servomechanism, or

● provide an either/or terminal pair where users can select either the inverting or the non-inverting terminal, depending upon the appropriate signal phasing needed in the specific application. In the second instance, once terminal selection is made, the other terminal typically is unused although nothing precludes its use as a difference generator.

Use as a difference generator circuit is rather straightforward. Users simply connect the feedback to one of the terminals and the command to the other. If loop phasing is incorrect, the two connections can be swapped to correct the phasing. There is only one precaution: **the user should inspect the schematic for resistor values to assess the input impedances.**

Input impedance of the inverting side of the circuit is the value carried by R_i. On the non-inverting side, the input impedance is $R_a + R_b$. Sometimes the circuit designer deliberately selects $R_a + R_b$ to equal R_i. In this combination, the gains still can be controlled.

On the other hand, if the circuit designer has selected other values for R_a and R_b, the two input impedances will be different. In that case, the load on the command signal will be different from the load on the feedback signal. This may or may not be a problem because of application-specific considerations. In any event, the user should always calculate the loading errors on both inputs and take appropriate action.

Used as an either/or terminal pair, differences in input impedances still exist and there is another precautionary note: **because this is an either/or situation, something should be done with the unused terminal.** The choice is the user's and can have a significant effect on this circuit. The unused terminal can be left unconnected or connected to ground (circuit common).

When using the inverting terminal as the single input, it turns out that the state of the non-inverting input is a *don't care* situation. The non-inverting terminal can be left open or shorted to common with minimal effect. On the other hand, if the non-inverting terminal is used, the connection or non-connection of the inverting terminal can have a 2:1 gain change in a circuit that is otherwise scaled for 1:1.

The effect can be seen by considering Equation (7.50). If the non-inverting input is being used, then v_{in1} signifies the active input terminal. If the other input is left open, the effective value of R_i is infinite rather than the value coded on the resistor. If this is the case, ratio R_f/R_i goes to zero and reduces the effective gain between v_{in1} and V_o.

If the resistances have been selected to provide a 1:1 gain on both inputs, the gain in this situation from v_{in1} to V_o will be 2 instead of 1. The rule for using this circuit should always be **short the unused terminal to circuit common**. This will always produce gains as given in Equation (7.50), even though in the either/or terminal pair situation, it is a *don't care* connection.

Inverting summing amplifier

An inverting summing amplifier, Figure 7.26, has inputs v_{in1}, v_{in2}, and v_{in3}. This type amplifier is used when users must input several voltages to the circuit card. The actual number of inputs is totally at the discretion of the designer with commercial amplifiers having from one to as many as seven.

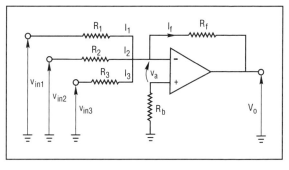

Fig. 7.26. This inverting summer circuit is commonly used in servo and proportional valve electronics. The circuit (arbitrarily showing three inputs) eases problems for the electronic designer because the number of inputs he can include is unlimited. The circuit also eases problems for the user because unused inputs can be left open or shorted.

For example, in a three-input application, one input may be the command, the second the feedback, and the third a dither voltage. In another application, Figure 7.27, several of the inputs can be switchable set-points or command voltages while only one is used for feedback. In this circuit, a user merely selects a preset command voltage and the output of the inverting summer is the negative sum of the selected command and the feedback.

Like the two-input differential amplifier and the multi-input inverting summing amplifier (sometimes called an inverting summer), there is not a single gain, but a gain for each individual input. The expression for the output voltage will help understand the function of the circuit and can best be seen by summing currents at the inverting terminal of the op-amp. Because the current into the op-amp inverting terminal is small, the feedback current must be equal to the sum of the four input currents. Thus

$$I_f = I_1 + I_2 + I_3, \qquad (7.52)$$

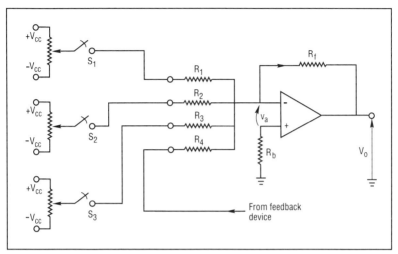

Fig. 7.27. This inverting summing amplifier circuit many times is used to switch in one of several possible preset command voltages by closing S_1, S_2, or S_3. If all input resistors are equal, the order in which inputs are connected is totally arbitrary.

where

$$I_1 = (V_1 - v_a)/R_1, \tag{7.53}$$

$$I_2 = (V_2 - v_a)/R_2, \tag{7.54}$$

$$I_3 = (V_3 - v_a)/R_3, \tag{7.55}$$

and

$$I_f = (V_a - V_o)/R_f, \tag{7.56}$$

all of which can be substituted into Equation (7.52), so that

$$(v_a - V_o)/R_f = (V_1 - v_a)/R_1 + (V_2 - v_a)/R_2 \tag{7.57}$$
$$+ (V_3 - v_a)/R_3.$$

Recall that an op-amp amplifies the very tiny voltage difference that exists between the inverting and non-inverting terminals, v_a. That is,

$$v_a = -V_o/A_{OL}, \tag{7.37}$$

159

which can be substituted into Equation (7.57). Now

$$-V_o/A_{OL}R_f - V_o/R_f = V_1/R_1 + V_o/A_{OL}R_1 \qquad (7.58)$$
$$+ V_2/R_2 + V_o/A_{OL}R_2$$
$$+ V_3/R_3 + V_o/A_{OL}R_3.$$

Note that because the open loop gain of the op-amp, A_{OL}, is a very large number, Equation (7.58) can be approximated as

$$V_o/R_f = -V_1/R_1 - V_2/R_2 - V_3/R_3, \qquad (7.59)$$

and solving for V_o,

$$V_o = -V_1R_f/R_1 - V_2R_f/R_2 - V_3R_f/R_3 . \qquad (7.60)$$

In this equation, the output voltage consists of three component parts with each component representing one of the three inputs. Furthermore, the output is a function of the **negative sum** of the three inputs, with each input multiplied by its own gain factor. That is, V_1 is amplified by gain factor $-R_f/R_1$, V_2 is amplified by gain factor $-R_f/R_2$, and so on. Note that this circuit has no theoretical limit as to the number of inputs that can be connected to the inverting terminal. If there were an amplifier which had n input resistors, each of the n inputs would have its own gain factor.

This circuit is so prevalent in modern servo and proportional electrohydraulics that each practitioner should be well versed in its purpose, function, and use. When reviewing schematic diagrams of commercial amplifiers, it is likely that this is the circuit that users will deal with or encounter most often. Most major manufacturers of this equipment supply amplifiers that have an inverting summer as the user interface.

In a servo system feedback control situation, the inverting summer generates the error or discrepancy between the command and feedback signals. Because the inverting summer, unlike the two-input differential amplifier, forms the negative sum of its inputs rather than the difference, it is the user that is responsible for phasing the input voltages to form a difference. That is, when using a negative feedback control system, it becomes necessary to generate a difference between command and feedback. This difference is called the *error voltage*:

$$\epsilon = error = V_o = V_{comm} - V_{fb}, \qquad (7.61)$$

where ϵ is the discrepancy between command and feedback, ie, the error, V_{comm} is the command voltage, and V_{fb} is the feedback voltage. If this error is generated using an inverting summer, then the gain for two of the inputs must be the same. It is not unusual for them to have a value of one.

That is, if in Figure 7.27 and in Equation (7.59), all the input R's and R_f were the same value (100 K is as good as any, for example), then Equation (7.59) becomes

$$V_o = -V_1 - V_2 - V_3. \tag{7.62}$$

Because the error is comprised of only the command and feedback constituent parts, only two inputs are needed; simply set the unused inputs to zero. The convenience of this interface circuit is that the unused inputs either can be left open or shorted to common. It is another completely *don't care* situation.

The input selected to remain unused is totally arbitrary. For the sake of explanation, assume that input 1 will be used for the command and that input 3 will be used for feedback and input 2 will be unused. Now, Equation (7.62) simplifies to

$$V_o = -V_1 - V_3, \tag{7.63}$$

and this can be altered to reflect the problem at hand:

$$V_o = -V_{comm} - V_{fb}. \tag{7.64}$$

Immediately from Equation (7.64) it is seen that output voltage is the negative sum of the feedback and command voltages, but users know that they must form the difference between the command and feedback as given in Equation (7.61). Now the inverting summer must be implemented so it will provide a difference between the two voltages rather than their sum. This can be accomplished by inverting the algebraic sign of the command voltage. (Actually, inverting the sign of the feedback voltage does the job, but inversion of the command is more convenient for this explanation). Notice that if negative values always are input for the command voltage, the double negative sign results in a net positive, or Equation (7.61), the desired result:

$$V_o = -(-V_{comm}) - V_{fb}.$$

The sign inversion is the responsibility of the circuit user. The designer has provided the means for generating a negative sum and users must modify equipment external to the amplifer to form the difference. The rule for using the inverting summer is easy: **when using the inverting summer as a feedback system input stage, the user must see that the command and feedback signal have opposite algebraic signs.**

This rule assures that the difference is generated and that a positive command voltage, for example, will be offset, cancelled by, or compared to a negative-going feedback voltage. Output voltage V_o will be the system error. When the command and feedback voltages are balanced, the output voltage is zero.

In this example, the input resistors were deliberately selected to provide the same gain for the command signal as the feedback signal. When the input resistors can be selected as they can be for some commercial servo amplifiers, it is possible to compare one voltage with a different voltage and still produce zero output. This is desirable when, for example, the command voltage generator ranges from, say, zero to five volts, but the feedback transducer ranges from zero to -10 volts.

To keep the resolution as fine as possible it is always advantageous to have the maximum input command voltage coincide with the maximum feedback voltage. That is, when the command is at $+5$ volts, the maximum system resolution occurs when this voltage is offset or cancelled by the maximum feedback voltage, -10 volts in the case at hand. The process the system designer uses to make this happen is called *scaling the servo*. It is done by proper selection of the input resistances in Figures 7.26 and/or 7.27.

For example, given the situation that command is from 0 to 5 volts and feedback is from 0 to -10 volts, it is quickly seen that the algebraic signs are correct for an inverting summer but the values are not. Returning to the earlier situation where the command was fed to the number 1 input and the feedback was connected to the number 3 input, note that if we change the value of R_3 so that it is twice the value of R_1, then

$$V_o = -V_{comm}/R_1 - V_{fb}/2R_1 . \tag{7.65}$$

Here, the $+5$ volts command voltage is exactly offset by a feedback voltage of -10 volts, the desired result.

The command now has twice as much effect as the feedback, or the feedback has only half the effect of the command. Be aware that exactly the same change in scaling could have been achieved by making the R_1 resistance one-half the R_3 resistance. In that case, the command would be amplified by a gain of two rather than de-amplifying (attenuating) the feedback by one-half. Now, the user can choose which resistor to change to change scaling.

Is one method preferred over the other? There is no hard and fast rule but when there is no other overpowering reason, it is safer to use the choice in which one resistor is increased. This is because it usually is safer to increase input impedance because it creates less load on the sending device. If the output impedances of the sending devices are very small, the choice is completely arbitrary.

It is emphasized that **the user must ensure that the servo loop has been properly scaled.** If the user-interface circuit is an inverting summer, the selection of one or more resistors is required. It is usually easy for the field practitioner to remember that the input resistors must have a ratio exactly the same as the ratio of the extremes of the voltages that are to be scaled. That is, if a -2.5-volt signal is to be offset by a $+10$ volt signal, the input resistors must be scaled 4:1.

While it is not always easy to remember which resistor should be larger, it becomes easier remembering this rule: **when scaling feedback and command voltages by changing input resistors in an inverting summer, the larger voltage always is connected to the larger input resistor. The ratio of the resistances must be the same as the ratio of the voltages to be scaled**.

Example 7.6. A two-input inverting-summer amplifier has two input $20 \text{ K}\Omega$ resistors. Complete the values of Table 7.2.

Table 7.2—Given input voltages		
V_1, volts	V_2, volts	V_0, volts
$+2$	$+4$	a.
-1	$+5$	b.
-3	-3	c.
-2.5	$+2.5$	d.
$+4.117$	-4.117	e.

Solution 7.6. The op-amp output voltages for the five situations indicated in Table 7.2 are:

$V_o = -V_1 - V_2$.
a. $V_o = -(+2) - (+4) = -6$.
b. $V_o = -(-1) - (+5) = -4$.
c. $V_o = -(-3) - (-3) = +6$.
d. $V_o = -(-2.5) - (+2.5) = 0$.
e. $V_o = -(+4.117) - (-4.117) = 0$.

Example 7.7. For the inverting summer of Example 7.6, what is worst-case loading error if (A). The command voltage is to be supplied by a 10 K, 10-turn pot, while the feedback is to be supplied by a low output impedance magnetostrictive position transducer with an output impedance of $25 \, \Omega$ and (B). Both command and feedback signals are to be supplied by 10 K pots?

Solution 7.7. (A). The percent loading error can be estimated using Equation (7.33):

$$E_l(_{in \%}) = (100)R_s/R_r. \tag{7.33}$$

It is known that the source impedance of a potentiometer maximizes at its mid position and that the source impedance is one-fourth the total resistance of the pot. Therefore, the source resistance of the command pot is 10,000/4 or 2500 Ω. Now,

$$E_{l\ (in\ \%)} = (100)(2500/20,000)$$

$$= 12.5\%$$

(B). When the command and feedback sources are identical, the amount of loading is the same in each branch, and in the feedback control scenario, loading errors are cancelled. This system is referred to as *ratiometric* and in the general case, both drift-induced errors and loading-induced errors are cancelled. Such systems obviously are desirable but, alas, are not always workable, mostly because of practical considerations such as cost constraints.

Example 7.8. An inverting summer is used to compare a 0-to- -2.56-volt command voltage to a feedback voltage which ranges from 0 to $+10$ volts. The amplifier is currently outfitted with 100 K resistors on all three user-input terminals and R_3 is socketed for easy replacement. (A). What value should be used for R_3 so that the full range of the command voltage coincides with the full range of the feedback voltage, and how should the signals be connected to the amplifier? and (B). How would one go about obtaining the resistance required in A?

Solution 7.8. (A). Knowing that the input-resistance ratio must equal the ratio of the voltages to be scaled,

$$R_x/R_y = V_x/V_y.$$

The two voltages and one of the resistances, R_y, must be equal to 100 K. Now

$$R_x = (100K)(10/2.56)$$
$$= 390.625 \text{ K}\Omega.$$

In this particular case, the unknown resistor has been selected to be greater than the existing 100 K resistors on the board. This is consistent with the idea that it is usually safer to select input resistors so that the input impedance is increased rather than decreased.

It also means that socketed resistor R_3 is the one to be changed and its value must be 390.625 K. Additionally, the feedback voltage, larger in magnitude than the command voltage, must connect to this larger resistor. Therefore, the feedback must be connected to terminal 3 and the command can be connected to either terminal 1 or 2. The choice is arbitrary.

164

(B). Finding a 390.625 K resistor will be difficult to impossible. One way to do it economically is to connect a fixed resistor and an adjustable resistor in series and adjust the combination to the requisite value. Values for the resistors are somewhat arbitrary, but a good starting place might be to randomly pick a standard and common 330 K resistor and select the potentiometer to be 100 K. If the variable resistor is not multiturn, it might be tricky to adjust the network to the precise value needed. If that is the case, the adjustment sensitivity can be reduced by adding a second variable resistor of about 10 K resistance.

The 100 K potentiometer should be adjusted first to a value close to but less than the target value. Then, the final value can be acquired with the 10 K pot. This is commonly called a *coarse-fine adjustment system*. Circuit-board designers do not allow for the easy incorporation of such a complex arrangement of resistors, so mounting these new components will be a problem. They probably will have to be screwed fast to the inside of the cabinet with two leads routed to the resistor sockets on the card. This provides some degree of industrial hardening in an emergency but the arrangement invites tampering by the insatiably curious.

An alternate method is to recognize that 390 K is a standard resistor value and a search might turn up one within the tolerance and with the precise value needed. However, not all voltage ratios yield resistors that are so close to standard values. Consider the situation if the election had been to reduce R_3 and connect the lower command voltage to that terminal. The required resistance is 25.6 K, which is more difficult to find than 390 K; 25 K is a standard but non-preferred value, and also will be difficult to find.

Some commercial amplifiers have the ability to adjust either the command channel or the feedback channel to provide any arbitrary scaling that may be necessary. When available, this sort of amplifier is preferred to the Rube Goldberg approaches suggested here, but only because they eliminate the cumbersome mounting problems.

Single-ended to differential conversions

The circuit in Figure 7.28 converts single-ended voltage v_{in} to a double-ended or differential output, V_o. One side of the single-ended signal is referenced to circuit common. Most voltage signals encountered in electrohydraulics are single-ended. The reason for converting to double-ended signals is that a differential amplifier has much better noise immunity. By converting to double-ended or differential operation, data can be transmitted over longer distances even in environments where the 60 Hz noise component is severe.

The circuit in Figure 7.27 uses an operational amplifier to drive a matched NPN/PNP-transistor pair. One side of v_{in} is referenced to circuit ground but output V_o is taken as the differential voltage between the two collectors.

Any transistor, by virtue of the slight amount of forward bias voltage needed to overcome the threshold in the base of the transistor, has a slight dead zone very similar to over-lap in the spool of a directional-control valve. In the circuit of Figure 7.28, however, the dead zone around zero input is effectively eliminated by connecting op-amp feedback resistor R_f from the point where the two transistor emittters are tied together rather than from the op-amp output.

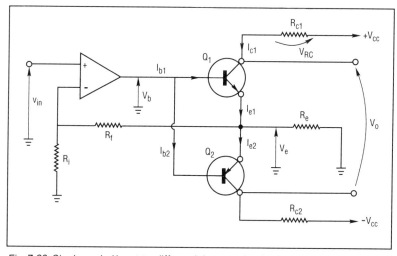

Fig. 7.28. Single-ended input-to-differential output circuit with dead-zone correction. This op-amp, with two complementary transistors, can convert single-ended input v_{in}, with one side referenced to common, to differential or double-ended output V_o, where neither side is referenced to ground. By connecting the op-amp feedback voltage from the emitter of the transistors, the designer has overcome the dead zone that comes from the 0.5 volts needed to get the transistor bases forward biased. This is a typical servovalve driver stage.

The feedback voltage is the voltage across R_e with respect to ground. When op-amp output V_b is near zero, there tends to be no base current into either transistor so there is no emitter current and no voltage across R_e. As input voltage v_{in} is increased in the microvolt range, the op-amp output rises, to say, 0.01 volts, which is not enough to overcome the base to emitter diode so neither transistor base is conducting. There is no voltage across R_e either, so there is no feedback.

This means that for low op-amp output voltages caused by extremely low input voltages, the op-amp is working without feedback and the gain is extremely high. But as soon as op-amp output reaches about 0.5 volts, the transistor begins to conduct, there is a voltage across R_e, there is feedback, and the op-amp operates with a feedback-controlled gain governed by the various resistors. The net result is that the circuit displays extremely good linearity through the zero point as well as converting from single- to double-ended output.

The gain of this circuit can be approximated by Equation (7.66), the derivation of which is left to the interested student:

$$G = -(1 + R_f/R_i)(R_c/R_e). \tag{7.66}$$

Noise sensitivity of the op-amp comparator

The op-amp comparator circuit was demonstrated previously as a level detector. When used in that application, circuit output changes state from one saturation limit to the other as the noise-free triangle wave passes through V_{ref}, Figure 7.29. Each time the output changes state, it is said the *output has been triggered*. Trigger is a generic term used in electronics and

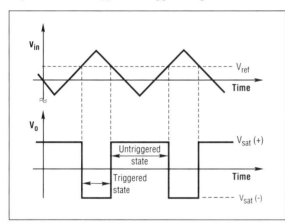

Fig. 7.29. Idealized triggering of a comparator op-amp with triangle-wave input occurs whenever the triangle input exceeds the reference voltage, V_{ref}. Triggering causes the output to snap from high to low.

some interpretation of its use perhaps is necessary. For example, a trigger is an event that is sensed that triggers or alters circuit output; output may rise from negative to positive or vice-versa. Which change-of-state occurs depends upon many application-dependent factors not of concern here. It is only necessary to understand that the term trigger applies to a change in state that corresponds to an event that has taken place.

For obvious reasons, the same circuit also can be called a *threshold detector* or a *level detector*, and when the reference voltage is zero, the circuit becomes a *zero-crossing detector*. A serious deficiency arises, however, when the signal input voltage carries some high-frequency noise, Figure 7.30; this noise often causes false triggers. While Figure 7.29 has a noise-free input signal, Figure 7.30 does not.

False triggers can be a problem for the downstream circuit which is intended to detect a specific trigger and then act. If a position transducer

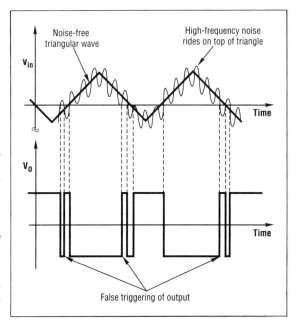

Fig. 7.30. Assuming the downstream cycle counter is set to count the minus-to-plus transitions, noise on the incoming signal will cause false triggering of the op-amp comparator and, consequently, the cycle counter will register a higher count that actually occurred.

on a cycling cylinder generates a triangle wave as discussed earlier, for example, the purpose of the circuit could be to count the total number of cycles. The downstream detector would be an electronic totalizing counter which could be adjusted to count each time, say, the minus-to-plus transition occurs and ignore the plus-to-minus transition.

Obviously, the noisy signal indicated in Figure 7.30 will cause extraneous counts because of the false triggers. Because noise tends to be a random phenomenon, it is unlikely that any scaling factor would correct the total count. The circuit and signal will give an erroneous value in the totalizing counter. Even more insidiously, there normally will be no evidence of the effects of noise until someone gets suspicious and investigates. The Schmitt trigger with its inherent, controllable hysteresis and the mono-stable multivibrator with its built-in time delay, can do wonders to minimize false triggering problems.

Schmitt trigger

The Schmitt trigger is a waveshape-squaring circuit used to minimize false triggering associated with noisy data signals. Noise rejection, or noise immunity as it is sometimes called, can be observed in the waveshapes of Figure 7.31. Note that the upper trip-point voltage needed to snap the output from plus saturation to negative saturation differs from that input required for the opposite snap — the lower trip-point voltage.

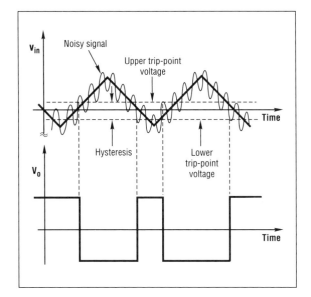

Fig. 7.31. The Schmitt trigger circuit has a designed-in hysteresis which creates a difference between the input voltage needed to trigger the output and that needed to reset the output. By adjusting the upper and lower trip-point voltages, the circuit can be given a certain amount of noise immunity, minimizing false triggers.

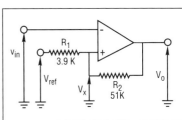

Fig. 7.32. Schmitt trigger circuit helps provide noise immunity because of its inherent hysteresis. Indicated resistance values are the results of Solution 7.9.

The result is that once the output changes state, the small noise signal cannot snap the output back and create false triggers.

Because of this, the downstream counter will record only the correct number of minus-to-plus transitions. It should be obvious that there are some noise amplitudes so large that they could still overcome the hysteresis and cause false triggers. For this reason, the upper and lower trip-point voltages can be designed into the circuit to meet the expected noise levels of the particular application.

For example, the Schmitt trigger is used as the input stage to electronic frequency meters and frequency-to-voltage convertors. Unlike a conventional op-amp analog amplifier circuit, the Schmitt trigger is characterized by positive feedback, Figure 7.32. Note that the circuit has two inputs. V_{ref} is a constant DC-reference voltage derived from the power supply, whose value may be fixed at the time of design or may be adjustable so the user can set the trigger level for the situation at hand.

Noisy input v_{in} is the signal whose level must be detected to cause a change in the output voltage.

If non-inverting voltage V_x is positive, then anytime that v_{in} is *below* V_x, output voltage will be *at positive saturation*, $V_o(+)$. On the other hand, when v_{in} rises above V_x, the output will snap to negative saturation limit $V_o(-)$. The positive feedback offered by the $R_1 — R_2$ voltage divider assures that the output will snap quickly between the two saturation limits. Furthermore, because of the positive feedback, V_x changes sign so that input voltage v_{in} must fall below the value that caused the output transition before the output can again return to its original state. This, of course, is hysteresis and is the characteristic which gives the circuit its noise immunity.

Design of the Schmitt trigger circuit consists of determining the voltage divider ratio for R_1 and R_2 and reference voltage V_{ref}. This requires an analysis of the voltages at which the trigger output is to change states. The input required for triggering is determined solely by V_x which is derived from output voltage V_o and reference voltage V_{ref}. Table 7.3 contains the notations used in the development of the Schmitt trigger circuit.

Table 7.3 — Nomenclature for derivation of design equations for Schmitt trigger circuit	
V_{ref}	Reference voltage
v_{in}	Input signal voltage
V_o	Schmitt trigger output voltage
$V_o(+)$	Positive saturation output
$V_o(-)$	Negative saturation output
V_x	Variable input voltage at non-inverting input terminal
R_1, R_2	Voltage divider resistors
V_{ut}	Input voltage at upper trip point
V_{lt}	Input voltage at lower trip point
ρ	Voltage divider ratio, $R_1/(R_1+R_2)$

These statements are true. When

$$v_{in} > V_{ut}, \text{output} = V_o(-), \qquad (7.67)$$

and when

$$v_{in} < V_{lt}, \text{output} = V_o(+). \qquad (7.68)$$

Since tripping takes place by comparison of input voltage v_{in} to non-inverting terminal voltage V_x, V_{ut} and V_{lt} are specific values of V_x which also relate directly to the input voltage; V_x is critical.

Using the voltage divider and superposition,

$$V_x = V_{ref}R_2/(R_1 + R_2) + V_oR_1/(R_1 + R_2). \tag{7.69}$$

Here, recognize that

$$\rho = R_1/(R_1 + R_2), \tag{7.70}$$

and

$$1 - \rho = R_2/(R_1 + R_2). \tag{7.71}$$

Substituting Equations (7.70) and (7.71) into Equation (7.69),

$$V_x = V_{ref}(1 - \rho) \ V_o\rho. \tag{7.72}$$

For the upper trigger point,

$$V_x = V_{ut} = V_{ref}(1 - \rho) + V_o(+)\rho, \tag{7.73}$$

and for the lower trigger point,

$$V_x = V_{lt} = V_{ref}(1 - \rho) + V_o(-)\rho. \tag{7.74}$$

Equations (7.73) and (7.74) can be solved simultaneously to determine required reference voltage V_{ref}, and voltage divider ratio ρ. This assumes that the other quantities are known or specified, which is indeed the case in a design situation:

● from a knowledge of the input voltage range that v_{in} will likely take and the noise immunity required, V_{ut} and V_{lt} can be reasonably estimated, and
● saturation voltages $V_o(+)$ and $V_o(-)$ are set by the values of output from the bi-polar power supply with approximately 10% allowance for op-amp drop. Furthermore, the positive and negative values in most bi-polar supplies are equal, sign notwithstanding.

The design equations are derived by solving, first, for ρ in Equations (7.73) and (7.74), equating the results, and then solving for V_{ref}. Starting with Equation (7.73),

$$V_{ut} = V_{ref} - \rho V_{ref} + V_o(+)\rho. \tag{7.75}$$

Collecting terms,

$$V_{ut} = V_{ref} + [V_o(+) - V_{ref}]\rho. \tag{7.76}$$

Solving for ρ,

$$\rho = (V_{ut} - V_{ref})/[V_o(+) - V_{ref}]. \tag{7.77}$$

Using a similar procedure on Equation (7.74),

$$\rho = (V_{lt} - V_{ref})/[V_o(-) - V_{ref}]. \tag{7.78}$$

Of course, with a bi-polar supply $V_o(-)$ is expected to be a negative value. Continue by equating Equations (7.77) and (7.78), that is

$$(V_{ut} - V_{ref})/[V_o(+) - V_{ref}] = (V_{lt} - V_{ref})/[V_o(-) - V_{ref}]. \tag{7.79}$$

Clearing both denominators gives

$$(V_{ut} - V_{ref})[V_o(-) - V_{ref}] = (V_{lt} - V_{ref})[V_o(+) - V_{ref}]. \tag{7.80}$$

Expanding both sides,

$$V_{ut}V_o(-) - V_{ref}V_o(-) - V_{ut}V_{ref} + V^2_{ref}$$
$$= V_{lt}V_o(+) - V_{ref}V_o(+) - V_{lt}V_{ref} + V^2_{ref}. \tag{7.81}$$

The V^2_{ref} terms cancel, leaving V_{ref} as the only unknown. After collecting terms and solving,

$$V_{ref} = [V_{ut}V_o(-) - V_{lt}V_o(+)]/[V_o(-) - V_o(+) + V_{ut} - V_{lt}, \tag{7.82}$$

the desired result. With a symmetrical bi-polar supply,

$$V_o(-) \approx -V_o(+), \tag{7.83}$$

so that

$$V_{ref} = -V_o(+)(V_{ut} + V_{lt})/[-2V_o(+) + V_{ut} - V_{lt}]. \tag{7.84}$$

Equation (7.84) along with either Equation (7.77) or (7.78) form the design relationships.

Example 7.9. It is necessary to design a Schmitt trigger which operates from a 15-volt bi-polar power supply. The incoming signal is expected to be ± 10 volts, and the design is to overcome a $\pm 10\%$ noise threshold.

Design the circuit.
Solution 7.9. Allowing for about a 1-volt drop in the op-amp at saturation,

$$V_o(+) \approx 14 \text{ volts.}$$

With the 10% noise rejection specification and a symmetrical input voltage specification, they can be interpreted as

$$V_{ut} = +1 \text{ volt}$$

and

$$V_{lt} = -1 \text{ volt.}$$

Now using Equation (7.77),

$$V_{ref} = [-14(1 - 1)]/[-28 + 1 - (-1)]$$
$$= 0.$$

The result is not surprising, given the degree of symmetry required.
Using Equation (7.77),

$$\rho = (V_{ut} - V_{ref})/[V_o(+) - V_{ref}]$$
$$= (+1 - 0)/(14 - 0)$$
$$= 0.071.$$

This is the voltage divider ratio. We know from Equation (7.70) that:

$$\rho = 0.071 = R_1/(R_1 + R_2),$$

or

$$R_1 = 0.071R_1 + 0.071R_2$$
$$R_2 = (R_1 - 0.071R_1)/0.071$$
$$= 0.929R_1/0.071$$
$$R_2 = 13.08R_1.$$

Standard resistor values which provide the needed ratio must be selected from Table 7.4. Clearly, the 3.9 — 51 combination is the closest choice. Actual values are relatively unimportant, as long as the resistances are above a few thousand ohms. The circuit, Figure 7.32, meets the design objectives.

Table 7.4 Standard resistor values		
Selected R_1 @ standard value	Calculated R_2: $(13.08)R_1$	Nearest standard value, K
1.0	13.08	12
1.2	15.69	15
2.0	26.16	27
2.2	28.77	27
2.7	35.31	33
3.3	43.16	39
3.9	51.01	51
4.7	61.47	56
5.1	66.70	68
5.6	73.24	75
6.8	88.93	100

Mono-stable multivibrator

The mono-stable multivibrator, Figure 7.33, often called the one-shot multivibrator, receives a variable-length pulse and delivers a pulse of fixed length. The circuit is used as a frequency-to-voltage convertor. It can be designed to produce either positive- or negative-going outputs. Note that a characteristic of the circuit is that it triggers or fires on the leading edge of the input waveshape.

A common use of the mono-stable multivibrator is as a *debouncer*, *contact bounce eliminator*, or *deglitcher* circuit. Limit switches, electrome-chanical relays, keyboards, and other such switch arrays are notorious for

Fig. 7.33. Typical input and output waveshapes of a mono-stable multivibrator circuit. The multivibrator triggers off the leading edge of the input and generates an output whose duration is T seconds, regardless of the on or off time of the input pulse. When new leading edge occurs before output is reset, new leading edge is rejected. This circuit can be used as a contact debouncer or a frequency-to-voltage converter.

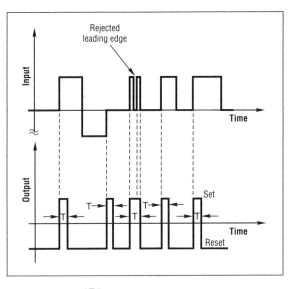

174

contact bounce. When actuated, the contacts close and go home with some force and kinetic energy. Because of this, the contacts often open and close several times before finally settling in the closed position. The whole process may take no more than one or two milliseconds, but if switch output is detected by either the op-amp comparator or the Schmitt trigger, neither can reject the bounces because they represent a 100% swing in voltage. The hysteresis of the Schmitt trigger is effective only if the noise component is below a certain designed threshold. Contact bounce, on the other hand, produces voltages that cover the entire range of detected signal. The mono-stable multivibrator circuit offers an ideal solution to contact bounce because of its built-in time delay.

The mono-stable multivibrator receives the first event, say the initial contact closure which could be a rise in voltage from zero to supply voltage, for example. Once the output switches to its opposite state or level, all addition input triggers are ignored during the time that the output remains there. Once switch output returns to its quiescent state, it can accept the next input trigger.

It is obvious, then, that a properly designed mono-stable multivibrator will have a stable output state whose duration is slightly longer than the time necessary for all input bounces to vanish but not so long that it misses the next valid switching event. Consider a keyboard deglitcher. When using a poorly designed computer keyboard, for example, occasional single keystrokes will put multiple characters on the screen. This situation can be frustrating because the computer will indeed think that all those characters were desired. On the other hand, if the mono-stable multivibrator is added to deglitch, the multivibrator will dictate the maximum rate at which a typist can type. If a second key is struck while the previous keystroke debounces, it is ignored — which also is a frustrating situation. The compromises a designer makes can spell the difference between a successful or unsuccessful product.

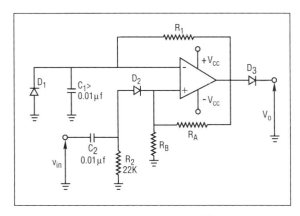

Fig. 7.34. Generalized circuit schematic of a mono-stable multivibrator. Output V_o is at positive saturation for a fixed time determined by time constant R_1C_1. The output is initiated by the leading edge of v_{in}. Any subsequent leading edges occurring during T will be rejected.

Turning to the generalized mono-stable multivibrator circuit, Figure 7.34, consider that during the absence of input voltage v_{in}, there will be a small negative voltage across D_1 and C_1 (due to the diode's threshold) when V_o is negative. The $R_A — R_B$ voltage divider places the non-inverting op-amp terminal at a negative value which provides positive (regenerative) feedback, sustaining the output at its negative value. Should the output become positive, C_1 then charges through R_1 heading for positive saturation.

Eventually the C_1 voltage, also applied to the inverting terminal, rises above the $R_A — R_B$ divider voltage at the non-inverting terminal, causing the output to snap to negative saturation. Thus, the stable output state of the multivibrator circuit is negative saturation. The multivibrator does not free-run because diode D_1 prevents a negative build-up of voltage other than the forward bias of the diode. Obviously, R_A and R_B must be selected so that their divided voltage must be greater than the bias voltage of D_1.

When a steeply rising signal appears at the input, it is differentiated through C_2 and R_2, sending the leading edge of the pulse through D_2 into the non-inverting terminal. If the leading edge of the pulse exceeds the bias voltage of D_1 on the opposite op-amp input, it will cause the output voltage to snap to positive saturation. Because of the $C_2 — R_2$ differentiation, the effect of the leading edge of the input pulse quickly vanishes.

Meanwhile, with the output at positive saturation, C_1 begins heading for positive output saturation through R_1. Some time later, however, C_1 voltage exceeds the $R_A — R_B$ positive boot-strap voltage, snapping the output back to its stable, negative state. Thus, the output was in its stable state for a time determined by the charging rate R_1C_1 and the value to which it must rise, set by the $R_A — R_B$ voltage divider. It can be seen that the voltage across C_1 is critical to the operation of the circuit and provides the necessary insight to quantitatively analyze its operation. See Figure 7.35.

We recognize that v_{c1} is a rising exponential:

$$v_{c1} = V_{o,\,sat} - (V_{bias,\,D1} - V_{o,\,sat})\epsilon^{-T/R_1C_1}, \tag{7.85}$$

where $V_{bias,\,D1}$ is negative. For switching to take place,

$$v_{c1} = V_{o,\,sat}R_B/(R_A + R_B). \tag{7.86}$$

Therefore,

$$V_{o,\,sat}R_B/(R_A + R_B) = V_{o,\,sat} + (V_{bias,\,D1} - V_{o,\,sat})\epsilon^{-T/R_1C_1}. \tag{7.87}$$

To know stable time T, transcendental Equation (7.87) must be solved.

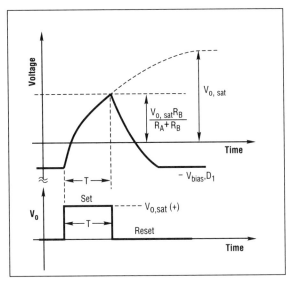

Fig. 7.35. Wave-shape at the inverting terminal of the op-amp produced by the mono-stable multivibrator circuit.

Some algebra is necessary:

$$\epsilon^{-T/R_1 C_1} = [R_B - (R_A + R_B)/(R_A + R_B)]V_{o,sat}/(V_{bias,D1} - V_{o,sat}). \tag{7.88}$$

Taking the natural logarithm of both sides and rearranging,

$$T = R_1 C_1\{ln(V_{o,sat} - V_{bias,D1})/[V_{o,sat}R_A/(R_A + R_B)]\}, \tag{7.89}$$

which can be used to determine the $R_1 C_1$ time constant for given de-bounce time T.

Chapter Eight

Special Circuits for Electro-hydraulic Control

Pulse width modulation (PWM) is a technique commonly used to operate electrically controlled proportional valves. The technique is popular because it:

● allows a large amount of power to be delivered to a load, say a proportional-valve coil, while consuming minimal internal power in the final output amplifier stage, and

● produces a beneficial dithering effect (keeping parts in a state of constant agitation) which can reduce stiction-induced hysteresis when the PWM frequency is appropriately low.

The form of the PWM waveshapes, Figure 8.1, is based on the concept that a load can be controlled proportionally by switching voltage on and off. The voltage pulse is made to swing from zero to full supply voltage and also made to vary the relationship of its on-time to off-time. By making the voltage switching rate so high (a high PWM frequency) that

Fig. 8.1. PWM voltages at different modulation levels. The receiving device is controlled in a smooth, gradual manner rather than the bang-bang response that square waves might indicate. The control is smooth because the receiver can respond only to the average value of the wave shape.

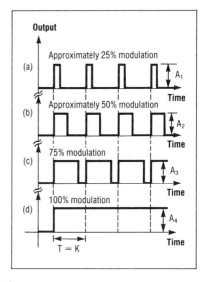

the receiver can only respond to the average value, the technique achieves its control function. Even though the switching rate is high it still can be low enough, depending upon the intent of the designer, to create a dither.

To control the ratio of on-time to off-time, the average current sent to the load is varied. For this discussion, the receiver is a proportional solenoid or perhaps a DC voltmeter. These devices respond to the *average* value of the PWM signal, given the conditions described. But if the receiver were an oscilloscope which reacts much faster than the PWM signal, the oscilloscope would display the actual PWM waveshapes on its screen, similar in appearance to the curves in Figure 8.1.

Power output stage

To understand the complete PWM circuit, first consider its power-output stage which is nothing more than discreet NPN power transistor Q_1, Figure 8.2(a). This transistor has the solenoid coil connected between the transistor's collector and the positive side of the DC power supply, $+V_{cc}$. Meanwhile, the base receives PWM square-cornered voltage v_b as shown in the accompanying oscilloscope trace, Figure 8.2(b). The PWM voltage normally swings from zero to nearly maximum supply voltage $+V_{cc}$. Base input resistor R_b has been selected along with large signal gain β of Q_1, such that a base input voltage equal to $+V_{cc}$ causes Q_1 to saturate.

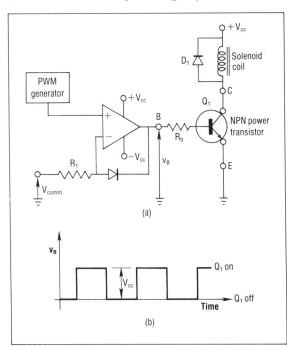

Fig. 8.2. PWM power output stage circuit, (a), drives proportional solenoid coil. Output waveshape, (b), is fed to power-output transistor Q_1. R_B and gain of Q_1 are selected so that Q_1 goes from saturation to cut-off as base voltage v_B goes from $+V_{cc}$ to zero.

That is, Q_1 fully turns on when its base reaches $+V_{cc}$. Of course, when base voltage signal v_B drops to zero, there is no base current and Q_1 shuts off completely, meaning that Q_1 merely switches from fully on (saturated) to fully off (cut-off). Q_1 behaves like an electronically controlled on-off switch. Indeed, it is not at all erroneous to replace the transistor with an on-off switch, Figure 8.3. Q_1 switches synchronously with the base voltage waveshape, v_B, Figure 8.2(b), which is also the PWM source signal.

Now, if v_B stays high for a long time, and zero for a short time (long and short being relative terms), the coil thinks it is powered with a high current. Conversely, if v_B stays zero for a long time and high for a short time, the coil reacts as if its current is a low value which, on average, it is.

Now digress a bit to look at the power consumed by Q_1 when it is operated in the PWM on-off mode. Consider the circuit, Figure 8.4, in which the collector-to-emitter current is labeled i_{ce} and a notation is in place to measure collector-to-ground voltage v_c. Collector saturation resistance R_{cs} has a value $< 1\ \Omega$, normal for a power transistor. Current i_{ce}, and voltage v_c define the power consumed by Q_1. That is

$$W_{Q1} = v_c i_{ce}. \tag{8.1}$$

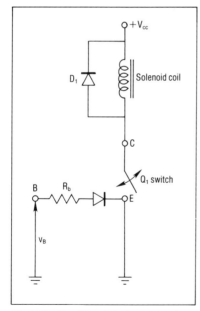

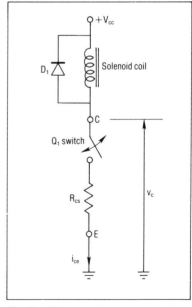

Fig. 8.3. On-off switch Q_1 can replace power-output transistor of Fig. 8.2.

Fig. 8.4. This circuit is used to analyze the power consumed by power-output transistor Q_1 in the PWM mode.

At any instant, then, the volt-ampere product of Equation (8.1) describes instantaneous power.

With some reasonable guesses, at least on a qualitative basis, the current and voltage waveshapes to be expected in the circuit of Figure 8.4 can be constructed. Consider that Q_1 is operating as an on-off switch and acts in synchronism with the PWM base voltage. Therefore, when the switch is open,

● there is no current and

● with no current, Kirchoff's Law demands that supply voltage V_{cc} be dropped entirely across Q_1, so

● when transistor voltage is high, transistor current is zero.

On the other hand, when Q_1 is closed and conducts,

● the transistor has only small net resistance R_{cs}

● with small resistance there will be current, but

● voltage v_c also will be small.

In short, when collector voltage is high, current is low and vice-versa. This, then, suggests the waveshapes of Figure 8.5. Therefore, the product of current and voltage is always low, and power, W_{Q1}, consumed by Q_1 is minimal.

Using typical values, the ratio of power delivered to the load (the solenoid) to power consumed by the transistor would be on the order of about 10:1. In a 30-watt coil, power consumption of the output transistor is about 3 watts. This is a significant point because it reduces power supply requirements, the transistor and heat sinks can be downsized, and the latter may even be even eliminated. All act to reduce product cost without compromising quality or performance. Powerful stuff!

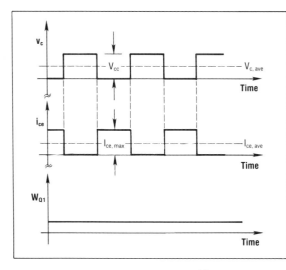

Fig. 8.5. Voltage, current, and power waveshapes for the power-output PWM transistor. When current is high, voltage is low and vice versa. The result is that power consumed by Q_1 is lower than the implied product of average collector current times average collector voltage.

The waveshapes of Figure 8.5 and the above conclusion must be viewed in the context of a typical, intuitive analysis. In that approach, one would measure the *average* collector voltage and *average* collector current and then calculate the power (watts) by multiplying the two. This approach is **incorrect** and will lead to an erroneous evaluation of the power consumed by output transistor Q_1.

To understand why this is true, imagine that we have values for the waveshapes of Figure 8.5. Assume that V_{cc} is, say, 12 volts and that maximum collector current $I_{ce,max}$ is, say, 2 amperes. Averaging a waveshape technically involves integrating to find the area, but if we inspect the current and voltage waveshapes, they look as if the modulation is about 50%. Thus, their averages would be about 6 volts (half the maximum), and about 1 amp. Their product is 6 watts, which is twice the earlier estimate of 3 watts.

Which is correct? The earlier estimate of 3 watts is. The reason 3 watts is correct is that use of average current and average voltage is **wrong** for finding power in circuits which have time-varying values, such as the case in point. It is necessary to find the average of the instantaneous volt-ampere product. The voltage and ampere waves must be multiplied together and then averaged. If the individual waves are averaged and then multiplied, the result is incorrect.

A clearer example of this is to consider the AC power in the home. Clearly the average current and average voltage is always zero and yet all electric appliances in the home work very well. When one multiplies the sinusoidal voltage wave times the sinusoidal current wave, the average value of the product is **not zero**. It is the true power.

The voltage and current waveshapes of Figure 8.5 suggest that the volt-ampere product is zero but that is not the case. There is always some power consumed because:

Fig. 8.6. In the generic PWM modulator, (a), on- and off-time varies, (b), as command voltage changes. This example PWM generator is viewed as having two subparts: a triangular wave oscillator and a pulse width modulator section.

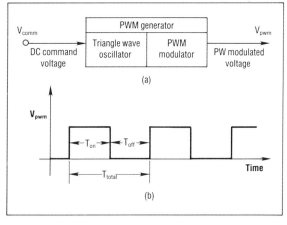

● saturation resistance R_{cs} is **not** zero. Therefore collector voltage does not go to zero when Q_1 comes on and current is high, and
● there is a finite time required for the transistor to switch.
During that transition period, current is rising while voltage is falling and vice-versa. This leads to a non-zero volt-ampere product during switching. Clearly, the faster the transistors, the more efficient the circuit.

Now consider the block diagram, Figure 8.6(a), of the circuit which generates the PWM input to the power output stage, called a PWM generator and the related output waveshapes, Figure 8.6(b). Although there are a number of practical implementations of the PWM generator, only a two-part example is covered here:
● a triangular-wave oscillator, and
● a modulator op-amp which is simply an adjustable level detector or op-amp comparator.

Triangular wave oscillator

The triangular-wave oscillator circuit schematic, Figure 8.7, produces voltage V_T at its inverting terminal with a waveshape shown in Figure 8.8(a), and produces op-amp output voltage V_q, Figure 8.8(b). The circuit can best be understood by inspecting Figure 8.7 and noting that feedback through the R_A — R_B voltage divider couples the output to the non-inverting op-amp input. This is the first clue that this is not a conventional amplifier circuit; it has positive feedback.

Begin the qualitative investigation of the circuit schematic by imagining that there is a short circuit across capacitor C. This forces the inverting terminal of the op-amp to zero volts. Next imagine that electrical power supply $\pm V_{cc}$ has just been energized. Further, imagine that the op-amp is not perfectly balanced so that its output is, say, slightly positive. That slight positive voltage is coupled to the non-inverting terminal through

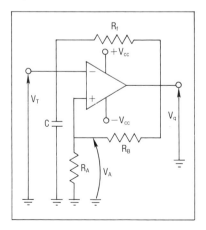

Fig. 8.7. Basic circuit of a triangular-wave oscillator. Positive feedback through R_B and R_A interact with negative feedback through R_f and C to produce a free-running oscillator. Inverting voltage is approximately a triangular wave while V_q is a square wave.

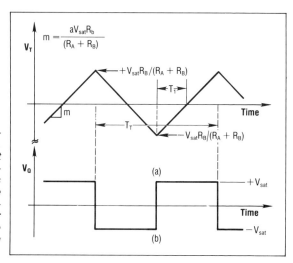

Fig. 8.8. Non-invert-
ing voltage V_T, (a),
and op-amp output
V_q, (b). It is the triangular wave which is
used in the example
pulse width modula-
tor. The triangular
wave appears at the
op-amp's inverting
terminal.

the $R_A - R_B$ voltage divider. This makes the non-inverting terminal slightly positive, which is amplified in a non-inverting manner. This, in turn, causes voltage at the V_Q output terminal to go even more positive, creating more positive input and so forth.

The end result is that output terminal voltage V_Q immediately snaps to its positive saturation limit, which is slightly less than the V_{cc} supply voltage. This action is regenerative feedback and always causes the output to run away to a saturation limit. Had the op-amp started in the opposite direction, that is, if the imbalance were toward the negative output side, output would have quickly snapped to the negative saturation limit. While it is impossible to predict which way it will go, the direction fortunately is not important; in either case, output goes to a saturation limit.

Now for the sake of discussion, assume that the output goes to positive saturation $+V_{sat}$. Then imagine that the short around capacitor C is removed. Capacitor C starts out at zero volts due to the short but its voltage begins to climb immediately toward $+V_{sat}$ because of feedback resistor R_f. The rate at which C charges is determined by the $R_f C$ time constant. Recall that op-amp output is at $+V_{sat}$ and therefore the non-inverting terminal also is positive but less so than $+V_{sat}$ by the amount of the $R_A - R_B$ voltage divider ratio, which is usually 1:10 or less.

For numerical purposes, suppose there is a saturation voltage of 10 volts and an $R_A - R_B$ voltage divider ratio of 1:10. The non-inverting terminal would be at $+1$ volt. Meanwhile, capacitor C starts at zero, trying to charge to $+10$ volts using R_f current. As long as inverting voltage V_T is less than the non-inverting voltage, the positive value holds V_O in positive saturation. At some point, however, V_T, in its quest to reach $+V_{sat}$, rises to put the inverting terminal at a positive value greater than the 1 volt on the non-inverting input.

This excess voltage at the inverting terminal is amplified but in an inverting manner, causing the output voltage to head toward negative saturation. Now, the regerative feedback through R_A — R_B causes the output to snap quickly to $-V_{sat}$. At that instant, V_T is at about $+1$ volt, but it charges through R_f connected to the output of the op-amp. Immediately, capacitor C begins to discharge, heading for $-V_{sat}$. Eventually, V_T goes sufficiently negative to cause the output to snap back to $+V_{sat}$, and the cycle repeats itself ad infinitum.

The result is that voltage at the op-amp output terminal is a square wave with amplitude $+V_{sat}$ to $-V_{sat}$, but voltage at the inverting terminal is approximately a triangular wave. It is the triangular wave that is necessary for the PWM modulator stage.

Design of the PWM circuit begins with recognition that the general form of the voltage at the inverting terminal is given by

$$V_T = V_{ss} - (V_{ss} - V_o)\epsilon^{-at}, \tag{8.2}$$

where

$$V_{ss} = +V_{sat}, \tag{8.3}$$

$$V_o = \text{initial voltage}, \tag{8.4}$$

and

$$a = 1/R_f C. \tag{8.5}$$

Now, assuming that the limits of saturation are approximately equal in both directions,

$$+V_{sat} = -(-V_{sat}). \tag{8.6}$$

Then

$$V_A = V_{sat} R_A/(R_A + R_B). \tag{8.7}$$

These values are substituted into Equation (8.2), so

$$V_T = V_{sat} - [V_{sat} - V_{sat} R_A/(R_A + R_B)]\epsilon^{-at}. \tag{8.8}$$

After finding a common denominator,

$$V_T = V_{sat} - [V_{sat} R_A/(R_A + R_B)]\epsilon^{-at}. \tag{8.9}$$

To determine the PWM frequency, assume that the amplitude of V_T is small, so that the charge rate of the capacitor is essentially constant. This is controlled by the $R_A - R_B$ voltage-divider ratio. The smaller this ratio, the more linear the triangle wave. The 1:10 attenuation ratio assumed earlier is reasonable. The slope of the triangle voltage can be found by taking the derivative of V_t with respect to time:

$$slope = dV_T/dt = [aV_{sat} R_B/(R_A + R_B)]\epsilon^{-at}. \tag{8.10}$$

Continuing with the small amplitude assumption, it is true that

$$dV_T/dt \approx [aV_{sat} R_B/(R_A + R_B)]\epsilon^{-a(0)} \tag{8.11}$$
$$= a V_{sat} R_B/(R_A + R_B). \tag{8.12}$$

Now, a straight line equation for V_T can be written using the generalized form

$$y = mx + b, \tag{8.13}$$

or, in this case

$$V_T = aV_{sat} R_B t/(R_A + R_B) - V_{sat} R_A/(R_A + R_B), \tag{8.14}$$

where

$$slope = m = dV_T/dt = aV_{sat} R_B/(R_A + R_B), \tag{8.15}$$

$$x = t,$$

and

$$b = V_o = - V_{sat} R_A/(R_A + R_B). \tag{8.16}$$

These values and interpretations can be visualized in Figure 8.8(a), where it can be noted that the waveshape has essentially uniform slopes and the wave cycles linearly between $+V_{sat} R_A/(R_A + R_B)$ and $-V_{sat} R_A/(R_A + R_B)$. Note that the time for ¼ of the wave to be completed is labeled T_1, the time for the wave to go from its most negative peak to zero volts. Using this to substitute into Equation (8.14) and letting $t = T_1$,

$$V_T = 0 = aV_{sat} R_B T_1/(R_A + R_B) - V_{sat} R_A/(R_A + R_B). \tag{8.17}$$

Solving for T_1,

$$T_1 = R_A/aR_B. \tag{8.18}$$

Because this is ¼ of the total period,

$$T_T = 4R_A/aR_B, \tag{8.19}$$

and because the frequency is the reciprocal of total cycle time,

$$f = 1/T_T = aR_B/4R_B. \tag{8.20}$$

Using the value for a in Equation (8.5),

$$f = R_B/4R_AR_fC. \tag{8.21}$$

This equation is useful at design time because it relates the frequency to circuit parameters R_A, R_B, C, and R_f. Equation (8.7) is the amplitude of the triangular wave. Now it is possible to begin with an amplitude and frequency requirement, and select components which will produce them. With only two equations and four unknowns, there is an unlimited number of combinations of components which will work. It helps to know that resistors should be in the range of a few thousand ohms to a few hundred thousand ohms.

PWM modulator

Now look at a modulator, that circuit which converts the command voltage into the PWM signal described earlier. The modulator stage, Figure 8.9, is merely an op-amp comparator. The two inputs to the comparator are V_T, the triangular wave just discussed, and command voltage V_{comm}. Think of V_{comm} as the control input which causes the valve to shift.

Note that V_T is symmetrical about the time axis, Figure 8.10(a). Therefore, if command voltage V_{comm} is zero, op-amp output V_o, will be as shown in Figure 8.10(b). Each time the triangular wave passes through zero, comparator output snaps between $+V_{sat}$ and $-V_{sat}$. Because the

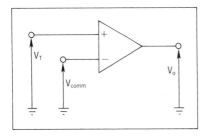

Fig. 8.9. An op-amp comparator is all that is needed to perform the modulation. V_T, the triangular wave, cycles continuously and causes output voltage V_o to snap between plus and minus saturation. V_{comm} controls the time when the output snaps and therefore controls on-time relative to off-time to create pulse width modulation.

Fig. 8.10. Modulator output voltage V_o and input triangular wave V_T, when V_{comm} equals zero for the comparator circuit in Figure 8.9. Whenever the triangle is above zero, the output is positive saturation. When the triangle is negative, output is negative saturation.

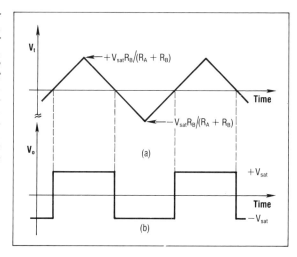

Fig. 8.11. Modulator input (a), and output waveshapes, (b). Changing the value of V_{comm} changes the point on the triangular wave at which the op-amp triggers. V_{comm}, then, sets the trigger level and controls the ratio of on-time to off-time of the output. Note that the output is a PWM signal.

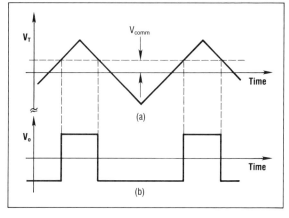

triangular wave is connected to the inverting terminal, output will be at negative saturation whenever the wave is above zero and in positive saturation whenever the wave is below zero. PWM is achieved when command voltage V_{comm} is variable but at a much slower rate than the triangular-wave frequency (also called the PWM frequency).

Consider now the variability of V_{comm}, and the op-amp becomes a level detector. Notice that the relative on-time to off-time at the op-amp output, Figure 8.11(a), is controlled by the strength of V_{comm}. To complete the PWM circuit, diode D_2 is added around the op-amp, Figure 8.12, to prevent op-amp output from going negative. This diode also protects the base circuit of power output transistor Q_1 from excessive reverse voltage.

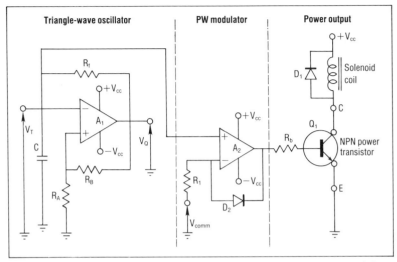

Fig. 8.12. Entire PWM circuit includes the triangular-wave oscillator, a modulator stage, and the power-output stage. Note that the triangular wave connects to the modulator and modulator output is used to switch Q_1 on and off.

R_1 has been added to the comparator (modulator) stage and forms the input resistor for the op-amp. Diode D_2 is the feedback *resistor*. Of course, its non-symmetrical resistance provides zero gain when the output of A_2 tries to go negative, preventing any negative output. We say that the output of A_2 is *clamped* at zero volts. Refer again to the waveshapes of Figure 8.11. Note that the negative portions of V_o will be gone and that when V_{comm} is at a high value, V_o has its minimum on time. If this is undesirable, the circuit designer could install an inverting op-amp to change the sign of V_{comm}, so that a positive value would create a positive and increasing PWM signal.

It is important to understand that this circuit controls only one solenoid. Because most proportional valves have two solenoids, the hardware will contain two circuits like the one in Figure 8.12. To build in some user-friendliness, proportional valve amplifier designers precede the two PWM stages with steering logic which steers a positive command voltage to one solenoid while a negative command voltage goes to the other solenoid.

Ramp generator

Ramp generator circuits are an electronic control option that can be integrated with a proportional valve amplifier. Ramp generators are especially popular when used with manual controls, such as those typically found on mobile equipment. A ramp generator can provide a

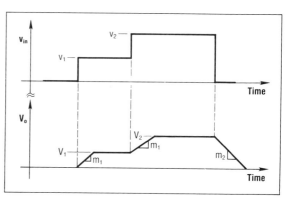

Fig. 8.13. Input and output waveshapes for a ramp generator. Ramp rates m_1 and m_2 control acceleration and deceleration, respectively, and are independently adjustable in most commercial hardware.

gradual opening of a control valve even though the operator's manual initiating command undergoes an abrupt change. This ability provides a degree of acceleration control, albeit imperfect. Nonetheless, use of a ramp control on a springy, noisy system can have beneficial effects.

Input and output signals for a ramp generator circuit, Figure 8.13, have three important waveshape characteristics which typify the way ramp generators are applied to industrial electronics:

● transitions in the output from one level to another are indicated as straight lines with slopes of m_1 and m_2

● output voltages eventually reach the same value as input voltages, and

● adjustability of rising output is separate from the adjustability of decreasing output.

Note that the rate of transition from zero to V_1 and from V_1 to V_2, Figure 8.13, are at a rate (slope) of m_1, while the transition from V_2 to zero is at a (perhaps) different slope of m_2. These slopes are normally two separate control adjustments associated, respectively, with acceleration and deceleration.

The heart of the circuit which performs the ramp function begins with an electronic integrator which, by itself, is insufficient. Recall that the output of an integrator continues to change as long as its input is not zero. The waveshapes of Figure 8.13 show that the output is required to change, but only until the output equals the input. A simple RC circuit, Figure 8.14, would do that but its output is exponential, Figure 8.15, not linear.

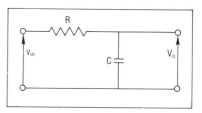

Fig. 8.14. RC circuit can be used as a ramp generator but response is exponential rather than linear as shown in Figure 8.13.

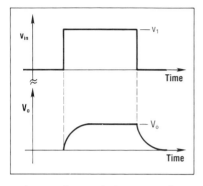

Fig. 8.15. Exponential response waveshapes of RC circuit of Figure 8.14. Output steady-state level equals input level, but the expontential response makes a less-than-ideal ramp generator. It is actually a low-pass filter.

A true electronic integrator is required but feedback is needed to stop the output from changing when output voltage reaches input voltage. Stage 1 of the basic ramp generator circuit, Figure 8.16, is simply an op-amp comparator which receives input or command voltage v_{in} and compares it to ramp output voltage V_o. If v_{in} exceeds V_o, first stage output voltage V_x immediately goes to negative saturation voltage. This voltage appears as a constant-value input to the integrator second stage. Feedback of output voltage V_o to the first stage assumes that V_x is at saturation whenever there is a discrepancy between v_{in} and V_o.

The constant value of V_x causes integrating capacitor C to charge through either $D_1 — R_1$ or $D_2 — R_2$ depending upon the value of V_x relative to the charge present on C. Should C be at zero volts while V_x is in negative saturation $(v_{in} > V_o)$, the sign inversion through stage 2 will cause integrating capacitor C to charge in the positive-going direction. A negative value for V_x dictates that the charging of C be done through $R_2 — D_2$ which means that the rate of change in V_o for an increasing v_{in} is controlled by the value of R_2.

Meanwhile, as V_o changes, it is fed back to stage 1. Eventually, V_o reaches the same value as v_{in} and V_x goes to zero; the change of C stops. Output voltage has reached the input voltage, the desired result.

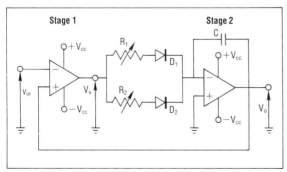

Fig. 8.16. Basic ramp generator circuit. R_1 controls the ramp for decreases in v_{in} while R_2 controls ramp rate for increases in v_{in}.

Should v_{in} be reduced, the charge present on C, output voltage, goes to positive saturation causing C to charge through $R_1 - D_1$. Thus R_1 controls the change rate for decreasing values of v_{in}. The way to remember this is that:

- R_1 controls ramp rate when v_{in} decreases, and
- R_2 controls ramp rate when v_{in} increases.

There are no other combinations to worry about. In commercialized versions of this circuit, adjustable resistors R_1 and R_2 are labeled as increasing and decreasing respectively, or accel and decel, etc.

Confusion usually arises in the interpretation of acceleration and deceleration in hydraulic cylinder circuits. That is, acceleration and deceleration occurs in the extend and retract directions. In the context of the ramp generator, here are the proper correlations:

- acceleration while extending is the same as deceleration while retracting and the same adjustable resistor controls them, and
- deceleration while extending is the same as acceleration while retracting and the other adjustable resistor controls them.

The rate of change of output, that is ramp rate, is controlled by resistors R_1 and R_2 along with integrating capacitor C and the amplitude of the saturation voltage level of V_x. That is

$$\Delta V_o = -V_{x.sat}/R_xC \int_0^t v_{in}\, dt. \tag{8.22}$$

The ramp rate or ramp slope is merely the coefficient outside the integral, namely

$$m_x = -V_{x.sat}/R_xC, \tag{8.23}$$

where x is either 1 or 2 depending upon increasing or decreasing v_{in}. Note that m_x has units of volts/second, the desired result.

The importance of Equation (8.23) is that it shows that the designer has control of ramp rate by varying V_x, R_x, or C. The user has control of ramp rate only through changes of R_x. Sometimes, users will remove an existing integrating capacitor and replace it with a larger one when the required ramps exceed the range offered by the maximum adjustment of R_x. **This procedure should be followed only by one who is knowledgeable in all of the consequences of making such changes**.

It is true that the saturation level of first stage 1 output $V_{x.sat}$ is not symmetrical. It is normal for the negative saturation value of the op-amp to differ with positive saturation value, sign notwithstanding. To compensate for the asymmetry and to avoid the difference in time required for the op-amp to come out of saturation, designers use zener diodes installed back-to-back to limit the value of V_x and prevent op-amp saturation,

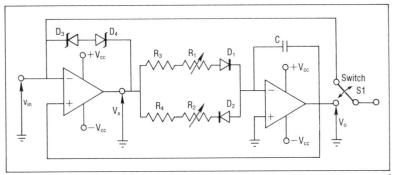

Fig. 8.17. Zener diodes around comparator stage prevent op-amp from going into saturation. They make the ± saturation limits of V_x symmetrical. Resistors R_3 and R_4 prevent oscillation by limiting loop gain, should R_1 and R_2 be set to their minimum limits.

Figure 8.17. The ramp rate given by Equation (8.23) is also the gain of the circuit. Because of the inverse relationship to R_x, it is necessary to limit the minimum value of V_x to prevent oscillation.

Oscillation (or instability as it is often called) occurs whenever there is feedback and the loop gain is high. Both feedback and high gain exist if R_x is not limited to a minimum value. The limitation is easily implemented by inserting fixed resistors R_3 and R_4 into the circuit, Figure 8.17. The price that must be paid, however, is that now there is some inherent **minimum, non-zero** ramp rate; now there is always some ramping present. The only way to totally eliminate ramping is to put in a bypass or enable/disable switch, S_1, Figure 8.17.

Deadband eliminators/correctors

According to the MSOE Lexicon III, Appendix A, a proportional valve is any electrohydraulic valve which has more than ± 3% center overlap or dead zone. The *deadband eliminator* (DBE) or *deadband corrector* circuit provides an electronic means to overcome the disadvantage of a valve with a large dead zone.

The DBE is an op-amp stage whose gain is very high in the region about valve null so that the spool cannot stop anywhere within the valve's overlap. This results in a flow-metering curve that passes through zero with no apparent overlap. Thus, so the argument goes, a proportional valve can be converted to a zero-lapped servovalve. The concept can be considered when looking at the hydraulic P-Q characteristic of a large-overlapped proportional valve, Figure 8.18, when tested at constant pressure drop.

When the dead zone of the valve is eliminated, the flow metering curve, Figure 8.19, appears to pass through the origin. It is emphasized that

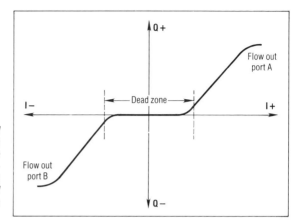

Fig. 8.18. Typical metering curve for a proportional valve at constant pressure. There is a dead zone caused by the overlap of the spool.

electronic compensation for a dead band can make very good looking flow metering curves as Figure 8.19 indicates. But in a real system, the valve will not function as well as might be suggested by the curves because:

● although the valve spool is electronically prevented from stopping in the dead zone, it still takes time to transport the spool through the zone. The curves in Figure 8.19 are always recorded very slowly, thus suppressing the spool transportation delay

● the dead zone of the valve is not really dead. It does meter some flow even though the amount of flow is only at leakage levels. Leakage is important in certain closed-loop systems, and

● a closed-loop system which seeks a valve shut-off condition, such as in a positional servo mechanism, will be unstable because the pressure gain is too high.

The reasons behind these points are beyond the scope of this electronic text. Suffice it to say that there will be improvements in system performance when DBEs are used but the improvements are not good enough to make a proportional valve into a servovalve.

Fig. 8.19. When a proportional valve spool is locked out of the dead zone, overlap appears to have been eliminated.

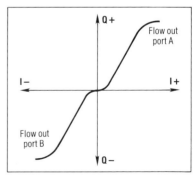

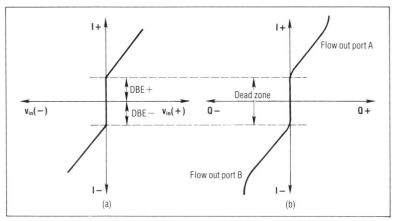

Fig. 8.20. Deadband eliminator curves, rotated 90°, indicate an abrupt jump in output flow for tiny input voltage changes about zero input. This prevents the valve spool from occupying a steady position in the valve dead zone. DBE transfer characteristic is (a), while (b) is valve metering curve.

The concept of using an op-amp circuit with a high-gain center region as a DBE can be seen, Figure 8.20, where the valve metering curve has been turned 90° from its normal orientation. Output of the DBE circuit is shown as a current, but in reality it is a voltage which eventually controls current in a proportional manner. Consequently, it is conceptually if not technically correct to depict the DBE as shown.

Looking at the DBE transfer characteristic, Figure 8.20(a), note the vertical region at zero input voltage. Since gain is the slope of the transfer curve, a vertical line indicates infinite gain. In reality, the actual gain is the open-loop gain of the op-amp which, although finite, is very large. The idea is that if input voltage is a very small, say, positive value, then the current immediately jumps to a value labeled $DBE(+)$.

Likewise, a small negative input results in an immediate jump to $DBE(-)$. These two points correspond to spool positions where the valve is just about to open. $DBE(+)$ and $DBE(-)$ are adjustable and can be tuned to the specific valve at hand. Under these conditions, the DBEs have been tuned to their theoretically optimum points. The fact is that when tuning them in a real system, their actual adjustments are quite another thing and, when used in conjunction with single rod-end cylinders, will be unequally adjusted.

The circuit, Figure 8.21, serves as an adjustable dead band eliminator. For the moment, ignore op-amp A_2. A_1 and A_3 then function as unity gain inverters, A_1 driving unity gain inverter A_3. The result is a non-inverting unity gain amplifier. Now A_2, which has no feedback around it, works as a simple op-amp comparator. If v_{in} swings between some small positive

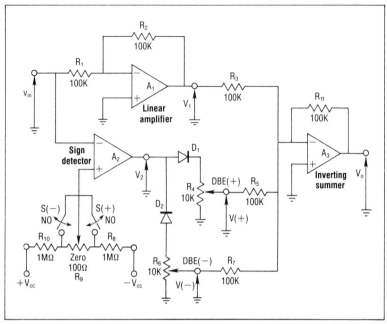

Fig. 8.21. Deadband eliminator circuit. It is necessary to hold S(+) closed while adjusting DBE(+), and the same is true for S(−) and DBE(−). The switches produce a very small voltage of the correct sign into the non-inverting terminal of A₂, the sign-detector circuit.

value and some equally small negative value, A_2 output V_2 will swing from negative saturation to positive saturation. Thus, A_2 is detecting the algebraic sign of v_{in}.

Diode D_1 couples positive output from op-amp A_2 to the $DBE(+)$ adjustment pot. Setting changes of $DBE(+)$ result in an adjustable positive voltage labeled $V(+)$. The range of adjustment is from A_2 positive saturation to zero.

Meanwhile, D_2 couples negative-going output from op-amp A_2 into the $DBE(-)$ adjusting pot. The wiper arm of $DBE(-)$ pot, $V(-)$, adjusts from zero to the negative saturation output of A_2. This pot controls how much of the A_2 negative output is coupled into A_3.

A_3 functions as an inverting summer which combines output of A_1 with $V(+)$ and $V(-)$. Note the three signals and the overall circuit transfer characteristic, Figure 8.22. Composite output V_o, Figure 8.22(c), is the negative algebraic sum of individual components. Also note, however, that the full amounts of $V(+)$ and $V(-)$ are not felt. Instead, only a fraction is coupled to summing amplifier A_3, Figure 8.21, because of the individual DBE settings.

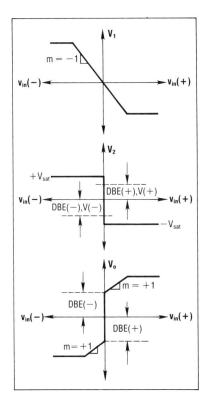

Fig. 8.22. Op-amp A₁, Figure 8.21, is a unity gain inverter with output waveshape (a). A₂, Figure 8.21, merely detects the sign of v_{in} and sends A₂ into positive or negative saturation depending on the sign of v_{in}. Note that A₂ inverts as well. DBE(+) and DBE(−) are potentiometer adjustments that take an adjustable fraction of the +/− values of V₂, namely V(+) and V(−), (b). A₃ in the preceding figure is an inverting summer which combines inverted v_{in}, V₁, V(+), and V(−), producing the output of (c).

Circuit zeroing is best accomplished by first assuring that v_{in} is zero. Shorting the input terminals gives such assurance provided that whatever source is connected to v_{in} is first removed. Set each of the DBE adjusting pots to about mid-range and then turn the 1000-Ω zeroing pot while measuring circuit output. V_o will swing rapidly from positive to negative saturation. It will be impossible to adjust exactly for zero output but it is unnecessary to set it closely.

The individual DBE pots can be set using switches $S(+)$ and $S(-)$, Figure 8.21. These switches correlate with $DBE(+)$ and $DBE(-)$ respectively. While holding $S(+)$ closed, adjust $DBE(+)$ while observing actuator response. Then close $S(-)$ and adjust $DBE(-)$ until the desired reaction at the actuator is observed.

Limit adjustments

Most proportional and servovalve amplifiers contain a limiting circuit that can be adjusted to regulate maximum spool shift. The circuit controls the amount of current (power) delivered to the coil to determine the length of spool stroke and thereby limit flow to and speed of the actuator. This limit circuit, Figure 8.23, sets the ceiling for output voltage V_o by limiting V_x, the input to op-amp A_4. The saturation voltage of A_4 provides its own maximum output, but it is not adjustable and the $+$ and $-$ limits are nearly always asymmetrical.

This limit circuit provides amplifier output variability and takes advantage of two important op amp characteristics — namely they:

● have very low output impedance so the op-amp can develop output voltage independent of current, and

● can deliver current to an external load **or** absorb current from an external source.

When no amplifier output limitation is desired, that is when the voltage ceiling is set as high as possible, $LIM(+)$, Figure 8.23, is set so there is a high negative voltage at the $LIM(+)$ pot wiper arm. The maximum voltage will be half the $-V_{cc}$ supply voltage because of the fixed 10-K resistor in series with the 10-K $LIM(+)$ pot. The unity gain of op-amp A_2 makes its output voltage go to half the $+V_{cc}$ supply because of sign inversion. This high positive voltage keeps the cathode of diode D_1 reverse-biased as long as V_x is low.

Similarly, clockwise (CW) adjustment of the $LIM(-)$ pot puts its

Fig. 8.23. The settings of pots LIM(+) *and* LIM(−) *of this limiter circuit determine the maximum and minimum values of* V$_o$ *below the saturation limits of* A$_4$.

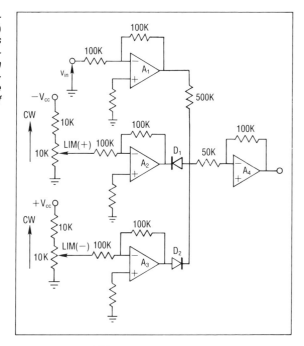

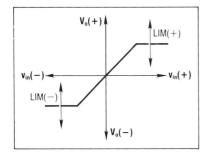

Fig. 8.24. LIM(+) and LIM(−) set the maximum output levels.

wiper at one-half of $+V_{cc}$ and through the inverting unity gain of op-amp A_3, puts output V_3 at one-half of $-V_{cc}$. Negative voltage on the anode of diode D_1 keeps it cut off for less negative values of V_x.

With those adjustments made, any v_{in} input voltage will be amplified by 1 with a sign inversion in op-amp A_1. Depending upon the amplitude of v_{in} and allowing that the amplitude could be large enough to saturate A_1, the value of V_1 would swing between $\pm V_{sat}$ for the A_1 op-amp. With V_1 at a saturation limit and the inverting pin of A_4 a virtual ground, one-half the saturation voltage would be measured at V_x. The 2:1 amplification (100 K:50 K) of op-amp A_4 would boost V_x to saturation of the opposite polarity. Conclusion: when $LIM(+)$ and $LIM(-)$ are set to their CW limits, the entire circuit has a gain of $+1$.

Changes occur when either or both $LIM(+)$ and $LIM(-)$ are taken out of their CW limits. Consider a reduced adjustment of, say, $LIM(+)$; now op-amp A_2 output V_2 will be less than $-V_{cc}$. Should v_{in} be large, V_1 will go to a large negative value but not into saturation. V_x will be one-half of V_1, and, of course, negative too. If the negative value of V_1 were more negative than V_2, then diode D_1 would conduct with A_2 absorbing current.

The net result is that the limit on V_x is established by the value of V_2 which is established by the setting of $LIM(+)$ pot. With V_x limited by $LIM(+)$, V_o is likewise limited but at a value double that of V_x. Similarly,

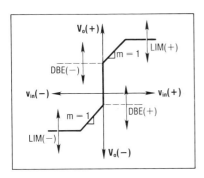

Fig. 8.25. The DBE adjustments control the jumps at the origin to compensate for the valve dead zone, while the LIM adjustments control maximum output. Understand that it is possible to adjust the circuits so that the valve has no proportioning region; the valve reacts only in an on-off manner.

199

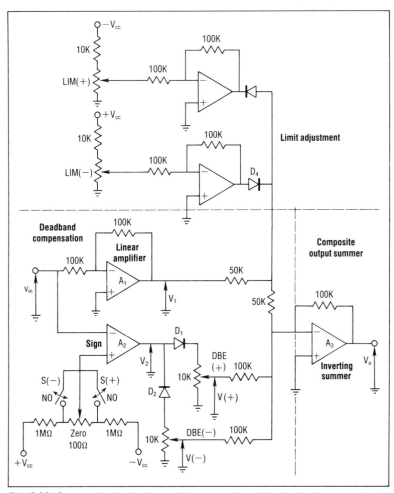

Fig. 8.26. Composite circuit shows interconnection of the limit adjustment circuit, deadband compensator, and composite output summer.

the *LIM*(−) pot governs output in the opposite direction. The transfer characteristic of the amplifier limit circuit, Figure 8.24, becomes the combined input-output transfer characteristic, Figure 8.25, of the composite amplifier circuit, Figure 8.26, which has both *LIM* pots and both *DBE* pots independently adjusted so that the electronic circuit can be tuned to the hydraulic circuit.

The *DBE* adjustments control how far the spool will jump when going across the valve dead zone. The *LIM* pot adjustments determine maxi-

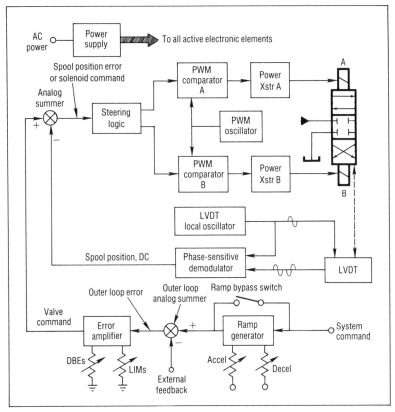

Fig. 8.27. Block diagram of typical PWM proportional valve amplifier.

mum spool shift in each direction. Note that the $LIM(+)$ adjustment sets the maximum positive output, but it is the $DBE(-)$ adjustment that is associated with positive output. This is a consequence of the phasing of the circuit relative to the labeling of the controls and illustrates how phasing affects user-friendliness.

That is, the designer would not want to print the circuit board with the labels as given. Instead, either the *DBE* sign labels **or** the *LIM* sign labels should be swapped. Where the $+$ or $-$ goes is completely moot now because the user has a choice of how the valve will be connected to the cylinder and whether extension is positive or negative.

Proportional valve amplifier

A commercial proportional valve amplifier, Figure 8.27, has several sub sections, most of which have been discussed:

Power supply. The power supply provides power to all op-amps as well as the solenoids. In most systems, power to the op-amps and other active chips is regulated while power the solenoids is unregulated. This is because solenoid current is typically one to three amperes (maximum) which would place an enormous burden on the voltage regulator. Mitigating this decision is the existence of the closure of the spool-position servo loop, which makes solenoid voltage regulation unimportant.

Power output transistors. These transistors act as on-off switches following the PWM signal. In conjunction with the transistors there is always a diode across the solenoid to prevent the inductive voltage kick from damaging the output transistor. There is one transistor for each solenoid.

PWM op-amp comparators. These comparators act as the PW modulators. They receive solenoid command voltage as well as a triangular wave from the triangular-wave oscillator which results in PWM. There is one PW modulator for each solenoid.

Triangular-wave oscillator. This oscillator generates the triangular wave. Interaction of this wave with the solenoid command (error) voltage and the switching action of op-amp comparators causes the width of the output to vary with command resulting in modulation of the pulse.

Steering logic circuit. The steering logic circuit listens to the command voltage and monitors its algebraic sign. If positive, the circuit steers the signal to, say, the *A* solenoid. If negative, the command is steered to the *B* solenoid.

LVDT local oscillator and phase-sensitive demodulator. The LVDT local oscillator and phase- sensitive demodulator is the electronic module for spool position. The local oscillator generates a low-power AC voltage of constant amplitude and fixed frequency, usually between 5 and 10 kHz. The return signal from the LVDT is likewise AC at oscillator frequency which is modified by the phase-sensitive demodulator. The demodulator interprets the phase of the LVDT return AC signal. If it is in phase with the oscillator, demodulator output is positive, corresponding to one direction of spool shift. If the return signal is 180° out of phase, the demodulator generates a negative voltage. Amplitude of the output corresponds to the amount of valve shift while algebraic sign corresponds to direction of spool shift.

Analog summer. The analog summer compares the analog voltage of the valve command voltage to the analog DC voltage of spool position. If they are equal, there is no solenoid command voltage and neither solenoid is powered. If the two voltages disagree, there is a spool position error which acts as a solenoid command. When this loop is properly phased, the command powers the solenoid to drive the spool-position DC voltage into agreement with the valve command.

Error amplifier. The error amplifier also houses the DBE and maximum spool-shift limit adjustments. It may or may not have a gain of one. It also may have a gain adjustment.

Outer-loop analog summer. The outer-loop analog summer receives system command voltage, and any external or outer-loop feedback voltage. If there is a discrepancy (outer-loop error voltage), it acts as the command to the valve.

Ramp generator. The ramp generator converts step, or sudden, changes

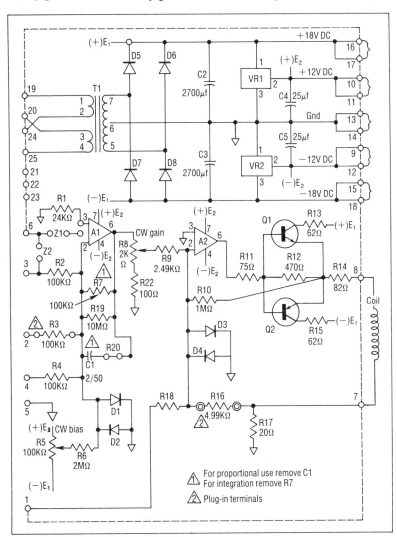

Fig. 8.28. Schematic of Moog 121-103 servocontroller.

in system command into linearly ramped voltages to result in a degree of system acceleration control.

Ramp bypass switch. The ramp bypass switch effectively disables the ramp generator.

It is evident that a proportional-valve amplifier is a complicated circuit comprised of a multitude of subfunctions. It is almost always matched to a specific valve although there are third-party vendors who supply amplifiers for specific valves. The reader is cautioned to assure that full compatibility exists when purchasing third-party electronics for proportional valves, especially the circuits which service the LVDT. It will soon become evident that servovalve amplifiers are much simpler devices, are much easier to use, and time and again are more amenable to mixed vendors.

Servo amplifier

A complete schematic diagram of the Moog 121-103 servo amplifier, Figure 8.28, consists of two major sections:
- the power supply which occupies the upper half of the schematic, and
- the signal-processing section which occupies the lower half.

This amplifier represents the sum and substance of a real, functioning, industrial amplifier for servovalve control. It should be compared to the proportional-valve amplifier just covered.

The power supply is straight-forward, but by way of summary, note that it contains:
- a dual-voltage transformer, allowing operation from either 115 or 230 V AC. The secondary is center-tapped
- four diodes connected to the center-tapped transformer to produce a bi-polar DC output
- integrated circuit voltage regulators VR_1 and VR_2 for the positive and negative voltages. Fixed outputs are ± 12 volts
- unregulated ± 18 volts and regulated ± 12 volts are available to the user at the terminal strip in the upper right hand corner. Note that $\pm E_2$ (± 12 volts regulated) are sent to op-amps A_1 and A_2 although the connections are not drawn on the schematic. Also note that unregulated $\pm E_1$ (± 18 volts) powers output transistors Q_1 and Q_2, and
- filter capacitors C_2 and C_3 are each 2700 μf. Capacitors C_4 and C_5 help reduce the cross-talk between A_1 and A_2 that might occur through the power supply.

The signal-processing section has three stages:

Preamplifier. Preamplifier A_1 and attendant resistances also serve as the user interface, input inverting summer, a place to convert to an optional integrating amplifier, and an optional means of scaling command and feedback.

Interstage section. The interstage section, comprised of A_2 and other components, receives a scaled output from A_1 through servo-loop gain control pot $R\,8$ and a current feedback signal from the voltage drop across current-sensing resistor $R\,17$. The primary feedback for A_2 is through $R\,10$, but note that it connects to the emitter output voltage of transistors Q_1 and Q_2 rather than to the op-amp output pin. This ploy removes the dead zone created by the 0.5-volt forward-bias voltage needed to get the bases to conduct.

Output stage. The output stage consists of transistors Q_1 and Q_2. Q_1 is an NPN type, while Q_2 is of the PNP variety. This arrangement allows Q_1 to conduct when the output of A_2 is positive. Q_2 is on only when A_2 output is negative.

The servovalve coil connects to user terminals 8 and 7 and will carry current either from 8 to 7 (call it positive) or from 7 to 8 (call it negative). Unlike the proportional valve, the servovalve torque motor is able to sense current direction and shift the valve one way for positive current and the other way for negative current.

An important characteristic of this and all servo amplifiers, is that it incorporates current feedback. When tracing into the board from terminal 7, note that the current, in returning to common, must pass through low-value resistance $R\,17$, 20 Ω. It is coupled to the inverting terminal of A_2 which sums the error voltage from $R\,8$ and the primary feedback through $R\,10$.

The result is that the existence of current feedback regulates the current to the servovalve coil. Current, not voltage, dictates the torque generated by the torque motor. Suppose that the unregulated $+18$-volt supply increased due to an increase in power from the electric company. This would tend to increase coil current, increase torque, and move the spool to a different position. However, existence of negative current feedback tends to reduce the drive voltage at the output of A_2 and tends to keep the current at its desired value. Thus, the lack of regulation of the Q_1 and Q_2 supply voltage becomes an unimportant issue.

Another, more subtle benefit of current feedback is that it *raises* the apparent output resistance of the amplifier. That is, the servovalve coil *looks back into the amplifier* and sees a much higher resistance than either 82 Ω ($R\,14$) or 470 Ω ($R\,12$). In the study of voltage amplifiers, this was undesirable because zero output impedance was the goal. But because the servo amplifier is a *current* amplifier, high output impedance here is desirable.

Recall that the time constant for inductive circuits is L/R. Therefore, if R increases, the time constant is shorter and the valve responds faster; thus all servo amplifiers have current feedback. An extra benefit is that terminal 7 allows the monitoring of the voltage across $R\,17$ and a look at the actual coil current on any kind of voltage measuring device. Terminal 7 makes a superb trouble-shooting point.

Some additional characteristics of this circuit are:

● diodes D_1, D_2, D_3 and D_4 might look like they short the inverting terminal of their respective op-amps directly to common. This is not the case because each diode requires about 0.5 volt before they conduct. Two diodes side-by-side, then, act to limit the maximum inverting-pin voltages to ± 0.5 volts. Think of them as small electronic relief valves

● input stage A_2, has three inputs through $R2$, $R3$, and $R4$, each 100 K. This permits the user to input three signals, typically command, feedback, and an optional dither

● resistor $R3$ is socketed so that a resistor with another value can easily be substituted to perform scaling. Output of A_1 is the servo error voltage. With other values for $R3$, it is possible for a command of, say $+10$ volts to be cancelled (nulled) by a feedback of -5 volts by making $R3$ a 50 K resistor and then connecting the feedback to it

● bias adjustment resistor $R5$ allows servo system zero to be displaced from either zero command or zero feedback, and

● during normal operation, resistor $R20$ jumper is severed, removing capacitor C_1 from the circuit. On the other hand, if an integrating amplifier is required, resistor $R20$ is installed and feedback resistors $R7$ (100 K) and $R19$ (1 M) are cut.

It should be apparent that the servo amplifier is a much simpler device than a proportional amplifier, and is generally much easier to use.

Chapter Nine
Digital Electronics

All of the circuits covered to this point have been of the analog variety. That is, the control information is carried in the *amplitude* or *frequency* of the control signals. For example, a high control voltage causes a large displacement in a proportional valve spool and results in high output flow. Similarly, a low control voltage results in low output flow.

In digital circuits, information is carried in various combinations of switches or gates that can be in either an on state (logical 1) or an off state (logical 0). These switches can be:

● mechanically operated such as household light switches

● electromechanical devices such as relays, controlled by voltages and controlling other relays, and

● transistorized or solid state devices called *gates*. Their status is determined by the presence (on state) or absence (off state) of a voltage at the input and/or output.

Information is anything that can be coded and carried in on and off combinations of several switches. For example, Paul Revere used digital coding when he placed lights in the North Church steeple to tell his fellow revolutionaries how the British were coming: one if by land, two if by sea. Of course, Paul didn't realize he had used digital logic and he probably didn't realize that with two lights, he could have forewarned of as many as four different, mutually exclusive events.

Using today's technology, the following codes, Table 9.1, could paraphrase Revere. Two lights could signify any of four possibilities because there are four on-off combinations with two binary variables. Each light

Table 9.1 - Revere code		
Lights		Attack code
Left	Right	
Off	Off	No attack
Off	On	By land
On	Off	By sea
On	On	By air

can exist in either an on or off state. Such devices are called *binary* because of their two possible states. Although signal amplitude carries no information, amplitude is important in establishing whether the switch is on or off. Again, using Revere's digital scheme, light intensity is an analog of quantity. His lanterns had only to be bright enough so that the observers could tell whether the lights were on or off. The brightness carried no other information. Similarly, in digital electronics, voltage ranges for a logical 0 and for a logical 1 must be defined so that on can be distinguished from off. There are two *logical families* in use today:

● TTL or transistor-transistor logic, and

● CMOS or complementary metal-oxide semiconductors.

TTL logic

The definition of on and off for TTL logic devices is clearly indicated, Figure 9.1. It is the circuit designer's responsibility to build circuits which interpret a voltage between +2.4 volts and +5.0 volts as on or logical 1, and any voltage between 0.0 volts and +0.8 volts as off or logical 0. Some circuit designers use inverse logic wherein the high voltage is a logical 0 and the low voltage is a logical 1, but this interpretation is not used here. It is the responsibility of the user or the one who does the interfacing to assure that digital sending devices always transmit voltages which conform to the scheme indicated in Figure 9.1. To violate logical levels is to invite receiving circuits to misinterpret data and thus reach erroneous conclusions.

The designer of circuits using TTL devices must allow for the permitted variations in high and low voltages, and collector supply voltage must be between 4.75 and 5.2 volts. When a user interfaces with TTL circuits, he must be aware that:

● input signals must be above +2.4 volts to be reliably interpreted as high, and must be below +0.8 volts to be interpreted as a logical low

● high output signals may be as small as +2.4 volts and low outputs may be as great as +0.8 volts

● when several receiving devices are connected to a single TTL output terminal, the number of receiving devices cannot exceed the *fan-out*

Fig. 9.1. Any voltage between +2.4 volts and +5.0 volts is interpreted as a logical 1 or on. Any voltage between 0.0 volts and 0.8 volts is interpreted as a logical 0 or off. Voltages between 0.8 volts and 2.4 volts are undefined.

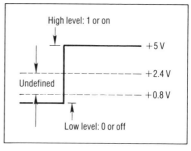

capability of the sending device which does the outputting, and
●when a sending device is used to drive a TTL input port, only 40 to 50
μA is needed when the input signal is high.
However, the input device must be capable of receiving 1.6 mA when low
and yet keep its voltage below +0.8 volts. The process of the receiving
device accepting or absorbing current from the sending device is called
sinking. The receiving device is the sink which absorbs the transmitted
current.

CMOS logic

CMOS logic is newer than TTL and its use is growing because it
requires far less power for equivalent functions, which makes it ideal for
battery-powered circuits. CMOS also is more versatile in terms of collector supply voltage range and logic levels for high and low interpretations.
CMOS elements can have a collector supply voltage anywhere from +5
to +15 volts. The output value of the high state covers a similar range.
Because a negative supply connection is provided, the value of the low
state is not used. Instead, that terminal is connected directly to circuit
ground, leading to 0 volts as the low-state value. Additionally, the output
state changes when the input reaches about 45% of the supply voltage,
therefore the ranges of the high and low states are broad. The wider the
range of high and low levels, vis-a-vis TTL logic, leads to less ambiguity
and greater noise immunity.

The upper bound on the CMOS low state, Figure 9.2, varies with the
circuit designer's choice of supply voltage. Therefore CMOS circuits are
not standardized from designer to designer as are TTL circuits. Note that
in the supply voltage range from 5 to about 8 volts, the CMOS signal levels
are approximately the same as in TTL circuits. Understand, however, that
one cannot expect to interface the two types of circuits without some loss
of reliability.

Although CMOS chips are low consumers of power, they are four to 10
times slower than equivalent TTL functions. Because they have high

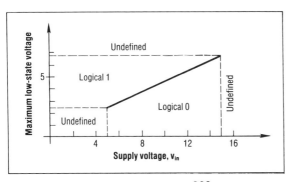

Fig. 9.2. CMOS high
and low interpreta-
tions depend upon
the supply voltage
the circuit designer
chooses.

input impedances, these chips are subject to damage due to electrostatic charge that can occur during handling. Walking on carpets or wearing wool or certain synthetic-fabric clothing can create a problem. CMOS chips require special handling to eliminate electrostatic charge.

Logic circuits and gates

Electronic circuits for digital signal processing are designed to generate, modify, and/or interpret the combinations of on-off signals from some digital source or sending device. These circuits are called *logic circuits, logic gates, gate circuits*, or simply *gates*. A gate consists of a combination of resistors and transistors interconnected to achieve the desired logical function(s).

The elementary or primary logic functions are:
- NOT (logical inversion)
- AND, and
- OR.

Additionally, other ancillary logic functions are:
- NOR
- NAND, and
- exclusive OR.

NAND and NOR gates are available as integrated circuit chips at local electronics stores and can be used to create the primary AND, OR, and NOT functions. For this reasons, some designers have come to adopt either NAND or NOR functions as their favorite circuit building blocks. This author prefers the primary functions of AND, OR, and NOT, but only because of their basic nature. There is nothing inherently superior about the choice of basic building blocks — only preference.

Here are the input/output actions of the three primary functions:
- a NOT produces a high output when the input is low and a low output when the input is high. Thus it also is called a *logical inverter* or, simply, an *inverter*. It has one input
- an AND requires more than one input and produces a high output only when all inputs are high, and
- the OR also requires more than one input and produces a high output when any one or more of its inputs is high.

When these functions are implemented as electronic hardware, those pieces of hardware are called *gates*. Thus, gates are the hardware elements that perform *logical functions*.

Internal construction of the logical inverter

The internal schematic for a certain TTL inverter, Figure 9.3, indicates how the integrated circuit chip designer selected and interconnected the components. While these design processes are beyond our scope, the circuit gives some insight of the insides of a particular gate. Hereafter,

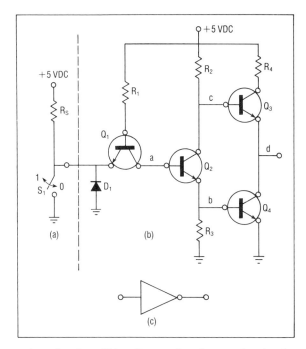

Fig. 9.3. The TTL in-
verter is the basic
element from which
all other logic func-
tions are built. A
high voltage or logi-
cal 1 input results in
a low voltage or logi-
cal 0 at the output.

other circuits will be discussed at the gate level rather than the transistor
level.

The inverter or NOT gate, Figure 9.3, contains NPN transistors Q_1, Q_2,
Q_3, and Q_4, and has one input and one output. The input signal is
controlled by external switch S_1. Note that S_1 is connected to provide a
short circuit path to circuit common when closed. When S_1 is open, the
gate-input terminal goes high because of the connection to $+5$-V DC
power supply through R_S. The switch acts as a sink when it is closed
because it carries current from the gate's Q_1 emitter.

This is a necessary and desirable trait. We shall see shortly that closing
S_1 *steals* current from Q_2 when S_1 is closed, and blocks the Q_1 emitter
when open, directing current through Q_1 into the base of Q_2. Thus, the
opening and closing of S_1 causes the transistors inside the gate to switch
on and off.

When reviewing the operation of the basic transistor, it is important to
understand that the change from an analog function of the basic transistor
to a digital function of the gate involves equal parts of gate design (resistor-
transistor selection) and amplitude of signal input. Recall that the transistor is a continuously variable, current-controlled amplifier. A small input
current results in a proportional output current and, within saturation
limits, a larger input current results in a larger output current.

The design of a logic gate begins with the statement of logic levels. That is, the issue of what voltage constitutes a logical 1 or on and what voltage constitutes a logical 0 or off. If the designer elects to use TTL, voltage levels have been established. The circuit of Figure 9.3 is a TTL circuit, so we proceed with the TTL values just as the designer would.

The gate designer's challenge is to select components that balance these parameters and elements:
- transistor current gains (β)
- resistances, and
- input voltage levels so that output transistors always operate either fully saturated or fully cut off as required to perform the requisite logic function for input voltage levels of 0 or 1.

Fortunately, designers have taken care of these things when we purchase an integrated circuit chip. As chip users, we are responsible only for providing the signal source, Figure 9.3(a), and connecting it to an unspecified load which does not exceed the fan-out capability of the gate. As all these matters have been taken care of, we proceed to the inverter, Figure 9.3(b).

When S_1 is open, the input to the gate goes high through the R_S connection to $+5$ V DC. This puts a reverse bias on the N-type emitter of Q_1, cutting off emitter current. Meanwhile, the P-type base material of Q_1 is connected to $+5$ V DC through R_1. This allows conduction from the base of Q_1 to its collector. This collector (line a) is essentially at zero volts through the base-to-emitter connections of Q_2 and Q_4.

Q_2 and Q_3 are conducting. Saturation of Q_2 causes its collector (line c) to go low, which in turn shunts base current away from Q_3. That is, current through R_2 prefers to go through the collector-to-emitter path of Q_2 rather than entering the base of Q_3. This causes Q_3 to be off or non-conducting from collector to emitter. At the same time, current through R_1, the base-to-emitter of Q_2, and the base-to-emitter of Q_4, causes Q_4 to be conducting.

Now, with Q_3 off and Q_4 on, the output terminal voltage is near 0. For proper TTL operation, output voltage must be $\leq +0.8$ volts at this time. Recall that at the start, S_1 was open, that is the input voltage was high and had produced a low output, the desired result. The output is the *inverse of the input*, or the output is the *NOT of the input*.

When S_1 is closed, the input is low or logical 0. This causes the base-to-emitter junction of Q_1 to conduct, making the base of Q_1 go low. The collector of Q_1 (line a), not being connected to the supply voltage also goes low, cutting off base current in Q_2 and Q_4. This causes the collectors to be non-conducting, making them go high. High Q_2 collector voltage (line c) causes Q_3 to conduct. The combined action of Q_3 conducting and Q_4 being non-conducting makes the output go high. This is again, of course, the inverse of the input. Figure 9.3(c) is the logical

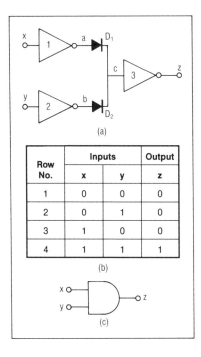

(a)

Row No.	Inputs		Output
	x	y	z
1	0	0	0
2	0	1	0
3	1	0	0
4	1	1	1

(b)

(c)

Fig. 9.4. A two-input AND gate, (a), constructed with inverters and diodes, along with AND gate truth table, (b), and logic symbol, (c).

symbol for the inverter. It is possible to build AND and OR gates from inverters and diodes.

Two-input AND gate

The two-input AND gate, Figure 9.4(a) is constructed of three inverters and two diodes. Recall that an AND gate will produce a high output only when both inputs are high. How this circuit will perform can best be seen by understanding the basic function of the inverter, and by starting with the assumption that gate output z, Figure 9.4(a), is a logical 1. Working backward through the circuit, required inputs x and y can be determined.

If z is at a 1 level, the input to inverter 3, signal c, must be 0 due to the basic operation of the inverter. What conditions are required for signal c to be 0? Consider some possibilities: if signal a were high, D_1 would be forward biased, making signal c high. Output z cannot be high. Similarly, if signal b were high, D_2 would be forward biased making signal c high; again this is impossible.

Thus it is clear that if output z is to be high, **both** signals a and b must be low, creating the requisite level for signal c. Of course, signals a and b are the logical inverses of inputs x and y, respectively. Therefore, **both x and y** must be high for output z to be high.

213

The truth table for any two-input AND gate, Figure 9.4(b), is a summary of the output state of the gate for all possible combinations of inputs. This holds for **all** truth tables, whether they are for AND, OR, NOT, NAND, NOR, or other combinations of gates. For any two-input gate, only four possible 1 or 0 input combinations are possible. Therefore, this truth table has four rows. Each row expresses one of four input combinations.

Row 1 shows both x and y at a 0 level and the output also is at a logical 0. Row 2 shows x at a 0 level while y is at a 1 level while z remains at 0. Row 3 shows x at 1 and y at 0, again with z at 0. Finally in Row 4, where x and y are both logical 1 at the same time, output z switches to a 1 level. There is a logical 1 output only when both inputs are high. The logic symbol for a two-input AND gate is shown in Figure 9.4(c).

Once one understands how the transistors of Figure 9.3 operate, such schematics are discarded in favor of gate symbology, Figure 9.4, and those of subsequent gates. As users of gates available as integrated-circuit (IC) chips, one need not know the internal details. We need only know if we are dealing with TTL or CMOS logic. It is unimportant whether the gate is designed from transistors, inverter gates, NOR gates, or whatever. It only is necessary to understand in the case of an AND gate, that the output will be high only when all inputs are simultaneously high.

Fig. 9.5. A two-input OR gate, (a), is constructed using three inverters, with appropriate truth table, (b), and logic symbol, (c).

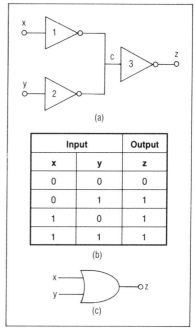

Input		Output
x	**y**	**z**
0	0	0
0	1	1
1	0	1
1	1	1

(b)

(c)

Two-input OR gate

An OR gate, Figure 9.5(a), can be constructed with inverters. While this is a two-input OR gate, the idea can be extended to any number of inputs. When comparing Figures 9.4(a) and 9.5(a), note that the OR gate made with inverters results from the removal of two diodes that were part of the AND gate. This is best understood by observing the function of Q_4, Figure 9.3(b). Q_4, because of the design of that circuit, will be either fully on and conducting or fully off and electrically open.

Imagine that two outputs of the inverters of Figure 9.3 are connected output-to-output as indicated by the connections of inverters 1 and 2, Figure 9.5(a). In that imaginary case, the single S_1 of Figure 9.3(a) would double and thus correlate to x and y, Figure 9.5(a). Such a scheme is depicted, in part, in Figure 9.6.

Because these Q_4 transistors, just like the pulse width modulation transistors, are either fully on or fully off, they act as on-off switches that either make or break a connection to ground. Imagine, in Figure 9.6, that $Q_{4,1}$ is on and conducting: it acts as a short to ground. If, at that time, $Q_{4,2}$ should go off and act as an open circuit, its action, absent $Q_{4,1}$, would cause output 2 to go high. However, if $Q_{4,1}$ is at that moment shorted to ground, the signal at c must be zero regardless of the state of $Q_{4,2}$.

Thus we conclude that signal c can never go high if either $Q_{4,1}$ or $Q_{4,2}$ is

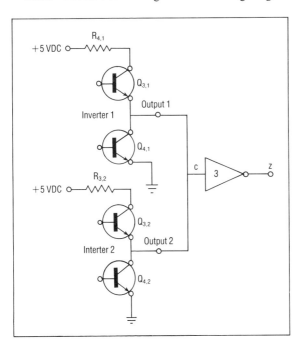

Fig. 9.6. The two output transistors, $Q_{4,1}$ and $Q_{4,2}$ interact with one another such that when either is conducting (on), output of the other is shorted out.

215

conducting. Of course, as $Q_{4.1}$ and $Q_{4.2}$ are output stages of two inverters, their respective inputs must be high for either of them to be shorted. Thus, we conclude that signal c, Figures 9.5(a) and 9.6, will be at logical 0 when **either** x or y is at a logical 1 or when they **both** are at logical 1. Signal c, however, is inverted through inverter 3 so that output z is 0 when signal c is high. For signal c to be high requires **both** x and y to be low. Thus z will be zero only when both x and y are simultaneously at logical 0. This leads to the truth table, Figure 9.5(b), of a two-input OR gate. The OR gate produces a high-level output when either input is high and also when both inputs are high.

Other gates

The name of the NOR gate, Figure 9.7, is a contraction of NOT and OR. In view of this, it is not surprising that the NOR logic symbol is similar to the OR gate logic symbol. If an OR gate is coupled to an inverter at its output, the result is a NOR gate. The NOR gate's output will be high only when both inputs are low. The reader is urged to compare the NOR gate truth table, Figure 9.7(b), with the OR gate truth table, Figure 9.5(b). The inverse operation should be apparent.

In a manner similar to the NOR gate, the NAND gate symbol, Figure 9.8, is an AND gate with a small circle to indicate an inversion, and its name is a contraction of NOT and AND. Comparing the truth tables of the NAND and AND gates shows that output z is the exact inverse from one to the other.

The exclusive OR gate, Figure 9.9, is a special variation of the OR gate with the condition that the output will be low whenever both inputs are

Fig. 9.7. The NOR gate symbol, (a). Its truth table, (b), indicates a high output only when both inputs are low. The NOR gate is the inverse of the OR gate.

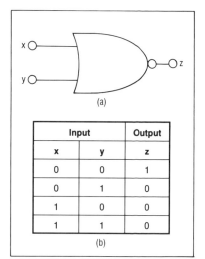

(a)

Input		Output
x	y	z
0	0	1
0	1	0
1	0	0
1	1	0

(b)

high, as well as when both are low. One way of looking at this circuit is that it produces a high output whenever the two inputs **do not** match one another. Note that with the addition of an inverter in the output, the circuit would produce a high output whenever the two inputs **do** match each other.

Circuits with memory

Electronic circuits that have memory are referred to generically as flip-flops and counters. They actually are two different but similar devices. The most common example of a mechanical flip-flop is the on-off switch used in the home to control lighting. Because it shares so many things in common with its electronic counterpart, it serves as a familiar component to help explain the principles of memory devices.

The mechanical on-off switch has memory. That is, once it is set, it remains that way until a subsequent event occurs to change it. One can enter a strange room with a conventional light switch, and if the lights are on, one knows that someone has turned them on. That person need not be present for us to know that, because the lights being on is evidence enough. We don't know who turned the lights on, or how long ago; we just know that they are on. That fact is stored in the switch.

The event which changes the switch state can be fleeting. That is, the

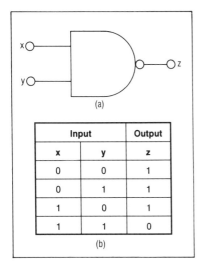

Input		Output
x	y	z
0	0	1
0	1	1
1	0	1
1	1	0

(b)

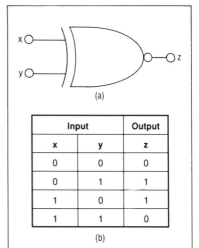

Input		Output
x	y	z
0	0	0
0	1	1
1	0	1
1	1	0

(b)

Fig. 9.8. NAND gate symbol, (a), is an AND gate with a small circle to indicate inversion. A NAND gate produces a logical 0 when both inputs are high, as indicated in truth table (b).

Fig. 9.9. Using an exclusive OR gate, (a), there is a high output whenever x is high or when y is high but not when they both are simultaneously high or low, as truth table (b) indicates.

217

stranger who turned the lights on entered the room, flipped the switch, and then vanished. The passing is noted only by the position of the switch. The stranger's passing and flipping, a fleeting event, is stored in the position of the switch. Note that if an attempt is made to activate the switch to the on position, nothing happens because the switch already is on. If switch status is to change, it requires an opposite-going input; the switch must be moved to the off position. The switch has two inputs: from on to off if on, and from off to on if off. It has memory because the last input is stored in the present switch position. This memory is characteristic of the electronic flip-flop.

The electronic counter is a special version of the flip-flop. The most familiar mechanical counter is the automotive odometer. It is a decimal counter (base 10), but has many characteristics of an electronic flip-flop-based counter. An odometer usually has six registers or six significant digits and the *least-significant digit* (LSD) usually displays increments of $\frac{1}{10}$ mile. Each digit is called a decimal *register*, a register being defined as a place to store one digit or symbol. This constitutes memory because the register retains its last value whenever the car stops. The last value is retained even during shutdown.

The LSD is connected directly to the wheels of the vehicle and therefore reacts to the number of revolutions the wheels have made. Of course, the display is *scaled* so that it does not show revolutions but rather miles traveled and does so with reasonable accuracy. The LSD, we know instinctively, changes most rapidly. Each successive more-significant digit changes 10 times less rapidly than its mate on the right; the more-significant digits change less frequently than the LSDs. The more-significant digits change at a *lower frequency* than the LSDs. An important use of counters is as a *frequency divider*, a device which reduces frequency.

An odometer has one input, that is the connection between the wheels and the LSD, but there are as many outputs as there are digits. The output of each digit becomes the input to the next more significant digit. All of these characteristics apply to an electronic counter, the major differences being mechanical vs electronic and decimal-vs-binary coding.

RS flip-flop

The basic electronic memory element is called an *RS flip-flop* or the *set-reset flip-flop*, Figure 9.10(a). The circuit requires two AND gates and two inverters. Note that each AND/inverter combination is a NAND gate, so it is possible to use two NAND gates as well.

It is common notation in electronic literature to identify the output of a flip-flop as Q. Furthermore, because of the way they are built, there always will be two outputs even though these outputs are the opposites of one another. Therefore, the second output is designated as $\overline{Q}$. The Q with the bar on top is the logical notation of the *inverse of Q*, sometimes called the

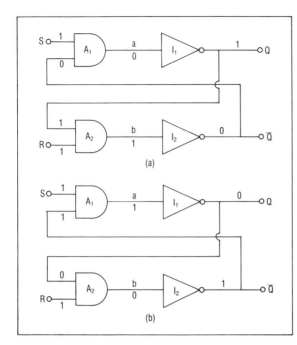

Fig. 9.10. Set-reset flip-flop can be constructed with two AND gates and two inverters. RS flip-flop is in its on state (a), and in its off state (b). They require that R and S be normally at a 1 level and that switching take place only when a 0 input occurs.

NOT of Q, or simply *NOT Q*. They are not independent of one another, a fact which is explicit in the choice of Q and $\overline{Q}$. That is when Q is high, $\overline{Q}$ **must** be low and vice versa. This is true of the RS flip-flop and the light switch, and is tantamount to saying that the switch cannot be off while it is still on. Now that may seem so obvious as to sound stupid, but when inspecting logic circuits, it seems easy to start believing incorrect things.

To digress for a moment, it is important to realize that the use of two outputs, Q and $\overline{Q}$ is redundant. That is when measuring the voltage at Q and finding it high, we say that the flip-flop is *set* or on. Now if $\overline{Q}$ is measured, we will find it to be low. Both measurements say the same thing. There is no new information gained from one output that cannot be gained from the other. Extending this to the light switch analogy, after looking at the light there is no need to look at the switch, and vice versa unless, of course, the light bulb is burned out. Then it does become necessary to look at both but that then is a troubleshooting affair rather than normal operation.

This situation also is true of the flip-flop. Suppose that Q and $\overline{Q}$ are measured and we find that both are, say, high. Only a malfunction can cause this situation. The main point is to emphasize the dependence of Q and $\overline{Q}$ in normal operation. Suppose a light-emitting diode was put on the $\overline{Q}$ terminal. When the LED is on the flip-flop is off, in its reset state. In

219

normal operation, another LED on Q would be redundant from an informational point of view.

Looking at Figure 9.10(a) to analyze the flip-flop circuit, it is assumed to be in its on state. That is the assumption that Q is at a 1 level demands that $\overline{Q}$ be 0. Working backward from output Q, inverter I_1 requires that its input signal a is logical 0. Similarly, because Q is 0, signal b must be at a logical 1. Because signal b, the output of AND gate A_2 is at a 1 level, both its inputs also must be 1. That is accommodated with feedback of Q to A_2 while R is a logical 1.

Jumping back to A_1 with its logical 0 output for signal a, at least one of the inputs to A_1 must be logical 0. This is accommodated by feeding $\overline{Q}$ back to A_1. S in Figure 9.10(a) is set at a 1 level for the moment for the sake of symmetry. Soon, it will become apparent that it is a requirement.

The outputs, Figure 9.10(b), are assumed to be in the opposite logical state. That is, Q is at a logical 0, indicating that the flip-flop has *reset*; signal a must be a 1 level and signal b must be a logical 0. It can be seen that S must be a 1 level, now identified as a requirement. R is shown at a 1 level which, in the current situation, is a *don't care* input. However, it was concluded earlier that it must be a logical 1.

Thus we see that of the two possible states, either can be sustained indefinitely as long as both R and S are held at the 1 level; there are two stable states. Some literature refers to the circuit as a *bistable* flip-flop because of its two stable states. It has *latching* properties in whichever state it is in; it holds itself there.

If the circuit continued in its latched state forever, the circuit would be quite uninteresting if not worthless. Usefulness comes as a result of being able to change states just as is possible with the light switch. The changing of states requires that the R or S input change to a 0 level. To see the

Fig. 9.11. Placing inverters in the R and S channels of the RS flip-flop allows R and S to normally be at logical 0. A logical 1 is required at R or S to change the output state. Simplified RS flip-flop logic symbol, (b).

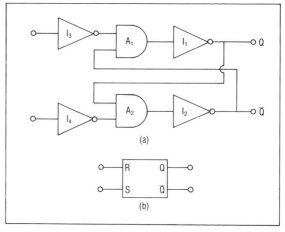

(a)

(b)

effects, consider that the flip-flop is set as shown in Figure 9.11(a). Now consider that S changes from a logical 1 to a 0. Because the output of A_1 already is at a logical 0, the change of S to 0 has no effect.

That seems reasonable, because if I_1 already is on, it cannot become more on, competely consistent with the light switch: on is on. Things are either on or off in the digital world. Capability to be more on or less on is strictly an analog concept. But look at what happens if reset signal R changes to logical 0 even for a moment: first, signal b must go to a logical 0 because of AND gate A_2. This forces $\overline{Q}$ to go to logical 1 which will be felt immediately at the lower input to A_1.

Because S is held at a 1 level, A_1 has two logical 1 inputs, sending its output to 1. A logical 1 at the input of I_1 forces Q to a 0 level which immediately is felt at the upper input to A_2. Of course, the output of A_2 was already 0 due to the zeroing of R, but at the instant that Qs 0 state is felt at A_2, R can return to logical 1 and the flip-flop self-sustains or latches in its new, reset state. Note that further zeroing of R has no effect. To change the state requires a subsequent change at the S input.

As presented, the circuit requires that R and S **normally** be at logical 1, and that switching requires a momentary change to a logical 0. Technologically, this is not a problem, but it may be disconcerting. Therefore another circuit, Figure 9.11(a) is offered which requires R and S to be at a 0 level as their normal state and the presence of a 1 becomes necessary to change the output. When all the elements of the Figure 9.11(a) circuit are included in a single package, it is normally drawn using the symbol of Figure 9.11(b). It is understood that 0 is the normal state of R and S and that a change to logical 1 changes the state of the output.

Electronic counters and the JK flip-flop

The electronic counter has, as its basic building block, a flip-flop which is *toggled* from one state to another. There is one input, called a *toggle* or T *port*. The flip-flop is toggled by inputting a pulse train of 0s, each followed by a 1, Figure 9.12. The first pulse sets the flip-flop while the second resets

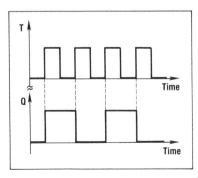

Fig. 9.12. A train of toggle pulses causes the counter output to switch from set to reset. The output changes at one-half the frequency of the input.

it, the third sets it again, and so on ad infinitum. In most versions of the counter, the set and reset terminals are available to the user. The external terminals are universally labelled J and K for set and reset, respectively, Figure 9.13. This version requires four AND gates and two OR gates to create a toggled counter from an RS flip-flop. AND gates A_1 and A_4 can be thought of as being *armed* or *disarmed* depending on the current output state of the flip-flop.

If the flip-flop is currently reset, a logical 0 is at Q and a logical 1 at $\overline{Q}$. The 1 at A_1, due to $\overline{Q}$, arms A_1 while the 0 at A_4, due to Q, disarms A_4. Now, the next toggle pulse at T passes through the armed A_1 but is blocked by disarmed A_4. Consequently, the T pulse is felt only at the internal S port and sets the fip-flop. This results in arming A_4 and disarming A_1 so that the next incoming T pulse is felt only at the internal R port. That next T pulse resets the flip-flop, and so on.

There is a problem with this counter circuit as thus far conceived. Imagine that T becomes a logical 1 and then stays there instead of quickly returning to 0. Note then, that if the flip-flop is now say, reset, the T input will be propagated to the S port resulting in the flip-flop being set. But, when Q goes high and $\overline{Q}$ goes low, A_1 and A_4 are, respectively, disarmed and armed. Arming A_4 then gates the steady T signal to the internal R port, immediately resetting the flip-flop.

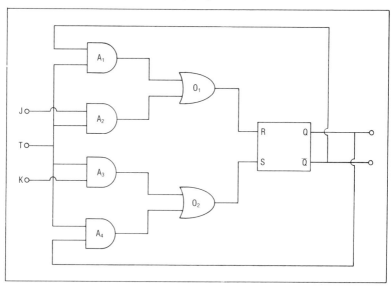

Fig. 9.13. *The RS flip-flop is converted to a toggled, binary counter by adding four AND gates and two OR gates. J and K are the labels given to the external set and reset terminals. A_1 and A_4 steer the next toggle (clock) pulse to the appropriate R or S port. Note that a 1 at J or K is felt at R or S only when a T pulse also is present.*

Of course, the reset rearms A_1 and again disarms A_4, causing yet another change in the state of the flip-flop. These changes of state will continue as long as T remains at a logical 1. This situation must be avoided. It is essential that T remain high only long enough to cause the switch in the flip-flop but not so long as to cause a second change; the T input circuitry needs modification.

The proper conditioning circuit for the T input channel must generate a pulse of fixed duration regardless of how long T might stay high. A one-shot multivibrator is just such a circuit and must be added to result in the circuit in Figure 9.14. It is characteristic that one-shot multivibrators generate a fixed-duration and amplitude output pulse regardless of the duration of the input. Amplitude of the input need only be large enough to cause the one-shot to trip. When all the elements of Figure 9.14 are incorporated into a single package, the result is the JK flip-flop.

Multi-stage counters

The JK flip-flop, when operated in its toggled mode, alternately changes output status with each successive pulse at the T port. As such, it has an output frequency one-half the T frequency. It also counts up to a total of *one* and then resets itself to zero. It can count one event! A subsequent event shuts it off again. Clearly, as a counting circuit, it has

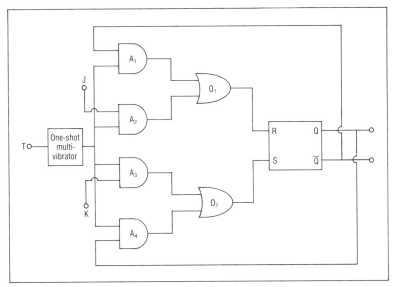

Fig. 9.14. Addition of a one-shot multivibrator to the T *input channel assures that any given* T *pulse will not be erroneously interpreted as being on too long or too short, because the one-shot output always is of fixed duration.*

223

limitations which begs the question, "Is it possible to interconnect JK flip-flops to count to values higher than one?" The answer: "But of course."

A three-stage counter, Figure 9.15, counts up presumably from 0 to a maximum of 7 and then resets itself to 0. The JK flip-flops are *leading-edge* triggered, in that a *rise* in the T pulse is what causes the respective output to change state. (There also are trailing-edge triggered JK flip-flops but their existence is only noted.) Now, each time the T port experiences a rise in voltage of sufficient amplitude, the output of the flip-flop changes state resulting in the so-called timing diagram, Figure 9.16. Assuming that all three flip-flops are reset before starting, then each subsequent T pulse toggles FF_1 from on-to-off-to-on, etc.

Because the flip-flops are leading-edge triggered, it is necessary to couple FF_1 to FF_2 and so on, using the $\bar{Q}$ output signal. This produces a counter which counts up. Coupling the Q outputs to the next T port causes a down count. In Figure 9.16, note that each pulse is numbered. Also note that the 0 — 1 patterns at outputs Q_1, Q_2, and Q_3. FF_1, receiving pulse train T produces Q_1, the most rapidly varying output. It is the *least significant bit* (LSB), just as the $\frac{1}{10}$-mile register is the LSD of the automotive odometer. A bit is the binary equivalent of a decimal digit.

Fig. 9.15. Three cascaded JK flip-flops can count up to seven. The eighth T pulse resets all flip-flops to 0s. Because the flip-flops are leading-edge triggered, the Q must be connected to the subsequent T port to achieve an up-count rather than a down-count.

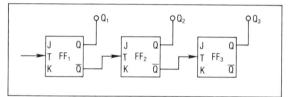

Table 9.2 - Timing summary			
Q_3 MSB	Q_2	Q_1 LSB	Pulse number
0	0	0	0
0	0	1	1
0	1	0	2
0	1	1	3
1	0	0	4
1	0	1	5
1	1	0	6
1	1	1	7
0	0	0	8
0	0	1	9

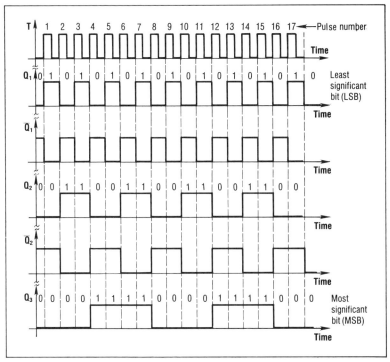

Fig. 9.16. Timing diagram for the three-stage counter in Figure 9.15 assumes that all three flip-flops are reset before the first pulse occurs. Each subsequent T pulse results in a unique 0 — 1 pattern at Q_1, Q_2, and Q_3, until the eighth pulse is received, which resets all three to 0.

For each T pulse in Figure 9.16, the 0 — 1 combinations are summarized, Table 9.2. There are only eight unique combinations including 000. Upon receipt of the eighth pulse, all the flip-flops go to their reset

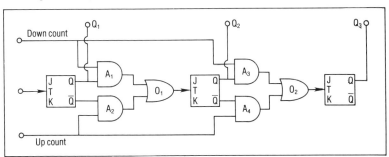

Fig. 9.17. The inter-stage AND and OR gates switch the counter from counting up to counting down.

225

states. Each row in Table 9.2 corresponds to the *binary equivalent* of the decimal value carried in the Pulse number column. The 101 combination in the fifth row is, for example, the binary code for decimal value 5. The Q and $\overline{Q}$ signals can be gated to the subsequent T port, Figure 9.17, to cause counting up or counting down. When the counter is used to accumulate pulses generated by an incremental encoder, it is necessary for new pulses to add on to the current count when the transduced motion is forward. But if the motion reverses, for example, the new pulses must subtract from the current count.

As long as the upcount port holds at a logical 1, Figure 9.17, $\overline{Q}$ is coupled to the subsequent stage and new pulses at the T port increase the count. On the other hand, if the down-count port is held at a logical 1 (the up-count port *must* hold at 0), any new pulses at the T port cause the counter to *subtract* from the current count. In this way, the counter contains a digital representation of the current position of the encoder. At the same time, the encoder and counter have *digitized* the encoder position. At the chip level, it is a binary representation but it is still a digital value.

Numbering systems

Successful design and construction of digital circuits require the coding of information so that it can be represented with on-off combinations in gates and memory. Then the information can be machine processed digitally and also can be read by other machines. To be read by humans, the information must be decoded.

Coding and decoding usually involves the conversion of numerical information to and from the familiar base 10 decimal system to the probably unfamiliar base 2 binary system. To understand how a computer or other digital control system controls electrohydraulic equipment, it is necessary to understand the binary numbering system and its offshoots: hexadecimal (base 16) and binary-coded decimal (BCD).

Table 9.3 - Four digit decimal register				
Significant position				
Most			Least	
4	3	2	1	Position number
10^3	10^2	10^1	10^0	Weighting factor
3	8	9	2	Register

$$2 \times 10^0 = 2 \times 1 \quad = \quad 2$$
$$9 \times 10^1 = 9 \times 10 \quad = \quad 90$$
$$8 \times 10^2 = 8 \times 100 \quad = \quad 800$$
$$3 \times 10^3 = 3 \times 1000 = 3000$$
$$\text{Sum} = 3892$$

Any *user friendly* system will perform the necessary conversions, but to understand how to make the necessary interfaces, to use them, and to know their limitations, it is essential to understand how coding and decoding take place. That means knowing and understanding the binary and hexadecimal numbering systems. The best place to start understanding them is to look at the familiar decimal system.

Decimal numbering system

Generally, there are two parts to consider in any numbering system be it decimal, base 39, or whatever:
- the symbols or set of symbols, alone and in combination, and
- the quantity represented by the symbols.

The symbology is arbitrary, but the quantity that the symbols represent must be the same regardless of the symbols that are used. When dealing with place- or position-weighted systems, the order in which the symbols appear affects the quantity being represented. For example, the decimal symbol set 38 does not represent the same quantity as decimal set 83 although the characters are the same. Their order is important because each position has a *weight* which is distinct from all other positions.

Consider a 4-digit register like a trip odometer that displays a current mileage of 3892, Table 9.3. Note that the position number begins in the right column with the least significant position and increases when moving left. Note that the weighting factor begins with 10^0 and is arranged in ascending powers of 10. Generalizing,

$$\text{weighting} = 10^{(\text{position number} - 1)},$$

Table 9.4 - Total combinations, 4-digit register			
0	0	0	0
0	0	0	1
0	0	0	2
0	0	0	3
0	0	0	4
0	0	0	5
0	0	0	
0			5
	9	9	6
9	9	9	7
9	9	9	8
9	9	9	9

227

that is in position 3, weighting equals $10^{3-1} = 10^2 = 100$.

To understand this 4-digit register, consider the largest number that it can store or display: 9999. Then consider the total number of combinations that can possibly be displayed. While Table 9.4 might list and count them, the total list is too long to construct. Instead, note that the largest number it can store is 9999, and when 0000 is recognized as a legitimate number, there are 10,000 possible different combinations. It is true that

$$\text{number of combinations} = 10^{(\text{number of digits})}.$$

Also, see that the decimal numbering system has digits 0 through 9 or 10 symbols, 10 is the system base, and there is no single symbol for the base. Instead, the base can be denoted only by a combination of other symbols — in this case 1 and 0. Here is a generalized summary of the decimal numbering system:

- the number of possible combinations $= \text{base}^{(\text{number of digits})}$
- maximum value $= \text{base}^{(\text{number of digits})} - 1$
- weighting factor $= \text{base}^{(\text{position number} - 1)}$
- number of symbols = base, and
- symbol for the base = 10.

Notation scheme

When expressing quantities in other numbering systems, the digital industry unfortunately has borrowed the same set of symbols used in base 10 rather than inventing a new set for each numbering system. Therefore, it is necessary to use a notation convention so that everyone knows what base is under discussion. Henceforth, all quantities (where it may not be obvious) will be indicated as having a certain base by attaching a subscript to the quantity. For example, 3892_{10} is 3892 in base 10, 110110_2 is 110110 in base 2, and $FFB9_{16}$ is FFB9 in base 16.

Binary numbering systems

Using the generalizations derived from base 10 examples, these statements are true about the binary system:

- number of symbols $= 2_{10}$
- the symbols are 0 and 1, and
- the base is denoted as: $2_{10} = 10_2$

Consider a 3-bit (binary digit or position) register such as a three-position automobile odometer. Each position can hold, display, or indicate one bit, that is a 0 or a 1. First determine the maximum value that can be stored (all the following numbers are to the base 10):

$$\text{Max value} = \text{base}^{(\text{position number})} - 1$$
$$= 2^3 - 1$$

$$= 8 - 1$$
$$= 7.$$

Now, determine the total number of combinations of 1s and 0s (again all numbers are in base 10):

$$\text{number of combinations} = \text{base}^{(\text{number of positions})}$$
$$= 2^3$$
$$= 8.$$

Example 9.1. Consider binary number 101_2 stored in a register. Convert that binary number to its decimal equivalent.

Solution 9.1. Begin by constructing Table 9.5, as was used in expanding the base ten number in Table 9.3. Completion of Table 9.5 indicates that $101_2 = 5_{10}$.

Next, consider all the possible combinations in a 3-bit binary register, for example. First, we know there are 8 possible combinations, so we construct Table 9.6, which has 3 columns (one for each bit location) and

Table 9.5 - Three digit binary register			
Significant bit			
Most		Least	
3	2	1	Position number
2^2	2^1	2^0	Weighting factor
1	0	1	Register

$$1 \times 2^0 = 1 \times 1_{10} = 1_{10}$$
$$0 \times 2^1 = 0 \times 2_{10} = 0_{10}$$
$$\underline{1 \times 2^2 = 1 \times 4_{10} = 4_{10}}$$
$$\text{Sum} = 5_{10}$$

Table 9.6 - Possible combinations, 3-bit binary register			
2^2	2^1	2^0	Decimal
0	0	0	0
0	0	1	1
0	1	0	2
0	1	1	3
1	0	0	4
1	0	1	5
1	1	0	6
1	1	1	7

8 rows (one for each combination), plus a right hand column to carry the equivalent base 10 value for each binary combination. In this Table, note that with 3 place positions, there are 8 combinations of 1s and 0s. Each row in the Table has a *unique* 1 — 0 combination. There are no others than the ones shown.

When dealing with digital systems, it is necessary to be able to construct a table of all combinations quickly. This can be done easily with just a little practice. In Table 9.6, note the least significant bit (LSB) column, headed with 2^0. It is a series of alternating 0s and 1s until all rows are exhausted. Of course, this assumes that the table has been constructed with the requisite number of rows, in this case 2^3 or 8 of them.

Next, move to the next least significant bit column (2^1) and note that it has two 0s followed by two 1s until all rows are exahusted. The third column, the most significant bit, (2^3), is four 0s followed by four 1s. This pattern can be extended to any number of bits. As the number of bits increases, the number of combinations also increases, but exponentially.

Conversion of decimal to binary

In general, it is necessary to be able to convert from decimal to binary and back to decimal. The first step in converting decimal to binary is to determine the number of bits needed to represent the number. Then a table is made and each binary position is evaluated as having a 0 or 1. Without proof, the following formula is offered:

$$\text{number of bits} = \text{integer part of } [\log(x)/\log(2)] + 1, \qquad (9.1)$$

where x is the quantity to be converted to binary.

Example 9.2. Convert 2836_{10} to binary.
Solution 9.2. Using Equation (9.1),

$$
\begin{aligned}
\text{number of bits} &= \text{integer part of } [\log(2863)/\log(2)] + 1 \\
&= \text{integer part of } [3.457/0.30103] + 1 \\
&= \text{integer part of } [11.483] + 1 \\
&= 11 + 1 \\
&= 12 \text{ bits.}
\end{aligned}
$$

Table 9.7 - Conversion of decimal to binary												
(a)	13	12	11	10	9	8	7	6	5	4	3	2	1	Position number
	4096	2048	1024	512	256	128	64	32	16	8	4	2	1	Expanded weighting factor
2^{12}	2^{11}	2^{10}	2^9	2^8	2^7	2^6	2^5	2^4	2^3	2^2	2^1	2^0	Weighting factor
0	1	0	1	1	0	0	1	0	1	1	1	1	= Binary value

(b) Binary $101100101111 = 2863_{10}$

Now construct 12-bit Table 9.7(a). The decimal value of each weighting factor also is included to ease arithmetic. The conversion is complete when Table 9.7(b) has all the 1s and 0s that indicate the value 2863_{10}. Begin with the most significant bit and then obtain answers to a series of *yes — no* questions. Only 12 bits are needed for the conversion of 2863_{10}, but Table 9.7(a) has 13 bits to illustrate a point. First ask the question "Should there be a 1 in the 2^{12} position?" The answer is no because its presence would create a binary number that with a single 1, (whose decimal equivalent is in the Weight expanded column) exceeds the number being converted. Therefore, there must be a 0 in the 2^{12} position.

This also means that all higher bit positions to the left of the 2^{12} register also must be 0s. Here are the rules of this process: if the weighting factor of the register is $>$ the target number, the answer is no. The reverse also is true: if the weighting factor is $<$ the target number, the answer is yes.

Now proceed with the next question: "Is there a 1 in the 2^{11} position?" The answer is yes because weighting factor 2048_{10} is less than target number 2863_{10}, so a 1 is placed in the 2^{11} position. Next, subtract 2048_{10} from 2863_{10} because 2048_{10} has now been accounted for. With a balance of 815_{10}, now ask "Is there a 1 in the 2^{10} position?" The answer is no because 1024_{10} exceeds the balance of 815_{10}. So a 0 is put in the 2^{10}

Decimal	Hex	Binary			
0	0	0	0	0	0
1	1	0	0	0	1
2	2	0	0	1	0
3	3	0	0	1	1
4	4	0	1	0	0
5	5	0	1	0	1
6	6	0	1	1	0
7	7	0	1	1	1
8	8	1	0	0	0
9	9	1	0	0	1
10	A	1	0	1	0
11	B	1	0	1	1
12	C	1	1	0	0
13	D	1	1	0	1
14	E	1	1	1	0
15	F	1	1	1	1

Table 9.8 - Hexadecimal-binary code

position and the remainder stays at 1024_{10}. Now ask "Is there is a 1 in the 2^9 position?" The answer is yes because 512_{10} is $<$ the balance of 815_{10}. Then subtract 512_{10} from 815_{10} to get 303_{10}.

Then test the 2^8 position and conclude that yes, there is a 1 there. This yes — no process continues until all binary positions have been exhausted, Table 9.7(b). Answering 11 questions about the presence or absence of 1 or 0 in each bit position provides the binary equivalent number.

Hexadecimal numbering systems

The hexadecimal numbering system is a base 16 numbering system, commonly called the *hex* system. It is useful when working with micro computers because they are segmented into bytes of 8 bits each and each byte can easily be converted into two hex characters without a lot of arithmetic. From previous analysis, these things are known about a hexidecimal numbering system:

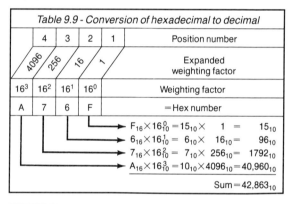

Table 9.9 - Conversion of hexadecimal to decimal

4	3	2	1	Position number
4096	256	16	1	Expanded weighting factor
16^3	16^2	16^1	16^0	Weighting factor
A	7	6	F	= Hex number

$F_{16} \times 16^0_{10} = 15_{10} \times 1 = 15_{10}$
$6_{16} \times 16^1_{10} = 6_{10} \times 16_{10} = 96_{10}$
$7_{16} \times 16^2_{10} = 7_{10} \times 256_{10} = 1792_{10}$
$A_{16} \times 16^3_{10} = 10_{10} \times 4096_{10} = 40,960_{10}$

Sum $= 42,863_{10}$

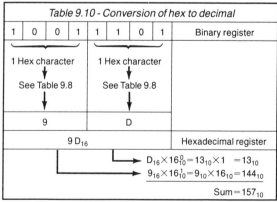

Table 9.10 - Conversion of hex to decimal

1	0	0	1	1	1	0	1	Binary register

1 Hex character — See Table 9.8 — 9
1 Hex character — See Table 9.8 — D

$9D_{16}$ | Hexadecimal register

$D_{16} \times 16^0_{10} = 13_{10} \times 1 = 13_{10}$
$9_{16} \times 16^1_{10} = 9_{10} \times 16_{10} = 144_{10}$

Sum $= 157_{10}$

- there are 16_{10} symbols, and
- the maximum value of one symbol is 15_{10}.

Table 9.8 shows all the characters and codes for a single hex character. There are 16 combinations, 16 characters, and the maximum value that can be stored is 15. A hex number requires four bits.

Example 9.3. Convert $A76F_{16}$ into a decimal.

Solution 9.3. First, construct weighting factor Table 9.9 for a four-character hex register. Hexidecimal numbers can be converted to decimal using the same technique used for binary numbers, except that the weighting factors are in $base_{16}$.

Note that one byte, the basic memory *chunk* in micro computers, is made of 8 bits. Note further that 4 bits are needed to define one hex character. Therefore, each byte can be represented by two hex characters. Consider a one-byte number, Table 9.10.

Bits, bytes, and high-level languages

The basic memory chunk for micro computers is made up of 8 bits. This means that the maximum value that can be stored in a 1-byte memory cell is given by the 8-bit value, 1111 1111. But this 8-bit *word* or byte is deduced from (using base 10)

$$\text{maximum value} = 2^{(\text{number of bits})} - 1$$
$$= 2^8 - 1$$
$$= 256 - 1$$
$$= 255.$$

This is a fairly small value, when considering the need for *number crunching* in a computer. Thus, to deal with larger quantities, fractional quantities and the like, the computer programmer must break decimal quantities into several bytes when working in machine language.

If the programmer uses an interpreter or compiler, the programs can be expressed in a high-level language such as BASIC, FORTRAN, PASCAL, ALGOL, C, etc. High-level language allows programmers to disassociate themselves from numbers at the byte level because the interpreter or compiler does all the needed memory management and arithmetic on numbers that occupy several memory locations.

Interpreters and compilers are special computer programs that translate high-level, english-like or mathematically structured instructions into machine language instructions. Interpreters sometimes are stored on internal erasable-programmable-read-only memory (EPROM) and begin executing as soon as the microcomputer is turned on. Some interpreters are stored on external bulk memory such as a disk or tape and must be loaded into the operating memory, called random access memory (RAM). The user must then start execution of the interpreter by using an appropriate system command.

Compilers are always stored on external bulk storage and must be loaded into RAM and then executed. The difference between an interpreter and a compiler is that the interpreter converts each high-level instruction into equivalent machine executable code or machine language as the instruction is encountered, and then executes the machine code immediately. Compilers go through the entire set of high-level instructions, called a computer program, and convert each instruction into machine language but do not execute the resulting machine code. Instead, they store the machine code, usually on disk, for execution at a later time. The result is that compiled codes usually execute faster because interpretation does not have to be done over and over again.

Fortunately, when programming in a high-level language, programmers can think in the familiar base 10 system. The disadvantage of high-level language is that it burdens the processor with management of, among other things, the decimal values while the computer works in binary. The speed of calculation, therefore, is slowed merely for having chosen a high-level language instead of machine language or assembler language. This is an important consideration when using the computer to control a hydraulic system. It is necessary for the computer to complete one sample of the entire control problem in about 1 or 2 milliseconds if the delay in the computer is to be kept manageable.

The fluid power world is an analog world. Information is carried in the magnitude of physical quantities such as voltage, pressure, speed, posi-

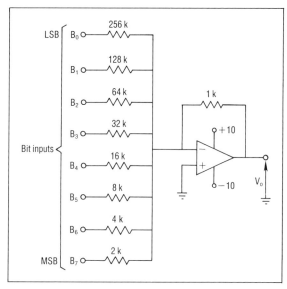

Fig. 9.18. An 8-input inverting summer op-amp circuit will perform an 8-bit digital-to-analog conversion. The individual bit inputs must either be 0.000 volts or 5.000 volts, then the output can be varied from 0.000 to 5.00 in 256 steps.

tion, and the like. It also is true that most controllers today are digital so there must be a digital-to-analog conversion process so control outputs of the computer are understood by the analog electrohydraulic system.

The general subject of digital-to-analog conversion is beyond our scope. It must remain sufficient that only some basic ideas will carry the reader through most problems that will be encountered in the fluid power world. A basic 8-bit digital-to-analog converter circuit, Figure 9.18, is set up for TTL logic which establishes a 1 level as being $+5$ V DC and 0 level as being 0 volts. In the converter, the normal tolerance of TTL logic levels (1 is any voltage greater than 2.4 volts and 0 is any voltage less than 0.8 volts) must be cast off and replaced with more precise voltages.

At the converter bit-input terminals, each 1-level bit must be at a precise, known and regulated value. The circuit anticipates that the voltages will be 5.000 and 0.000 for a logical 1 and a logical 0 respectively. Therefore, some necessary conditioning circuits are not shown. The circuit acts as a simple, analog inverting summer. Output voltage V_o is given by

$$V_o = -B_0/256 - B_1/128 - B_2/64 - B_3/32$$
$$- B_4/16 - B_5/8 - B_6/4 - B_7/2. \qquad (9.2)$$

Example 9.3. Consider the 8-bit binary number, Figure 9.19. Of course, the presence of a 1 corresponds to a voltage amplitude of 5.000 volts and a 0 signifies a voltage amplitude of 0.000 volts.

Solution 9.3. Output voltage can now be calculated using Equation (9.2):

$$V_o = -5/256 - 5/128 - 5/65 - 0/32 - 5/16 - 0/8 - 0/4 - 5/2$$
$$= -5[1/256 + 1/128 + 1/64 + 1/2]$$
$$= -2.949 \text{ volts.}$$

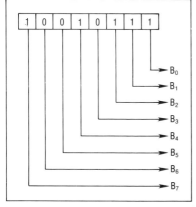

Fig. 9.19. Eight-bit binary number for Example 9.3.

The converter can convert any 8-bit pattern to an equivalent voltage. For the comparator to perform analog control, it must be outfitted with a digital-to-analog converter which performs the above calculation. These converters also are kown as *DACs, D/A converters,* or *D-to-A converters.* The 8-bit converter in question has a resolution of 1 part in 256 (2^8), or 0.003906.

Because of the 0 to 5-volt scaling, this corresponds to a voltage resolution of 0.01953125 volts. That is, with the requisite input bit pattern, any output voltage between 0 and 5 volts can be selected, but only in 19.5-millivolt steps. It is impossible to achieve any output voltage that is not an integer multiple of 0.01953125 volts. If intermediate values are needed for the application, more bits are necessary. Of course, more bits require more hardware, more regulation of 5.000 volts, more precision in the resistors, and finally, more money.

Programmable logic controllers and general-purpose microcomputers can be outfitted with D/A converters. They are available as add-ons or plug-in cards. There are quite a number of performance specifications to consider in their selection, but these are notable:

- resolution, that is the number of bits
- output voltage range, and
- range change method.

The first two have been discussed. Range change can be important in some applications, and some converters can change output-voltage ranges. Those versions that are changeable use hardware, or software. With hardware range changing, the usual methods use jumpers or switches on the board. This usually means some disassembly is necessary to get at the hardware, an inconvenient process. With software control, range can be changed by programming the host computer with the logic needed to make the decision. This is obviously more convenient but it is also more expensive.

Analog-to-digital conversion

Analog-to-digital conversion is the inverse of digital-to-analog conversion and is required so that the digital controller can *listen* to the analog world it controls. They are sometimes called *ADCs, A/D converters,* or simply *A-to-D converters.*

One method of A/D conversion is the successive approximation method, shown in combined block diagram/circuit schematic, Figure 9.20. Note that it uses the D/A converter as a port. The circuit functions as a null-seeking system just like a servomechanism, except that it is purely electronic. Operation of the circuit begins with firing of the Master Reset, which causes all Q_is in the 8-bit counter to go to logical 0s.

If there is a positive input voltage V_x, then there is a $+5$ volts or logical 1 at the output of OA_2, because the output of OA_1 is 0. The logical 1 from

OA_2 arms AND gate A_1 so that a subsequent clock pulse at the other AND input is gated through to the T input of the 8-bit counter. That pulse increments the counter by 1 which causes a new bit pattern at the 8 Q_i inputs to result in a new V_{FB}. If V_{FB} remains below V_x, output at OA_2, the sign-on error, remains at a logical 1 so the next clock pulse increases the counter by 1 count.

This process continues until such time that feedback voltage V_{FB} rises above V_x. At that time, output of OA_2 goes to logical 0 (diode D_1 prevents the output from going negative) and disarms AND gate A_1 so that

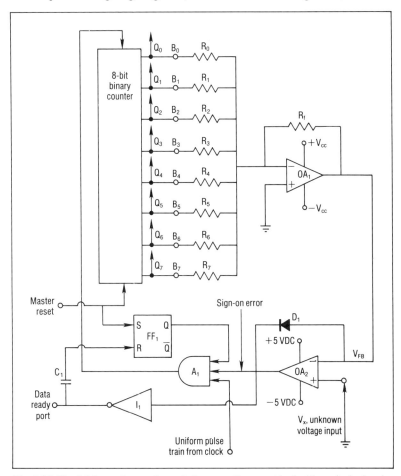

Fig. 9.20. The 8-bit counter continues to increase the count by 1 with each clock pulse as long as the sign of the error is positive (logical 1). When the sign changes, the correct bit pattern is held in the eight Q outputs of the 8-bit counter.

subsequent clock pulses are prevented from changing the counter. At the same time, output of inverter I_1 goes high, signalling that the counter has reached that bit pattern which corresponds to unknown voltage V_x. That is, it signals *Data ready*. The conversion process is done.

Although the circuit of Figure 9.20 is not used in commercial versions of A/D converters, it explains that:

● an initiating action must start the data conversion process. In Figure 9.20, that action is a momentary logical 1 at the Master Reset line. The Master Reset also *sets FF_1*, which arms one input of A_1

● the conversion process takes time

● when the conversion process is complete, it is signalled by a logical 1 at the Data ready port

● After the Data ready port goes high, the interrogating device can read the 8 Q_i counter outputs to fetch the binary value of unknown voltage V_x that existed at the instant V_{FB} exceeded V_x, and

● the value of the Q_i inputs *never exactly* coincides with V_x. It will only be within 1 bit.

There are several reasons why the circuit is Figure 9.20 is not used in commercial A/D converters:

● it is too slow and the conversion time depends upon the value of V_x. This is because the search is done in simple, incremental up-count fashion. A more rapid strategy is to do a binary search emulating the decimal-to-binary conversion algorithm presented in an earlier section. That search can be done in eight clock cycles, never more, never less. The circuit:

● does not allow for changing voltage range

● does not accommodate negative voltage, and

● has only eight clock bits.

The 8-bit A/D converter is popular on digital oscilloscopes, but for control work, 12 is the minimum number of bits and 16 are preferred.

Some of the characteristics important in selecting an A/D converter are:

● resolution

● speed of conversion, which also affects throughput

● software/hardware rangeability

● number of data channels, and

● availabilty of control software.

Commercial A/D and D/A converters

There are a number of competing products that perform both A/D and D/A conversion is a single, plug-in package. The most common version has up to 16 A/D input channels and as many as two D/A output channels. They can be either 8 bit or 12 bit and some are as high as 16 bit.

Multiple-channel input is accommodated with the use of a *multiplexer*.

There is only one A/D converter on the card, but it is shared among all the input channels. That is if all 16 channels are active and in use, the multiplexer switches the converter to channel 1, the conversion is carried out and data is transferred to the host computer. Then the multiplexer switches the converter to channel 2 and so on, until all active channels are completed. This process necessarily slows the data acquistion process and deserves a little scrutiny.

Suppose that there is an A/D converter card which boasts 100 kHz throughput and 16 channels. This means that if there is only one A/D channel in use at the time, it is possible to sample or read that channel 100,000 times each second. But if there are four channels of input data for example, then 100,000 samples must be distributed over four channels. Each channel now can be read only 25,000 times each second. Additional input channels reduce the rate at which each can be sampled even more.

Additionally, all this assumes that the software controlling the A/D card is faster than the sampling process. **That assumption usually is not a good one.** For most hydraulic control system problems, it is necessary that all channels be scanned, all outputs be generated and sent to the D/A port(s), and any number crunching and control logic be completed in no more than 3 milliseconds. This is only a rule of thumb that can be overly conservative or overly liberal depending upon application-specific circumstances.

This 3 millisecond benchmark is referred to as the *digital up-date time*. As long as it is small in comparison with the slowest time constants in the hydraulic system, the digital controller can be treated as being instantaneous for all practical purposes. At 3 milliseconds, it will be fast enough for most high-performance industrial electrohydraulic servo systems.

Chapter Ten

Challenges of the Control Chain: Measurement, Data Transmission, and Noise Control

Transducers are used in the laboratory for collecting data regarding the status or performance of a component or system and also in a control environment wherein the data collected from the transducer is used to control a machine or process that the transducer is monitoring. Although many problems and challenges are similar in both categories, some issues are unique to the industrial control environment and are addressed here.

In an industrial-control setting, a transducer measures some system output variable, say shaft speed. Then, based upon the desired or command(ed) speed, an error is calculated and used to bring actual speed into closer agreement with command(ed) speed. Such applications are called feedback control systems and their general form, Figure 10.1, indicates how the measurement and control links are expanded into several subparts. This expansion is presented because it is necessary to investigate the measurement problem in some detail.

1. Measurand. Certainly, the primary consideration is the variable which must be measured and controlled. Selection of this variable dictates the nature of the output which, in turn, dictates system interfacing and signal-conditioning needs. If the variable to be measured is fluid temperature, for example, the nature of the signal from the temperature transducer most likely is of a different form and strength than if the measured variable is cylinder position.

Measurement link 2. The physical sensor. The heart of a transducer is its physical sensor. It might be a conductor that becomes deformed as is the case of a strain-gage transducer, or the sensor might make use of the Hall effect as do some encoders. Whatever the selection, it will affect other links in the measurement and control chain.

Measurement link 3. Sender signal conditioning. In this text, a transducer sometimes will be called a *sending device* and it will be helpful to distinguish between things on the sending end from things on the receiving end. Many transducers are equipped with integral signal conditioners or outfitted with nearby external signal conditioning equipment. Such signal conditioners may be simple amplifiers, phase-sensitive demodulators, or special band-pass filters. There are hundreds of possibilities but only a limited number will be reviewed.

Handshaking, indicated between boxes 3, 5, and 6, and between 6, 5, and 3 in the reverse direction, Figure 10.1, is the term the digital industry uses to explain that two digital devices that want to share data must coordinate the availablity of the data at the digitization end with the interrogation process on the receiving end.

Measurement link 4. Data transmission medium. The data transmission medium is the method used to transmit information from the transducer to the receiving device. Again there are myriad possibilities, but in an industrial-control application, wires are usually the medium. On occasion, fiber-optic cable could be used to advantage if some special noise-control methods were necessary. In the case of an aerial lift, the medium could be an FM radio signal.

If the sending-end signal conditioner generates a 24-bit parallel digital signal, the data transmission medium must have 24 signal wires plus a

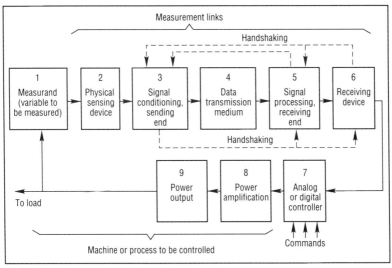

Fig. 10.1. A transducer and its support equipment form several links in the measurement-control, closed-loop chain. All measurement links may not be present or necessary in all systems.

ground wire. On the other hand, if the sending signal conditioner is an analog DC output device, the medium can usually be a simple two-conductor shielded cable. Only a few of the many possibilities will be covered here because apparatus such as FM radio transmitters and FM receivers/demodulators and their designs are left to qualified experts in those fields. Practitioners of the electrohydraulic art are advised to purchase such equipment as turnkey operational packages should they be needed.

Measurement link 5. Receiver signal processing. Signal processing on the receiving end may or may not be needed. The most common possibility is that the sending device transmits a 4- to 20-mA current-loop signal but the receiver requires a voltage — that is the receiver has a high input impedance. The typical industrial servo amplifier is an example of a voltage-processing receiving device. If a servo amplifier is the receiving device, a resistor, usually in the range of 100 to 500 Ω, will convert the current signal into a proportional voltage which the receiver can then process. Should the transmission medium be a radio signal, the receiving-end signal processor must be a radio receiver and a suitable radio-frequency (RF) demodulator.

Measurement link 6. The receiving device. The form this device can take has many possibilities but two common ones are a proportional-valve amplifier or a servovalve amplifier, most often called simply a servo amplifier. Given the popularity of programmable logic controllers in industry and the growing use of motion controllers, the receiving device of the future increasingly will be a special-purpose digital computer.

If the receiving device is a digital computer, interfacing decisions take on new dimensions. If the transducer generates an analog signal, an analog-to-digital converter will have to be somewhere in the measurement chain or in the receiving computer. If the physical sensing device is, say, an absolute-position encoder with parallel digital output, the encoder can be coupled directly to the parallel input port of the receiving computer.

Control link 7. Controller. A controller is a component which receives the conditioned data that represents the measured variable, compares it to the command, and issues any necessary corrective signal to the power amplifier. The controller could be an analog proportional or servo amplifier or it could be a special-purpose digital computer. The controller could even be a general-purpose desktop or laptop computer if it is configured with the proper hardware and software.

Control link 8. Power amplifier. For electrohydraulic control systems, the power amplifier is the driver stage of the servo/proportional amplifier. Motion controllers may have the power amplifier as an integral part of the controller. Amplifier output drives the valve coil.

Control link 9. Power output. The power output component is the hydraulic actuator: a cylinder or rotary actuator.

The loop formed in Figure 10.1 is the measurement-control closed-loop chain of which the measurement links form a vital part. It can be shown that the measurement device and its supporting equipment alone dictate the performance of a high-gain closed-loop system. That is, deficiencies in the measurement chain propagate one-for-one into deficiencies in the control of final system output. Transducer performance is crucial and its selection is critical. Unfortunately, the great number of possibilities that can be employed make the subject of transduction and interfacing confusing to those who are not familiar with the art.

Three elements

Usually, three elements of Figure 10.1 are chosen early in the design process or are mandated by application requirements:

● the control problem at hand usually dictates the measurand. For example, if one wants to control the speed of a motor, it is unlikely that a temperature-measuring transducer would be called upon to do this task; a speed transducer is the more likely choice. Once the measurand is selected, the choice of transducer most often narrows considerably: there are no commercially viable speed transducers in which strain gages perform the basic act of transduction; frequency-generation methods are more popular and can be cost effective. Suppose that a frequency-generation transducer has been selected; the signal conditioning equipment must then be able to process a frequency input as opposed to an amplifier for a strain gage bridge or thermocouple analog voltage

● application circumstances many times control the data transmission method. The transmission medium in most industrial hydraulic systems will be a multiplicity of wires, but if it is necessary to remotely control a farm tractor for example, radio waves may be a real possibility. If the distance between sending and receiving devices is great, a 4- to 20-mA current loop may be the choice. If there is a distance problem as well as a ground-loop noise problem, then opto-isolation and fiber-optic cabling may be called for. Whatever constraints and requirements apply, the data-transmission medium will significantly affect the nature and extent of the signal processing/conditioning equipment on the sending and receiving ends of the measurement chain, and

● the receiving device will affect interfacing decisions. If the receiving device can receive only digital signals, the receiving signal processor must produce digital outputs. If the receiver is an analog device such as a servo amplifier, on the other hand, the receiving signal processor must output analog signals. Carrying this point further: if the sending-end signal conditioner generates a high-level DC output (more than ± 1 volt) and the physical distance between the transducer and servo amplifier is just a few feet, there is no need for receiving-end signal processing; the servo amplifier does it all. Make note of this — the servo amplifier is at once the receiving device and the controller.

What we find then is an extensive jargon and terminology of transduction and control along with a block diagram that shows function more than it does physical hardware. This is not unusual in the technology of control systems. That is, the block labelled *Receiving device*, Figure 10.1, may in one instance be a piece of real and separate hardware such as an analog-to-digital converter. But it also may be, for example, nothing more than the 500-Ω resistor in a servo amplifier that converts a 4- to 20-mA current signal into a proportional voltage that the servo amplifier needs.

All of this recognizes that a great deal of the problem for the fluid power practitioner is one of terminology, definition, and common usage. Be aware that the diagrams used by controls-systems artisans probably will contain blocks that define function as opposed to depicting separate, identifiable boxes that one would buy at a store. The hardware needed to implement a function may come all in one box or in several boxes. It is impossible to predict without dealing with specific applications and choice of specific hardware.

Selection questions

When selecting actual hardware, **always ask these questions**: of all the functions needed to perform the desired control action, how many are contained in this specific piece of hardware and how many must be obtained with other pieces of hardware?

The answers to these questions will be enhanced if the fluid power practitioner can remember, understand, and appreciate the:

● overall picture suggested in Figure 10.1, and distinguish between function and hardware boxes. Eventually, the hardware boxes must be identified, but at planning and design time, it helps to consider only function

● basic physics of the transducer in question, because its operation will help select the transducer

● variety of formats in which data can exist. For example, when dealing with analog or digital signals, will the information be the frequency or the amplitude, etc

● various data transmission media and what factors assist in the decision to select one over the other. If application circumstances dictate a particular transmission medium, understand the signal conditioning/processing implications attendant therewith, and

● nature of the controller and whether the other elements in the measurement chain require a separate receiving device or can the receiving-device function be adequately performed by the controller.

Adding to this multitude of possibilities is the fact that there are so many different transducers that perform the same function. For example, there are at least 20 different ways to measure liquid flow. Each method uses its own particular technology, generates its own output data form, and requires its own special signal-processing equipment. Add to that the possibility that there are several different controllers and data transmission media, and the number of combinations becomes truly astronomical. What follows is the reduction of that astronomy into manageable proportions by looking at things the practitioner of the electrohydraulic art may encounter in the work-a-day world.

Forms and methods for data transmission

In the electrohydraulic control situation, components are connected in a chain-like fashion to form the feedback-control loop. The purpose of the several connections is to transmit information or data from one point to another in the loop to bring about the desired degree of control. Obviously, the information exists in a variety of forms at various points within the loop. For example, the transducer output may be a voltage. At the valve, input is usually a current. Within the actuator, information is in the form of a pressure and a flow, and so on.

When expanding the purely electronic elements within the loop, there are a variety of forms within that medium alone. The transducer probably outputs an analog voltage but within the controller, depending upon type, the data may exist as a digit in computer memory. In between, there may be pulse-position modulation, a frequency-modulation element, or even a double-sideband, suppressed-carrier, amplitude-modulated signal. Possibilities may be endless.

The general subject is covered in detail in an electrical engineering course called *Information Theory* or *Information Transmission*. The course deals with the many possible forms in which information can be processed and transmitted. To treat it exhaustively here would require substantial addition to this book. Fortunately, for the electrohydraulic engineer there are only a few forms used for data transmission.

There are two broad data-form categories that must be understood to cover most electrohydraulic applications: digital and analog. The subject of digital data already has been covered to some extent in the form of binary and hexadecimal codes, and the analog-to-digital and digital-to-analog converters. Electronic counters also have been discussed. Methods of processing digital data are an issue of software and should be described in a course in computer programming; they are not covered here.

In the following discussion, electronic counters will be used as components or black boxes in the control/measurement chain mostly to show methods of converting data from analog to digital form when the data is not a simple analog DC voltage. Because all these data forms are common in electrohydraulic control systems, they should be understood at least in a conceptual sense. The general subject of digital data transmission and processing is not included here. Instead, emphasis is placed upon the analog forms with digitization being a digression where appropriate.

245

ANALOG DATA FORMS

A family tree of the analog signal data forms likely to be encountered in electrohydraulic systems, Figure 10.2, shows the two major branches of the tree, namely DC and AC. Strictly speaking, the DC branch is really a subset of the AC branch, but fluid power technology normally does not make this distinction. The fact of the matter is that DC, by definition, is absolutely constant and therefore cannot transmit information because it never changes.

But, information is transmitted in the fact that the DC level **does** change. For example, when the output voltage of a pressure transducer changes, one knows that the pressure must have changed commensurately. That **change** is the data; it **is** the information.

But, the argument goes, if the voltage changes, then **by definition** it must be an AC system! The concept seems almost philosophical and for our purposes, that is how it is treated. But, it is more than that for the circuit designer because indeed, AC circuit theories must be used for designing this thing that is categorized as a *DC data transmission system*. In spite of these arguments, the tree of Figure 10.2 has a DC and an AC branch.

DC data transmission forms

While no standards govern the voltage level in the generation or transmission of DC analog signals, actual practice is slightly different. There are a large number of systems that use a 0- to 10-volt signal or a

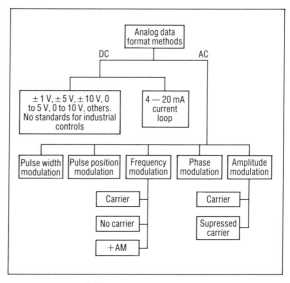

Fig. 10.2. The analog-signal family tree of data indicates the different forms that data may take in an electrohydraulic system. Several forms may exist in different parts of a single system.

± 10-volt signal. Most commercial transducers come with options that often include those values, or the transducers can be equipped with signal conditioning modules that provide that output. Furthermore, receiving devices that accept and process 10-volt signals are easy to design, economical, and commonly available. This also is true of 5-volt signals; 5- and 10-volt signals are consistent with the normal 5- to 24-volt range of DC power-supply voltages and each gives good noise immunity because the noise levels usually are well below the peak signal levels.

Some of the options that should be considered in a DC analog data transmission system are indicated in Figure 10.3. When the system uses voltage as the data-carrying variable with the so-called *high level* signals between 100 millivolts and 10 volts, the interconnection is very straightforward. A signal wire and ground connection are all that are needed when the interconnection distances are, say, below 20 ft. In any event, it is always good practice to use a *shielded, twisted pair* as the interconnecting method, understanding that shielding becomes more important as the separation distance increases. This shielded, twisted pair refers to the type of cabling that has a signal and a common conductor enclosed inside a conducting sheath usually made of braided wire called the shield.

When transmission distances exceed 20 ft, line 2, Figure 10.3, it may be

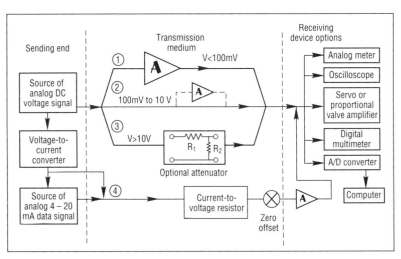

Fig. 10.3. *Either a voltage or a current source, located at the sending end of shielded and twisted-pair analog DC data-transmission lines 1, 2, 3, and 4, sends low-amplitude voltage (< 100 mV) in line 1; mid-amplitude voltage (100 mV to 10 V) through line 2, and high-level amplitude (> 10 V) through line 3 to the receiving device. The fluid power industry uses 250-or 500-Ω input resistors to convert the current signal to a proportional voltage. Any analog receiving device can be used depending upon needs of the application.*

247

desirable to include a buffer amplifier at the sending end of the data link. This amplifier provides a high input impedance for the transducer to look into and at the same time provides a low output impedance to drive the transmission line. Both impedances will work to enhance the noise immunity of the data link. When the voltage level at the sending end is less than 100 millivolts, amplification at the sending end is almost mandatory. This statment is made assuming that the receiving-end device, such as a proportional or servo amplifier, will best be served by a 5- or 10-volt maximum signal level. That may not always be the situation at hand, so the suggestion must be interpreted as a rule-of-thumb; each application has its own specific considerations that must be weighed.

Note that the correct position of the amplifier is at the sending end, especially if the distances are more than two or three ft. This will raise the voltage, probably to the 5- or 10-volt range, with the amplification taking place in the noise-protected environment of the sending device. With this increased voltage level, noise induced in the more-vulnerable interconnecting cable will have less effect than if the voltage were transmitted at the millivolt level. That is, the *signal-to-noise* ratio of the system will be higher when using a sending-end amplifier.

For signals that exceed 10 volts (the exception rather than the rule), it probably will be necessary to attenuate the signal so that it is in the 5- or 10-volt range. If the attenuator is placed at the sending end of the transmission line, it can pose a problem. Voltage divider R_1 and R_2, line 3, Figure 10.3, will undoubtedly increase the effective output impedance of the sending device and will reduce the noise immunity of the line. Another reason it may be neccessary to include a buffer amplifier at the sending end is to reduce the effective output impedance of the sending end. It may be possible to get by without the buffer amplifier if the attenuator is placed at the receiving end.

The 4-to-20 mA current loop, line 4, Figure 10.3, grew up in the process-control industries where transmission distances between senders and receivers are often measured in terms of miles instead of feet or inches. The 4-to-20 mA current loop, or simply the current loop, was invented to solve the noise problems attendant with such long lines. The current loop has found a niche in electrohydraulic control systems when noise immunity is desired and/or long distances are involved.

A current loop uses the concept of *duality* compared to the voltage method of data transmission. Using duality, the sending-device output stage contains a current amplifier rather than a voltage amplifier. Current amplifiers have high output impedances, usually in the kΩ range. In contrast, the ideal receiving device has zero input impedance. The reader is encouraged to compare this scenario with that of the ideal sender and ideal receiver for voltage transmission.

In practical terms, zero input impedance is an unachievable goal, so designers must settle for low impedance. In the case of servo and proportional valve amplifiers, the practice is to outfit the input stage of the receiving amplifier with a 250- or a 500-Ω resistor which converts the incoming current signal into a proportional voltage — what the amplifier was designed for. Note then, that Ohm's law tells us that with a maximum incoming signal current of 20 mA, the effective input voltage at the receiving amplifier is 5 volts with the 250-Ω resistor and 10 volts with a 500-Ω resistor, just about ideal. On the other hand, the minimum input current by standarized practice is 4 mA, which converts to 1 and 2 volts, respectively for 250- and 500-Ω input resistance.

One of the disadvantages of the current loop is that the incoming signal does not pass through zero although it may be necessary to have a condition which corresponds to zero. With the current loop, system zero must correlate to a non-zero input current. The usual practice is to split the current spread down the middle, making zero for the system coincide with 12 mA of input current. Now, the input signal is 12 mA ± 8 mA. To compensate for this, the receiving amplifier can be equipped with a zeroing, or offset, or bias control. Then, when the incoming current is 12 mA, the receiving system, ie the input to amplifier A, Figure 10.3, is zero. Of course, the sending end must be set so that the 12 mA output corresponds to the system zero condition. This may be done with the sending-end current-generating source.

The major disadvantage of the current loop is at the same time its major advantage. The data range is standardized from 4 to 20 mA so if the signal should ever go outside that range, it is an indication of a fault. The most unreliable part of any electronic equipment is the interconnecting cabling and the terminal connectors. If the data link in the current loop breaks, for example, the current at the receiving end goes to zero which is outside the permissible range. A simple op-amp detector circuit can sense this condition and take action to shut down the critical parts of the circuit or system. This probably is the one most important characteristic that has kept the current loop in continuous use for more than half a century.

Several devices can be on the receiving end. Certainly, if the purpose of the system is to merely measure a system variable such as shaft speed, the data may be observed on any one of several possible data display devices. The most common ones, Figure 10.3, include oscilloscope, analog voltmeter, or digital multimeter (DMM). On the other hand, if the system shown in Figure 10.3 is a subsystem of a control system, then the component on the receiving end may be a servo or proportional-valve amplifier or an A/D converter connected to a computer or programmable logic controller. Any device that listens to an analog voltage in the range that is being transmitted is a possible and viable receiving-end device.

The transmission of data by means of AC voltage invariably brings up the subject of *modulation* and *carriers*. In over-simplified terms, the modulation contains the information or data while the carrier is the vehicle that carries the data. The AC branch of the family tree, Figure 10.2, shows the most common forms for data likely to be encountered in electrohydraulic applications. While the tree is not exhaustive, it covers those used most often:

- amplitude modulation (AM)
- phase modulation
- frequency modulation (FM)
- pulse position modulation, and
- pulse width modulation (PWM).

The form of the modulation tells how the data is contained. Modulation form may be dictated by the kind of transducer on the sending end or it may be the result of necessary or optional signal conditioning.

The form of the modulation dictates the nature of the receiving device because it must be appropriately designed/selected to recover the data. The data recovery process, in general, is called *demodulation* and its purpose is to separate or extract the data from the carrier. The specific circuits that perform the demodulation vary from a simple diode for certain forms of AM to phase-sensitive demodulators for other forms of AM, to FM detectors. The possibilities are legion, but when the concepts of data form are understood the details of the circuits that process the signals become less important. These details can be safely left to the specialized electronic design engineers.

Amplitude modulation, carrier present. The most common example of AM is the commercial-radio broadcast band. That band uses those carrier frequencies that extend from 550 kHz to 1600 kHz or 1.6 MHz. Technically, this is called *double-sideband AM*. It is characterized by a radio-frequency (RF) carrier whose amplitude varies or is modulated in synchronism with the data, which is usually audio information such as voice or music.

The AM modulator is located at the transmitter site and is the final or output stage of the transmission electronics where the data and carrier waves come together. They form the modulated RF signal which is then sent to the transmitting antenna, Figure 10.4. It is the usual practice of electronic engineers to describe their processes mathematically, a practice that leads to a number of terms unfamiliar to the layman because one has to understand the mathematical concepts to place importance on the words.

In the case of AM, double sideband-with-carrier, the modulation process requires there be a mathematical multiplication of the data signal and the carrier signal for the modulation to occur. Given that this signal multiplication takes place, the transmitted signal then is of the form:

$$e_T = [A + B\cos(\omega_D t)]\cos(\omega_C t), \tag{10.1}$$

where ω_D is the frequency of the data or audio signal, ω_C is the frequency of the carrier, B is the amplitude of the data (audio) and A is the amplitude of the carrier when there is no modulation (audio signal) present.

From this point on, consider the signal mathematically. Expanding Equation (10.1) gives:

$$e_T = A\cos(\omega_C t) + B\cos(\omega_D t)\cos(\omega_C t). \tag{10.2}$$

In this form, see clearly that carrier frequency ω_C is present. The second term also is of interest because it contains the modulation or data, B.

A trigonometric identity says that the product of two cosine waves can be represented by two terms that contain the sum and difference of their angles. That is:

$$\text{Cos}x\cos y = \tfrac{1}{2}[\cos(x + y) + \cos(x - y)]. \tag{10.3}$$

When the identity of Equation (10.3) is applied to Equation (10.2), we see that $x + y$ is the sum of the data and carrier frequencies while $x - y$ is the difference between the data and carrier frequencies. Further, there are three frequencies present in the modulated or output signal: the carrier, ω_C; the carrier plus data, $\omega_C + \omega_D$; and the carrier minus data, $\omega_C - \omega_D$.

We say that the signal contains the **carrier plus the sum and difference** frequencies. The sum and difference frequencies are also called the

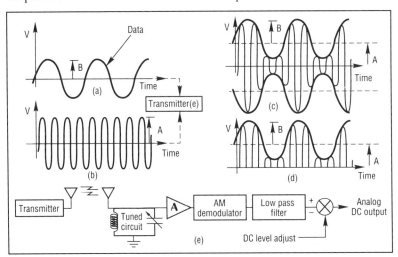

Fig. 10.4. Audio signal (a) combines with carrier signal (b) to form modulated signal that contains upper and lower sidebands (c) transmitted by the antenna, (e). A diode demodulator in a single-sideband transmitter passes one-half the signal for transmission, (d), and throws the other half away.

251

sidebands, and because both the sum and difference frequencies are present, the signal is called *double-sidebanded*. These revelations become apparent when the signal is studied mathematically. A more intuitive feel for the AM process can be seen in the four signals of Figure 10.4. The first signal, (*a*), is the audio or data signal that we are trying to send. It is the information. The second, (*b*), is the carrier frequency shown before it enters the modulator (multiplication) stage of the transmitter. At that time, it has constant peak amplitude A as given in Equations (10.1) and (10.2).

Next, modulated signal (*c*) results from combining the carrier signal with the data signal in the modulator. This signal is radiated by the antenna as the radio or RF signal and contains the carrier plus the sum and difference frequencies. It contains the sidebands called the *upper sideband* (sum frequency) and the *lower sideband* (difference frequency). The radiated signal is then picked up by a receiving antenna, which is connected to a *tuned circuit*.

This tuned circuit is a coil and variable capacitor in parallel which has an extremely high impedance at its resonant frequency. Varying the capacitor changes the resonant frequency, thus tuning the circuit to the carrier frequency of the radio signal. Other transmitters radiating at different carrier frequencies also are received by the antenna, but because the coil and capacitor are tuned to only one frequency, all other received frequencies see the tuned circuit as essentially a short circuit to ground. They are effectively shorted out so that only the tuned frequency is amplified by the receiving amplifier.

The data, identified as the *envelope* in Figure 10.4(c), then can be extracted with a simple diode. When passed through the diode, the signal, Figure 10.4(d), emerges but is only one half the input signal. Because the antenna signal contains both sidebands, it does not matter which way the diode is put into the circuit, because both halves of the wave contain the same information. The final stage of the demodulation process passes the rectified signal through a low-pass filter that removes the last vestiges of the carrier frequency. Be aware that the frequencies in Figure 10.4 are not drawn to scale. That is, carrier amplitude typically is 100 to 300 times higher than the data frequency: to wit, 5 kHz of data vs 1 MHz for the carrier.

Electronic engineers noticed the obvious redundancy in the double-sideband signal and lamented the wasted power. They invented the *single-sideband* transmitter which chopped off one sideband at the trans-mitter. All the radiated power then, could be put into the one sideband, increasing the useful range of the transmission. However, removal of one of the sidebands constitutes a distortion of the signal so the data is corrupted, but corrupted in a known and controlled way.

Anyone who has listened to single sideband on a double-sideband receiver knows the effect of the distortion. It is obvious to the listener that a voice is involved, but it is unintelligible. Receipt of the single-sideband signal and its demodulation require that the carrier be reinserted at the receiver site. Single-sideband radio transmission and demodulation is mentioned to round out the discussion of amplitude modulation; single sideband is not used in the fluid power work-a-day world.

Amplitude modulation, suppressed carrier, double sideband. Suppressed-carrier, double-sideband AM (SCDSAM) data transmission definitely is found in electrohydraulic control systems, Figure 10.5. There are a number of transducers that must use AC and many of them generate SCDSAM signals: synchros and resolvers, variable-reluctance pressure transducers, LVDT's, variable-capacitance pressure transducers, strain-gage transducers when AC is used to power the bridge, and potentiometers when AC is used as a supply voltage.

The SCDSAM signal is characterized by the the fact that the data envelope, Figure 10.5(a), modulates the amplitude of the carrier, Figure 10.5(b), as in the case of simple AM, but the envelope and the data pass through zero at the same time. Note that when the data passes through zero, the modulated signal undergoes a 180° phase change. These condi-

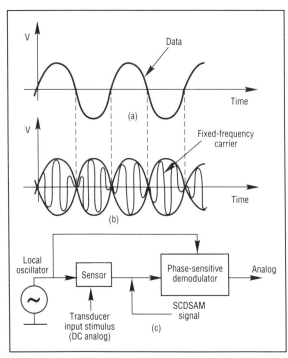

Fig. 10.5. Note that fixed-frequency carrier signal (b) of suppressed-carrier double-sideband AM (SCDSAM) transmitter undergoes a 180° phase reversal each time modulating or data signal (a) undergoes a sign change. This phase reversal requires a phase-sensitive demodulator, (c), to correctly recover the algebraic sign of the original data. Local oscillator outputs fixed-frequency, fixed-amplitude AC; circuit outputs DC with reconstructed algebraic sign.

tions are contrasted with the waveshapes of Figure 10.4.

Simple rectification fails to properly reconstruct the algebraic sign reversals in the data. A more sophisticated device, a phase-sensitive demodulator is required, Figure 10.5(c). This demodulator compares the raw transducer output to the local oscillator signal to maintain full sign sensibility. Of course, once the signal is demodulated, there is no evidence of the internal AC signal in the output. There are a number of commercial transducers which use internal AC, but with miniaturized onboard electronic signal conditioning, this is invisible to the user. Lest an incorrect impression be gained, it is emphasized that the synchro and resolver are potential candidates for phase-sensitive demodulation as described above, although they are not used this way in a commercial sense.

The reason they are not is because imperfections in the demodulation process would destroy the otherwise excellent repeatability of the synchro family of transducers. Instead, they are used in synchro-synchro or resolver-resolver pairs in which the second of the pair is at once a receiving device and a demodulator. Additionally, resolvers have been applied in fluid power applications when the output is conditioned by a special *resolver-to-digital* converter. The result is a rotary position-measuring transducer whose performance equals or exceeds that of digital shaft encoders.

Phase modulation. As its name implies, phase-modulation data forms are those in which the information is contained in the amount of phase shift between a reference signal and an output or data signal. Phase-shift modulation is used in certain ultrasonic flowmeters and torque transducers. In the torque transducer, imagine that there is a rotating shaft capable of producing a measurable amount of twist in the presence of a torque, Figure 10.6.

Output signals are shown as being nominally sinusoidal, Figure 10.7(a) and (b), but they need not be. In fact if the encoders are optical-incremental types, the outputs are essentially square waves. Assuming that as the

Fig. 10.6. Twisting the shaft causes a phase shift between two encoder signals and produces phase-modulated signals E_1 and E_2.

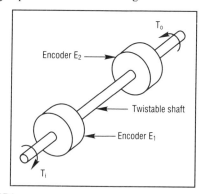

shaft turns, the incremental encoders initially are aligned so their respective outputs are directly in phase when there is zero torque transmitted through the shaft, the signal from Encoder 1 will be in phase with the output of Encoder 2.

Now, if there is a torque transmitted through the shaft, it will undergo some amount of wind-up or twisting. That wind-up means that the output encoder gets slightly behind the input encoder and can be seen as a phase shift between E_1 and E_2. The degree of phase shift is directly relatable to the amount of transmitted torque. The output voltage of Encoder 2 is a phase-modulated signal because the data is contained in the amount of phase shift between reference E_1 and the output.

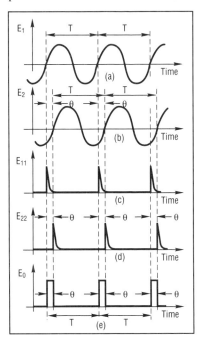

Fig. 10.7. Reference signal E_1 (a) compares with phase-modulated signal E_2 (b), can then be converted to pulse position modulated signals E_{11} (c) and E_{22} (d), and then to pulse width modulated signal E_O (e), using the circuit of Fig. 10.8.

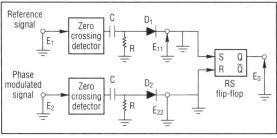

Fig. 10.8. This circuit converts phase-modulated signal E_2 of Figure 10.7 into PWM signal.

255

To extract the phase data, modulated signal E_2 must be compared to reference signal E_1; by itself, voltage E_2 is meaningless. Demodulation of the phase-modulated signal is easy once it is converted to a pulse-position modulated signal which in turn, can be easily converted to a PWM signal. The first step in the conversion process is to put reference signal E_1 from the torque transducer just discussed into a *zero-crossing detector*, Figure 10.8.

A zero-crossing detector is merely an op-amp comparator that produces a positive-going output anytime the input is greater than zero, plus an RC network at the output to differentiate the square wave. The differentiated signals are E_{11} and E_{22}, Figures 10.7(c) and (d), and appear as short-duration spikes. The E_{11} spike, having been derived from the E_1 reference signal, sets an RS flip-flop causing Q output E_O, Figures 10.7(e) and 10.8, to go high. Some time later, E_{22} from the phase-shifted or modulated signal provides a spike which resets the RS flip-flop. The result is that output voltage E_O is high only for the interval between when the reference goes through zero until the modulated signal goes through zero. The result, E_O, is a PWM signal in which the on-time is a measure of the torque transmitted by the torque shaft.

Provided that the shaft is turning sufficiently fast and that there is a large enough number of output cycles from each encoder, the PWM signal will be a high frequency. It is not difficult to calculate that frequency for any given set of hardware and operational scenario. Now given that the PWM signal has a sufficiently high frequency, any analog readout device such as an analog voltmeter can read the torque because the average or DC level of the E_O signal is directly proportional to the transmitted torque. This example has dealt with a torque transducer, but the principles apply to any phase-modulated signal.

Incidentally, the phase-shift torque transducer is not popular in the U.S. It is most often seen in the Far East because that is where the manufacturing and calibration technology has evolved. Note that this transducer cannot be calibrated statically; its shaft has to be turning to produce a measurable phase shift. This is a disadvantage that does not apply to strain-gage torque transducers.

Fig. 10.9. PWM digitization is done with a counter which accumulates clock pulses when the PWM signal is high. Value of digital data is proportional to the PWM on-time. PWM is high or positive when on.

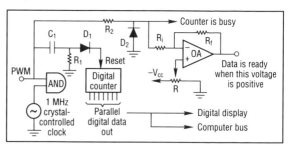

Digitization of a PWM signal. Digitization of a PWM signal is easily accomplished with a high-speed electronic counter, a precision stable clock pulse generator (clock), an AND gate, and some other analog elements to take care of handshaking, Figure 10.9.

The clock is any stable, electronic oscillator of the type used in computers or commercial electronic counters. The higher its frequency, the greater the resolution of the digitized output, but only if the counter has enough stages (digits or bits) to accommodate the resolution. The AND gate, Figure 10.9, is the basic logic element. Assuming that the PWM signal is high when it is on and that the frequency of the precision clock is substantially higher than the frequency of the PWM signal, the counter will accumulate counts only when the PWM is on, precisely the result we want.

At the conclusion of each of the on-intervals of the PWM signal, the counter contains a count which is directly and linearly proportional to the width of the pulse. Note that if we would like to have, say, a resolution of 0.1% or one part in 1000, that specification fixes the minimum relationship between clock frequency and the frequency of the PWM voltage. That is, it will be necessary for the clock frequency to be at least 1000 times greater than the PWM frequency. By way of example, suppose we wanted to digitize the PWM signal that powers a certain proportional valve whose PWM frequency is 400 Hz, a common value. This requires that the clock frequency be at least 400 kHz, which is not difficult with today's electronics. Given these values, see that when the on-time of the PWM voltage approaches almost the entire period of the PWM cycle, the maximum total count in the counter approaches 1000 which gives the desired 0.1% resolution.

The digitizer of Figure 10.9 is not atypical, in that it has to carry out some handshaking between it, the digitizer, and the thing that is going to interpret the counter. In the circuit at hand, during that time when the PWM signal is high, the counter is accumulating counts and the digitization is in progress. If the interrogation device (not specifically identified in Figure 10.9) were to read the counter before the PWM voltage went low, the reader would get an erroneous value. The only time that valid data exists in the counter is the interval during which the incoming PWM signal is low or at zero.

Note then, that the PWM signal itself contains all the information necessary to cause the handshake. If when ready to receive data, the reading device first looks at the *Counter is busy* line, Figure 10.9, and sees that it is high, the reader then knows the counter is being updated and data is **not** ready. On the other hand, if a poll of the Counter is busy line reveals a low or zero state, the reader knows it can read the counter to obtain a valid digitized value for the PWM input. In today's control-system technology, the reading device is probably a digital computer or pro-

257

grammable logic controller, which in turn is being controlled by software. The software would be the vehicle that polls the Counter is busy line.

Polling is a term applied to the process of an interrogating device wherein it looks at a given data line and checks for a special condition — in this case the special condition is a single bit, but it could be an entire nibble or byte. The reader is looking for a single bit to be low to start pursuing the data. The reader looks and does not find the requisite condition for data acquisition and then looks again, and again, and again and keeps on. Whether the computer looks and then looks again, or optionally goes off and does something else (payroll, turn on the TV, or whatever else may be the proper domain of the computer) is strictly a programmer's choice and the possibilities are all application specific. The circuit of Figure 10.9 only points out the concept of handshaking, and that handshaking is a requirement in all digital data communication.

Occasionally the circuit may fail. For example, suppose that the reader polls the Counter is busy line and finds it low. This indicates that the counter now holds valid data. But if during that very short time interval between polling and subsequently accessing the counter, the reset pulse should occur, it will set the counter to zero and the reading will be in error. There are ways around this problem but the circuit immediately becomes more complex.

For example, one ploy is to make the polling and reading processes take place simultaneously. Then the test can be made on the Counter is busy bit and if not low, the counter-reading discarded and the process continued until the busy bit does go low. Another way is to build a second register to hold the counter contents. Then occurrence of the reset pulse shifts the current contents of the counter, bit-for-bit, into the second register, and then resets the counter. This simplifies the handshaking logic because now, the second register always contains a valid number; it is merely out of date by as much as one complete PWM cycle.

A fatal flaw remains in the circuit that can be recognized when the reader attempts to read the second register at the same instant it is being updated. The solution for this problem is to use the reset pulse, the output signal from diode D_1, Figure 10.9, as the Data-busy bit. When it is high, the data is invalid. Generally, the number of problems is extensive and their solutions are the rightful province of digital electronic designers.

Frequency modulation. Using FM, the information is contained in the frequency of the signal rather than its amplitude. The two versions of FM are:
- deviation from a center or carrier frequency, and
- carrier frequency is the data.

The first is the method employed by the FM broadcast industry, and is not used specifically by the electric or fluid power controls industry. The second version, however, is very common in industrial controls.

258

FM, deviation-from-center frequency. The typical FM radio transmission system, Figure 10.10, has a local oscillator at the transmitter site that generates a fixed-and-controlled frequency carrier between 88 and 108 MHz for the FM broadcast band. At the time the data (audio signal) is of zero amplitude, an FM modulator in the transmitter sends the carrier signal to the antenna at the same frequency as generated by the local oscillator. When the audio signal goes positive, the modulator causes the transmitted frequency to increase commensurately and conversely; when the data voltage goes negative, the transmitted frequency decreases below the basic carrier frequency.

This is a difficult thing for some to visualize because the carrier is an AC voltage of very high frequency and the audio also is an AC voltage but of much lower frequency. Because the FM modulator causes the transmitted frequency to rise and fall as the modulation signal changes amplitude, it is the frequency of the transmitted signal that undulates rather than its amplitude. Furthermore, it is difficult to sketch an FM signal, which is clear and yet near scale. Figure 10.10 portrays a typical square-wave data modulation signal rather than a typical audio-modulation situation. Note that when the data is at zero amplitude, the modulated signal is at the base-carrier or center frequency. When the data voltage is positive, the

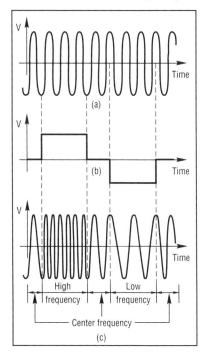

Fig. 10.10. The fixed-frequency, fixed-amplitude carrier signal (a) shifts about the center frequency by an amount that depends on modulating data signal (b). Combined signal (c) is the modulated output signal.

modulated signal frequency is some amount greater than the center frequency; when negative, the modulated signal is decreased in some amount from the center frequency. The demodulator in the receiver must extract the data by detecting and measuring the amount that the received frequency deviates from the center carrier frequency. It is unimportant to know how that is done.

FM, carrier is the data. In a popular rotational speed-measuring scheme, the shaft is outfitted with an incremental encoder. Encoder type is unimportant to this discussion. Because the measured shaft and the encoder shaft are physically coupled, output frequency of the encoder can be directly related to the shaft speed by an integer amount. The reasons for this have already been discussed. In this system, the data is in the frequency and when the encoder has 60 pulses/revolution, output frequency in Hz is exactly equal to shaft speed in rpm. Without doubt this is an FM system of data transmission. A common demodulation method is to simply input the FM signal into a digital electronic frequency meter, Figure 10.11, and read the speed.

Digitization of frequency. As stated earlier, frequency generation is a popular method of determining shaft rpm. The basic transducers are incremental encoders of the magnetic, Hall effect, or photo-optical encoding variety. The outputs of these devices are often referred to as being *digital signals* because they have only high or low values. This is erroneous, except to the extent that the signal is one bit of digital information. In speed or frequency measurement it is the frequency value that is sought. Frequency is an analog quantity and if it is to be interpreted by a digital controller, the frequency must be digitized. Electronic counting technology is the usual method of digitizing frequency.

The electronic, digital frequency meter or *electronic counter* as it is often called, uses a precise, crystal-controlled 1-MHz oscillator as its clock. Clock output is fed into a counter that can count to 10^6 and then reset to zero. Thus, the output of the million-to-one counter/divider produces a

Fig. 10.11. Block diagram of a digital frequency meter. The Master reset *forces the* Data counter registers *to all read 0. It also sets the* Million-to-one counter/divider *output high (1 level), gating the unknown frequency through the* AND *gate to the* Data counter registers. *One million cycles later, the* One-second gate *goes off with the* Data counter registers *holding the unknown frequency.*

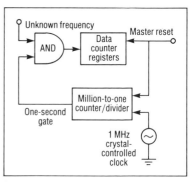

gate that is exactly 1-second long. It is also called a frequency-divider circuit because it accepts the clock frequency and outputs a frequency which is one-millionth of its input. Commercial counters use other divider ratios, which are usually panel-selectable. The example of a million-to-one is convenient, because it produces a 1-second gate.

The *Master reset*, Figure 10.11, is a bit that is set (usually from low to high) to start the digitization process. The Master reset all at once causes the counter/divider output to go high and sets all the registers in the data counter to zero. The counter/divider output remains high until one million input cycles have been received which happens to coincide with one second (1 MHz clock frequency). This precise, one-second gate is one input to a two-input AND gate, Figure 10.11. The one-second precision gate opens the AND gate so that unknown frequency cycles can be directed to the data counter.

The count in the data counter goes up by one digit each time a pulse is received from the unknown frequency signal. After one second has elapsed, the gate signal from the counter/divider goes to zero and stops any subsequent unknown signal pulses from reaching the data registers. At that instant, the count in the data registers is *frozen* with the number of unknown signal pulses that have entered the data counter in one second: the number of unknown cycles in one second. The frequency now is contained in the counter registers.

Commercial versions of electronic frequency meters usually provide a means for changing the internal gate time. That is, a one second gate and 1 MHz clock frequency are convenient for mental arithmetic because the combination produces a measure of frequency in Hz. An important disadvantage of this frequency measurement method, however, is that there is always a one-second delay between when the data acquisition process is initiated by the Master reset and when data is ultimately available. This may be prohibitively slow. In fact, in most electrohydraulic feedback control systems, a one-second data acquisition delay will render the control system useless.

To get around this problem, a shorter gate time, say 0.1 second instead of 1 second, is used. Now, there is only a 100-millisecond delay between Master reset and the availability of valid data. A shorter gate time produces further decreases in delay time, but resolution is lost unless clock frequency is increased. Note that with a 0.1-second gate, if the unknown frequency were, for example, 5 kHz, the data counter would accumulate only 500 counts in the gate time interval. The resolution of the digitization process would be 0.2% of reading. It is is easy to see that another decade of reduction in gate time would produce a tenfold increase in the resolution. This constitutes a random error in the measurement of the frequency.

The only way to maintain resolution is to increase clock frequency as gate time is reduced. But note that a 100-fold decrease in gate time must be offset by a 100-fold increase in clock frequency to maintain digital resolution at a target value.

Period digitization. An alternate method of digitizing a frequency signal is to use its period instead of its frequency. Many commercial electronic counters have the ability to switch from frequency to period measurement, but plug-in cards for digital computers and programmable logic controllers may not be so equipped without extensive software changes. It is true that as the frequency goes down, if one is to maintain a given digital resolution, the gate time must be increased if the clock frequency cannot be changed. In most counters, clock frequency **cannot** be changed, but gate-time change is commonly available. The result is that as the frequency to be measured and digitized gets lower, the delay time in data acquisition must increase; this quickly deteriorates into an untenable situation.

To circumvent the problem, it may be possible to measure the period of the incoming signal wherein the reciprocal of the frequency is digitized. That is the number of seconds or microseconds per cycle are measured rather than the number of cycles per second (Hz). To do so consists basically of swapping the unknown frequency of Figure 10.11 with the one-second gate, Figure 10.12. There, both the unknown input and the onboard precision 1 MHz clock are passed through Schmitt triggers to square them off. For period measurement, it helps to realize that the clock frequency is much higher than is the frequency of the incoming unknown. In fact it is absolutely necessary that that be true. Now, during one cycle of the unknown, several hundred or thousand clock pulses will pass. Noth-

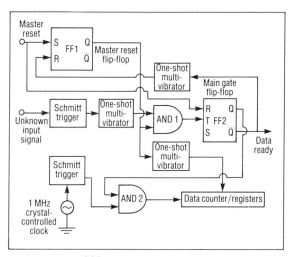

Fig. 10.12. The period-measurement function determines the number of clock cycles that occur in one cycle of the unknown-frequency input. This strategy maintains resolution without increasing data acquisition delay when the unknown frequency is low.

ing happens until receipt of a Master reset.

Master reset is *latched up* into its own flip-flop. The Q output is one input to *AND* 1 and arms it for the next pulse to come from the unknown input. Note that the Master reset also goes to reset the data counter/register at the same time that it arms *AND* 1, and Master reset also resets the Main-gate flip-flop. With *AND* 1 armed, the very next unknown input pulse causes the Main gate flip-flop to toggle from off to on. The second unknown input pulse toggles the Main gate flip-flop from on to off. In this manner, there is a voltage at the Q output which is high for one complete input period and then goes low thereafter.

When *FF* 2 switches from high to low, note that its $\overline{Q}$ output switches from low to high. The leading edge of the $\overline{Q}$ signal is detected with the one-shot multivibrator whose output goes to reset the Master reset flip-flop. This disables the entire measurement process until another Master reset signal occurs. However, after Master reset, the very next unknown input pulse is directed to the Main-gate RTS flip-flop, *FF* 2. With its Q output high, *AND* 2 is armed, allowing subsequent shaped clocked pulses to increment the Data counter/register.

Eventually, another unknown input pulse is received which can pass through armed *AND* 1 and cause the Main-gate RTS flip-flop to toggle to its reset state. It is at that instant, as explained before, that the leading edge of the $\overline{Q}$ output is sent to reset the Master reset flip-flop which locks out any further action until another Master reset. At that time, the Data counter holds the number of microseconds that elapsed during one complete cycle of the unknown input wave. That, of course, is the period of the unknown.

The interrogating device needs only to look at the $\overline{Q}$ output of *FF* 2 and whenever that voltage is high, valid data is in the Data register. Note that the total elapsed time between the receipt of the Master reset and the availability of data is not more than two complete cycles of the unknown input signal. The disadvantage of this system is that the amount of data acquisition delay is a function of the period of the data. This can be a problem when attempting to improve the responsiveness of a speed-control system.

Frequency-to-voltage conversion. If one is interested in remaining in the analog world instead of converting to the digital world, it is possible to convert the frequency of interest into a proportional voltage using the frequency-to-voltage conversion process. It is purely an analog process and like its digitizing cousin, there are time delays involved. These time delays may be invisible to the unwary, and therefore more insidious. An incoming frequency signal is first fed into a Schmitt trigger, Figure 10.13(a), to shape the arbitrary input waveshape into a square wave.

In general, incoming signal e_i, Figure 10.13(b), will vary in amplitude and frequency, but it is the frequency data that is of interest for conver-

263

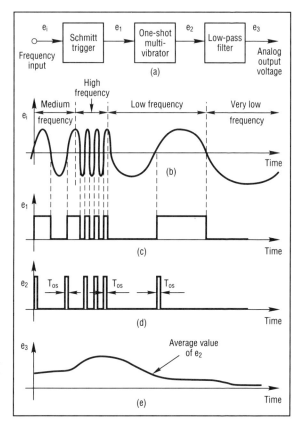

Fig. 10.13. Block diagram, (a), of a frequency-to-voltage converter produces analog DC output that is proportional to the input frequency but is delayed in time.

sion. Note that the Schmitt trigger not only squares the incoming signal but also generates a constant amplitude while the frequency is unaltered, Figure 10.13(c). The one-shot multivibrator is the device that really does the frequency-to-voltage conversion. Recall that the one-shot multivibrator receives an incoming pulse (it detects the leading edge of the incoming signal) and produces an output of exactly the same frequency, although on-time duration [T_{os}, Figure 10.13(d)], of the output pulse is the same from cycle to cycle. As subsequent pulses of fixed on-time get closer and closer, the average value of the voltage rises. As pulses get farther apart, the average voltage decreases.

In this fashion, the value of analog output voltage e_3, Figure 10.13(e), is linearly proportional to the frequency of e_i. Of course, raw output from one-shot multivibrator e_2 is filled with pulses. To smooth them, a low-pass filter must be used. This filter has substantial delay and can be detrimental in feedback control systems. There are a number of commercial frequency-to-voltage converters available on the market and before they are used in any feedback control system, the manufacturer should be consulted regarding time delays in the instrument. Published catalog data usually is evasive on this issue. There are models that often cost more money which are faster, but it is impossible to measure frequency without some amount of time delay in data acquisition.

Frequency-measurement summary. It should be apparent now that there is no way to use frequency data to measure speed without time delay. Furthermore, the amount of delay depends upon the hardware and in some instances, it depends upon the data as well. In feedback control of speed or flow, for example, it may be necessary to use frequency measurement for speeds in one range and period measurement in another range. Regardless, frequency generation remains a popular and cost-effective way to determine speed. Some investigations into the suitability of frequency methods should be made. Note that the tachometric methods of speed measurement do not have these time delays. These methods should be evaluated in critical speed- or flow-measurement situations.

Noise control in electronic systems

Electronic system noise control is more art than science, and its elimination is appropriately referred to as a *witch hunt*. Electronic noise is broadly defined as any unwanted variation in signal. The root of the term *noise* harkens back to the early days of telephony and radio when noise literally meant audible sounds through the headset or speaker. Certainly, the term retains that interpretation today and all of us know of the background noise that is associated with certain conditions in telephones and radio.

But now, noise has become a more generic term that refers to any unwanted signal regardless of whether it is audible or not. Control-system noise may be audible but it also may give evidence to its presence in an unexpected and/or unwanted twitch or vibration in a positional servomechanism, unexplained variation in manufacturing uniformity, or puzzling vibrations in some output member. The best approach to reducing noise to a tolerable level (theoretically it cannot be eliminated) is to identify its source. Generally, there are four common noise sources that should be considered at design time and at debugging time:

- electrostatic interference (ESI)
- electromagnetic interference (EMI)
- radio frequency interference (RFI), and
- ground loop.

Identification of the type of noise is crucial because each method of control is different. Most non-electronic engineers who have had to deal with noise find that it is unpredictable and therefore unmanageable. The problem is that in one instance, the source may have been ESI that can be controlled with proper shielding and grounding, and in a later situation the source was EMI that cannot be controlled with shielding and grounding. Yet the symptoms, especially when associated with the 60 Hz power-line frequency, are identical.

GENERAL RULES FOR CONTROLLING NOISE

These recommendations should be followed when constructing any electronic equipment for use in an industrial environment — an environment considered to be especially noisy:

● connect all electronic components so that the ground, low side, or circuit common all tie together. Never swap leads to change an algebraic sign, which may be necessary to correctly phase a servo loop, for example, unless the output is truly differential. Most electronic signals **are not** differential — they are single-ended. On the other hand, there are some situations where neither side of a receiving device is grounded, such as the coils of a servovalve. It is permissible to swap the leads of a servovalve in order to change the algebraic sign of the servo loop. Proportional valve-coil leads can be swapped but **only if there is no spool feedback position transducer**

● do not run AC power lines in the vicinity of electronic data lines. The current levels in the AC power lines usually are sufficiently high to cause their magnetic fields to couple into the data lines. If that is the case, electronic devices, such as servo and proportional valves and their amplifiers, most likely will respond

● run all signal (data) lines in twisted, shielded pairs

● run the AC power lines in twisted, shielded pairs, too

● consider a 4-20 mA current loop when data transmission distances exceed about 20 feet

● encase AC power lines in iron (not aluminum) conduit. Of course, the conduit is the shield, and

● connect the electronic circuit common to power ground (mother earth) only when necessary and only at one physical point in the entire electronic part of the measurement chain. When this rule has to be violated because component manufacturers have provided built-in grounding, follow the recommendations contained in the later parts of this chapter.

PARASITIC CAPACITANCE AND
ELECTROSTATIC INTERFERENCE

As stated in an earlier chapter, capacitance arises any time two conductors are separated by a dielectric. Of course, electronic equipment is built of conductors and those conductors most generally are separated by a dielectric — the insulation and the atmosphere between them. Therefore, all electronic equipment has *parasitic* capacitance. It is called parasitic because it exists merely because the circuit exists; there is just no way to build a circuit without it. As with hydraulic capacitance that arises because of fluid compressibility, capacitance is parasitic because no one has figured out a way to build hydraulic equipment without having an enclosed, compressible volume of fluid.

Parasitic capacitance of electronic circuits can be the cause of induced noise, expecially at power-line frequencies. Figure 10.14 shows a representation of how the power lines, the parasitic capacitance, and an electronic device (an amplifier) interact to create a noisy system. Note and understand that the capacitances in Figures 10.14, 10.15, and 10.16 represent real capacitances that exist and can be measured, but that they **do not** represent capacitors that have been hard-wired into the circuit. These capacitances are not pieces of hardware; the circuit must be viewed as an analytical schematic rather than the usual hardware schematic familiar to the fluid power practitioner. The capacitances exist only because on one has found a way to build the circuit without this type interaction.

In Figure 10.14, the power company is represented by the AC alterna-

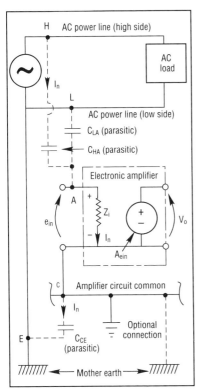

Fig. 10.14. Parasitic capacitance exists merely because of circuit construction and proximity of one circuit to another. There is parasitic capacitance C_{HA} between power line high side H and amplifier input terminal A. Due to the potential difference, small noise current I_n travels through C_{HA}, amplifier impedance Z_{in}, and returns to mother earth and the power company through parasitic capacitance C_{CE}. The voltage drop across Z_{in}, due to I_{in}, is amplified and appears at the output of the amplifier as 60 Hz noise voltage. The amount of noise in V_o depends upon physical distance, Z_{in}, and amplifier gain A. Note that if the optional earth connection is used, total parasitic impedance diminishes, raising I_n, creating a higher noise voltage.

267

tor in the upper left-hand corner, the mother-earth grounding connection in the lower left-hand corner, and the power lines and arbitrary load across the top. The amount of capacitance is very small, leading to a very high capacitive impedance, perhaps as high as 10^9 Ω. Amplifier input impedance, Z_{in}, may be about 100 kΩ.

Using the 10^9 Ω estimate for the parasitic impedance, and line voltage at 110-V RMS (about 311 volts peak-to-peak), there will be an AC current, the result of 311 volts divided by 10^9 Ω, or about 0.311 μA. That current, upon passing through the 100 kΩ input impedance will develop a voltage drop of about 31 mV (using Ohm's law). Depending upon the gain of the amplifier and a number of downstream factors, the induced noise voltage may be palpable.

This phenomenon is most dramatically demonstrated with an ordinary oscilloscope with the vertical sensitivity set to about one volt/centimeter or maybe a little less. Connect a lead onto the high side of the scope input and hold the lead in hand while observing the trace. It is not unusual to see a deflection of several volts. The amount of deflection depends upon the wiring in the vicinity of the scope, and the induced noise voltage is definitely increased by the presence of flourescent lights.

In analyzing this situation, the lead and the human hanging onto it are sometimes referred to as an *antenna*. This is technically incorrect because an antenna picks up an electromagnetic wave, whereas this phenomenon is electrostatic. The human is one plate of a capacitor and touching the wire puts that plate in touch with the lead and a human has more capacitor area than the wire. Therefore when dropping the wire, the amount of scope deflection decreases. This is similar to the reaction when one touches the antenna of an AM radio tuned to a weak station. The audio level increases but in this case the events have a different origin.

To test whether the induced noise is a capacitive (electrostatic) effect or an electromagnetic efect, one need only connect the low side of the oscilloscope to mother earth. If ESI is the culprit, the amplitude of the noise on the scope will increase, assuming that the low side of the scope input is not connected internally to mother earth. This is because parasitic capacitance C_{CE} has been shorted out, reducing the total capacitive impedance, increasing the current, increasing the voltage drop across Z_{in}, and resulting in a higher voltage. Were the effects caused by electromagnetic induction, grounding the scope to mother earth would have no effect.

To carry this investigation a bit further, in Figure 10.15 the scope (the electronic amplifier) has been connected to some source. Like all sources, it has output impedance R_S. Recall that the ideal voltage source has low impedance; if that be the case, R_S might be in the order of say, 10 Ω. Immediately the scope will show that all the noise voltage is gone! The reason can be seen looking at the path that noise current I_n must take from the high side of the power-company line to mother earth. Note that in passing through C_{HA} and entering the scope lead, the noise current can take one of two paths: it can go through the high impedance of the scope (usually about 1 MΩ) or it can go through the low impedance of signal source the R_S.

Clearly, the current will go through the signal source, it will produce very little voltage drop, and there will be no apparent noise on the scope signal. Even when you touch the high-signal side of the scope, the noise deflection will not be measurable. Bear in mind that this would not be true if source impedance R_S were large, say of the same order of magnitude as the scope input impedance. This further argues in favor of low-impedance sources as being the best matchup for high input-impedance voltage amplifiers.

Electrostatic shielding

To counteract the electrostatic effects of parasitic capacitance, the amplifer is placed inside a conducting case called a shield, Figure 10.16. The amplifer, literally, is placed inside a box. Note that the box need only

Fig. 10.15. When amplifier input is connected to a signal source that has low source resistance R_S, *there is a tiny increase in noise currrent. A significant noise reduction benefit is achieved, however, because low-source resistance* R_S, *diverts the major part of noise current* I_{ns} *away from high-input impedance* Z_{in}. *There is less noise voltage across* Z_{in}, *and consequently, lesss noise voltage at the amplifier output. Therefore, merely by connecting a low-resistance signal source to the voltage amplifier of and by itself, can have a 1000:1 noise reduction component leaving the amplifier input open.*

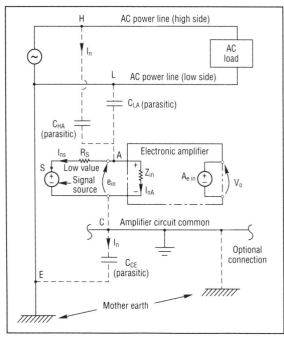

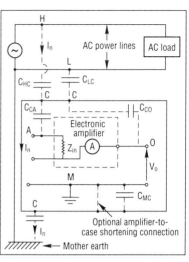

Fig. 10.16. When the amplifier is enclosed in a conducting case, noise current I_n, due to power line-to-amplifier parasitic capacitance is made to totally bypass Z_{in}, thus perfectly nullifying its effects. In doing this, however, an unwanted feedback path is created through C_{CA} and C_{CO}. All capacitances are parasitic.

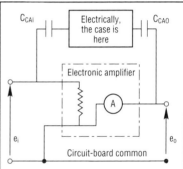

Fig. 10.17. Because of the encasing shield, parasitic capacitances C_{CAI} and C_{CAO} create a feedback path that can cause the high-gain amplifier to break into oscillation.

be a conductor; it does not have to be magnetic. Immediately, the shielding case provides a direct short circuit around the amplifier so that noise current due to parasitic capacitance completely bypasses the amplifier input terminals. The detrimental effect of power line-to-amplifier capacitance is absolutely cancelled. That's the good news.

The bad news is that now there is a substantial parasitic capacitance between the output terminal of the amplifier and the large area of the enclosing case. Plus there is a parasitic capacitance from that same case to the input terminal of the amplifier. This capacitance forms a feedback path from output to input, Figure 10.17. High-gain amplifiers, of which servo- and proportional-valve amplifiers are a part, are known to break into oscillation due to parasitic feedback. Oscillation frequency is several hundred to a few kHz. The symptoms are that the system responds sluggishly, and increases in gain do not improve responsiveness.

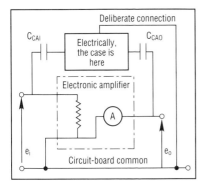

Fig. 10.18. Connecting the circuit-board common directly to the enclosing case kills the parasitic feedback and reduces the tendency for the amplifier to break into oscillation. It does not, however, kill parasitic capacitances C_{CAI} and C_{CAO}.

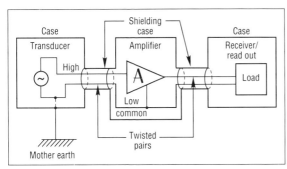

Fig. 10.19. Ideally, the electronic chain is totally encased in conducting shields and enclosures. All shields and cases must be electronically continuous and must be connnected to the shield at one or more points. Finally, if a mother-earth connection is to be made, it must be made at one point only.

The insidious part of this malfunction is that the effects cannot be seen with any DC measuring instruments; an oscilloscope is the only way to diagnose the problem. Adding to the insidiousness is that the response of the system mimics the performance of a contaminated servovalve. There is a way to prevent the oscillation problem, but the contamination problem is a matter for other study.

Killing the parasitic feedback path. Addition of the enclosing case got rid of the line-to-amplifier parasitic coupling but it created a new parasitic path that can lead to amplifier oscillation. That problem can be eliminated by making a deliberate connection from the common side of the amplifier board (card) directly to the encasing shield, Figure 10.18. This connection couples the input and output parasitic capacitances that are shorted to circuit common. Note that this is not mother earth here; this is only circuit-board common, the return point on the card, the center tap of the power-supply transformer. Now observe in Figure 10.18 that any current that enters C_{CAO} due to output voltage e_o is directed to common, rather than into C_{CAI}. This means that the parasitic feedback path has been effectively killed. The rule is simple: **always** place all electronic devices in a totally enclosing, conducting case and then connect the circuit board common to the case.

Shielding the electronic chain. To prevent undesirable effects of parasitic capacitance, it is necessary to enclose the entire electronic chain within the shield, Figure 10.19. Each element in the chain is placed within its own box or case and the cases connected together through the interconnecting shielded cable. The nature of the shielding is not critical from a technical point of view: it only is necessary that the shielding be a conductor. When each electronic component is in a separate case, a physical connection must be made from the cabling shield to the cases at both ends of the cable. Note that if a connection to mother earth is made, it should be at one point only.

GROUND LOOPS — CAUSE AND CONTROL

Electrical power companies always connect one terminal of their alternators to mother earth for reasons of safety. The side of the alternator connected to earth is called the *low side* of the power line. The low side also is carried by a physical wire between the alternator and the user site, Figure 10.20(a). Because the earth is a conductor, the low side of the line actually has some redundancy to it. That is, it is possible for the low wire to break, Figure 10.20(b), and yet a user's electrical apparatus will work because one side of the appliance is likewise connected to mother earth. Of course, electrical wiring codes require that the user's site be connected that way.

Note that should the low side of the power-transmission line break somewhere between the alternator and the user's site, current can still be delivered to the user's appliance but it most likely will be reduced because of the impedance of the earth path. With good earth conductivity, the user may not even detect the fault. The aim here is to show that under not-so-rare circumstances, substantial current can be in the earth at a

Fig. 10.20. Because there are earth connections at the alternator as well as at the user end (a), a user's appliances will still function if there is a break in the low-side line because of the earth's conductivity (b). In that case, however, appliance operation will most likely be at less than optimum performance

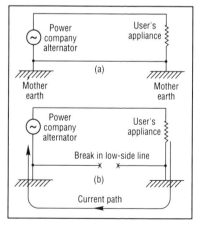

given point because of ground wire faults.

A ground loop exists whenever an electronic circuit is constructed so that the earth-borne current can find its way into the electronic-shielding system, Figure 10.21. All it takes is connection of the electronic system shielding to mother earth at more than one point in the electronic chain. Assume that this system is set up in a region where there are ground currents, I_g. Note that circuit common is connected to the shielding at points A and B, and that there are also *Earth connections* 1 and 2 as well. Although there is current I_g in the earth path, the earth is an imperfect conductor.

As a result, when the current arrives at the site of the first connection it is offered two paths: continue through the high impedance earth, or follow the very low resistance of the shield. The lower-resistance path will carry the bulk of the current. Regardless of how low the shield's impedance may be, it is not zero; there is some resistance R_{wire}. Ground currents can be on the order of a few amperes to hundreds of amperes depending upon local conditions. This shield current will create a voltage drop which will be felt at the input of the amplifier and will be amplified and sent down the electronic chain.

The obvious correction to the ground loop problem is to eliminate one of the earth connections. Then any ground currents are forced to remain in the earth where they belong. Understand that electrostatic noise and ground loop noise will generate signals in the electronics that are at line frequency, and it will not be apparent at troubleshooting time which type noise prevails in a given situation. Furthermore, if only one earth connection has been made but some manufacturers have internally grounded their equipment, another ground connection may be in place either through the electrical wiring or even through hydraulic and/or water plumbing. Do not assume that the only ground connections are those you have made or that are plainly visible.

Fig. 10.21. When improper practice has been followed and two connections have been made to earth, ground currents prefer the shield path with its lower resistance rather than earth resistance R_g. Current through the shield's resistance creates a small voltage drop that will be amplified, creating 60 Hz noise in the electronic signals. The electronic chain should never be connected to earth ground at more than one point.

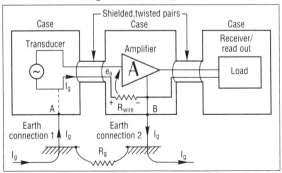

have made or that are plainly visible.

DIFFERENTIAL SIGNAL TRANSMISSION

The differential amplifier discussed earlier does not have a low- and high-signal side as does the more common single-ended amplifier. The differential amplifier has two input and output lines but neither is at board common, so the user has the option of interconnecting them to other differential devices in one of two ways. This permits a change of algebraic sign and it also offers improved noise immunity in the presence of ground loops. The noise immunity to ground loops arises because ground loop current in the shields is common to the amplifier inputs.

That means that the case voltage may be undulating at several volts because of the ground current, and the amplifier inputs may likewise be following the ground current. But because both input lines are going up and down in unison while the amplifier operates, the **differential** voltage output contains almost no ground-loop noise. It is true that when multiple connections to earth cannot be avoided, it may be necessary to design an instrumentation system which is differential rather than single-ended. Specialists in this technology should be consulted should this become necessary.

OPTO-ISOLATION

Opto-isolation makes use of light waves to interconnect a sending and a receiving device. When ground loop noise is severe and differential amplifiers are not practical, it may be necessary to optically isolate one component from another, Figure 10.22. For unstated reasons, the electronic chain has two points connected to mother earth. *OIT* and *OIR* are the optical transmitting and receiving devices respectively. The transmitter is usually an LED whose intensity is affected by the amplitude of its current. The receiver is a photo transistor whose collector current is affected by the light intensity impinging upon its exposed base material. In this way it is possible to couple data from the sender to the receiver without a direct electrical connection. The advantage of this is that there is an extremely large impedance offered to the ground current so that it prefers to stay within the earth path and not be diverted to the shield.

ELECTROMAGNETIC INTERFERENCE

Current in one circuit creates magnetic flux which links with the magnetic flux of another circuit to produce electromagnetic interference or noise. When the rate of change of flux is sufficiently great, a palpable noise can be felt in the linked circuit. There are no easy solutions to EMI. Only use of good design and fabrication practices will help minimize the problem. It is possible to control the receiving circuit to minimize the amount of flux linkage between it and whatever the source may be. This is done by

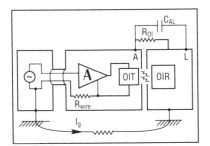

Fig. 10.22. Opto-isolation eliminates the ground loop problem even when receiving and transmitting ends are grounded, because the majority of ground current I_g passes through the relatively low resistance of earth path R_g rather than through very high opto-isolator resistance R_{OI}. The ground-loop problem is thus solved with opto-isolators.

always keeping signal lines away from power lines and always running the signal lines as twisted pairs. The twisting of the signal wires:
● reduces the amount of cross-sectional area that the wires encircle and minimizes the amount of flux linkage that otherwise may exist, and
● alternates the direction of each consecutive loop in the wires so that if there is a magnetically induced voltage in one twist, it will be offset by a voltage of the opposite phase induced in the adjacent twist.
It is emphasized that twisted pairing of wires is always the best practice.

Attempts should be made to reduce the amount of magnetic radiation at its source. For example, the most common source of 60 Hz magnetic radiation is the field created around current-carrying conductors. The higher the current, the greater the amount of magnetic flux and the greater the likihood that there will be an EMI voltage induced in any electronic equipment in the vicinity. Approaches to reduce this magnetic radiation include:
● twisting all power lines just like signal lines. This helps because the flux caused by the current in one conductor cancels the flux created by the opposite-going current in the mating conductor. This is true even for three-phase power lines as long as all three lines are twisted together, and
● encasing all power lines in **iron** conduits. This helps confine the magnetic field to the conduit, preventing its linkage with sensitive electronic circuits.

Many time there are unencased three-phase power lines in the industrial environment. It is possible to locate them with an ordinary portable AM radio receiver. Tune the receiver to a frequency where there is no signal and then walk around, converging on those places where the 60-Hz noise from the receiver is loudest. Those places are the source of the powerline-based magnetic fields.

RADIO-FREQUENCY INTERFERENCE

Radio-frequency interference can come from a multitude of sources:
● bona fide radio signals radiated by a nearby radio, TV, or radar station. Attempts to nip these generators at their sources are sure to be met with

derision if not hostility, and

● RF that is radiated when electrical contacts open or close with an arc. There is no specific frequency. Instead the signals are broad band containing thousands of frequencies. Because they can be of short wavelength, twisting and shielding signal wires may alleviate the problem. Controlling the problem is not at all a systematic process. One method is to use arc-suppression devices on relay and starter contacts, and to put varistors in series with AC coils to reduce inrush current. In extreme cases, it may be necessary to run separate power lines and transformers from the electrical substation because the short wavelength RF will sometimes find its way into the electronics through the power wiring. The wiring acts as a waveguide and directs the energy right to the place where it is not wanted. The symptoms of RF interference are usually the twitching of a servoaxis or sudden jump in a data display indicator that correlates with starting a motor or energizing an on-off solenoid.

Chapter Eleven
Physical Principles of Transduction — Part I

Every transducer uses a particular physical principle for its operation. A change of some variable causes a reaction in the transducer's sensing element that can be detected. For example, internal pressure applied to a tube causes an observable, resultant deformation of the tube. When the tube is semicircular, a small deformation of the tube produces a large movement of the tube tip. This transduction principle drives the popular Bourdon tube pressure gage. Another transduction example is the turbine flow meter: fluid moving past a propeller turns the propeller.

The following discussion explains some of the various physical phenomena used in commercial transducers. The insights gained will help the practitioner judge the suitability of a given transducer and will help in studying the nature of output signals for the measurement and control chain. The output signal dictates the nature of the necessary signal conditioning and thereby determines, or at least limits the way interfacing must be done.

CHANGES IN ELECTRICAL PROPERTIES
Thousands of commercial transducers take advantage of changes in the electrical properties of an element to produce a usable output. The advantage of using electrical properties for sensing purposes is that the support equipment must have an electrical component, and the output is an electrical signal that can be fed to one of several electronic signal conditioners. There are only three electrical properties that must be dealt with while considering transducers: resistance, inductance, and capacitance.

Resistance changes
The resistance of a given conductor depends upon its dimensions and its resistivity, a physical property of the conducting material:

$$R = \rho L/A, \tag{11.1}$$

where R is the resistance in ohms, ρ is the resistivity, L is the length of the conductor, and A is the conductor's cross-sectional area (assumed to be uniform over length L) through which electrical charges pass. In Equation (11.1), see that there are only three possible ways a resistance can change: change in resistivity, change in length, and change in cross-sectional area.

All conducting and semiconducting materials have a thermal-sensitivity property. That is, when the temperature of the material changes, its resistivity does too. The resistivity of metals increases with increased temperature, but the temperature coefficient of resistance in the resistive films used in many commercial-grade fixed resistors is negative. This, then, results in a decrease in resistance with a temperature increase for these films.

Semiconductors also exhibit a negative temperature coefficient of resistance but the rate of resistance change with temperature is much greater than with film. When commercialized, these semiconductor devices are called thermistors, Figure 11.1(a). They undergo large increases in resistance for small temperature changes and thus can be used as temperature transducers with proper calibration.

Semiconductors also are sensitive to the amount of light energy directed at them. That is, simply exposing the semiconductor to photons causes its resistivity to change. As light intensity increases, the semiconductor conducts more readily because its resistance decreases. The change in resistance can be detected as a change in current or a change in voltage; the commercial version is a photo resistor, Figure 11.1(b). Cou-

Fig. 11.1. Thermistor R_t and photo resistor R_p can be used in voltage-divider circuits as a temperature transducer, (a), or light detector, (b).

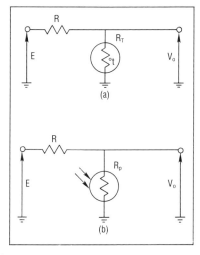

pled with a voltage source and a voltmeter or ammeter, the device becomes a usable photo detector.

Thermistors are completely encased in opaque envelopes that eliminate possible photonic effects. On the other hand, the photo resistor cannot be insulated from temperature changes, so it becomes necessary to ensure that no significant temperature change takes place in the environment of the resistor. Lacking that, the temperature change can be measured and a mathematical correction applied to detector output.

Geometric factors such as conductor length and cross-sectional area are used to make resistance changes in strain gages, Figure 11.2. Stretching a conductor of length L and area A makes the resistor longer while reducing its area, and results in an increased resistance. Conversely, squeezing the conductor from the ends makes it shorter and bigger around, decreasing its resistance. These resistance changes are typically

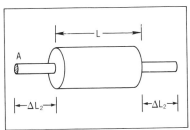

Fig. 11.2. When a conductor is stretched, its length increases while the area of its cross-section decreases. The smaller area increases the resistance of the conductor.

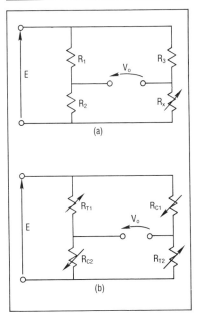

Fig. 11.3. Geometrically induced resistance changes are detected with a single active-arm bridge circuit (a), or a four active-arm bridge circuit, (b).

less than 0.2% of the total resistance of the element. To detect such small changes, a bridge circuit, Figure 11.3, is necessary.

Strained resistor R_x, Figure 11.3(a), is in a circuit called a *single active-arm bridge* circuit; resistors R_1, R_2, and R_3 complete the bridge. When this strain gage is used, the three resistors that complete the bridge usually are unstressed strain gages called *dummy gages* for obvious reasons. When R_x is unstressed, all four resistors are nominally the same and output voltage V_o is nominally zero.

But when R_x is strained or stretched, the bridge becomes unbalanced and produces a measurable output voltage. This voltage can be calibrated against the strain-inducing phenomenon and the result is a usable transducer. This is the principle that pressure transducers, force transducers (load cells), torque transducers, and drag-body flowmeters use.

Commercial transducers do not use the single active-gage bridge because the circuit lacks sensitivity. The alternative is the four active-arm bridge circuit, Figure 11.3(b). In this configuration with no strain in any gage, the four resistors nominally are identical in value and the bridge is in balance; there is no output voltage. The four gages must be arranged so they all experience the same temperature to automatically compensate for temperature sensitivity.

Furthermore, the gages must be arranged and mounted on the strained member so they experience different levels of strain. Ideally, resistors RT_1 and RT_2 experience tension while RC_1 and RC_2 experience compression. Now, when the measurand is applied, two gages undergo an increase in resistance while the others undergo a decrease in resistance. When arranged as shown in Figure 11.3(b), the bridge produces the maximum possible output voltage for a given strain and the circuit sensitivity is four times greater than in the single active-arm bridge circuit. The sensitivity of commercial transducers usually is given in millivolts of bridge output V_o per volt of supply voltage E when the transducer is subjected to rated, full-scale value of the measurand.

Note the construction and configuration of several versions of the SR-4 strain gage, Figure 11.4. This gage is available in single-, double-, and triple-element configurations, usually with resistance values of 120 or 300 Ω. Bridge supply voltage typically is limited to a maximum of about 12 volts.

Temperature variations affect a bridge circuit in two ways. First, there can be a zero shift because one gage is at a different temperature than the others. That is why it is desirable for all the gages to be at the same temperature. If all gages are of the same material and at the same temperature, the bridge circuit inherently rejects temperature variation as it affects zero or null. On the other hand, current through the resistors affects the sensitivity of the bridge: its gain, or volts of output per unit of measurand input.

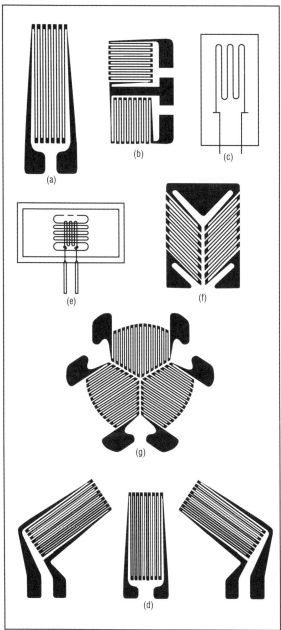

Fig. 11.4. SR-4™ strain gages are available in single-element, (a) and (c), dual-element (b), (e), and (f), or triple-element configurations, (d) and (g). Multiple-element gages measure strain along different axes of the strained member.

Courtesy of BLH Electronics, Inc.

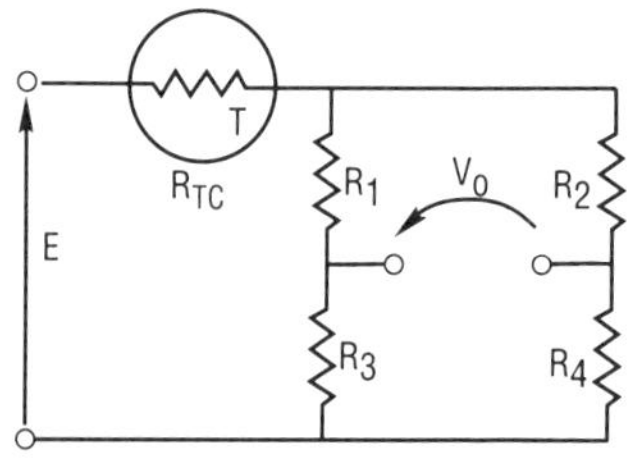

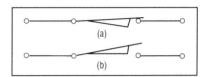

Fig. 11.5. Temperature-compensation resistor R_{TC} *has a negative temperature coefficient so that its resistance rises as gage temperature falls and vice versa. Thus transducer sensitivity does not change with temperature. The bridge circuit inherently compensates for thermal zero shift when all gages are at the same temperature.*

Fig. 11.6. An on-off switch changes resistance from zero to infinity when going from closed to open.

Secondly, temperature changes affect total resistance, current, and sensitivity. To compensate for sensitivity changes, a small resistance with a negative temperature coefficient-of-resistance is connected in series with the bridge, Figure 11.5, so total resistance and sensitivity remain constant over the usable temperature range. The process of matching the R_{TC} to the bridge is called *temperature compensation*. In spite of these efforts the result is always less than perfect, so a statement about the sensitivity to temperature variations of gain (sometimes called span) and zero comes with commercial transducers.

Lastly, a common device that makes use of resistance change to create a usable output is the simple on-off switch, Figure 11.6. Clearly, there are only two possible switch states, because it only can be fully open (infinite resistance) or fully closed (zero resistance).

Inductance and inductive coupling changes

Variations in magnetic properties also are used to make transducers. A conceptually simple device is the eddy-current detector that uses Lenz's Law. This law says that a voltage will be induced whenever a conductor is placed in a time-varying or AC magnetic field. The AC magnetic field, Figure 11.7, is created by a coil excited by an AC source. In practical applications using this principle, the AC source is a local electronic oscillator running at several kHz. The source powers a coil which produces a time-varying magnetic field around it.

If a conductor approaches that magnetic field, an *eddy current* is induced in that conductor and circulates as indicated, Figure 11.7. Because the conductor is imperfect, there is a small power loss and the conductor's temperature will rise. The energy causing the power loss must come from the the AC source so the current must increase slightly. Any

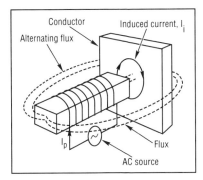

Fig. 11.7. Alternating flux creates an in-duced current in a nearby conductor. This results in a change in primary cur-rent which can be calibrated in terms of distance between the coil and the con-ductor.

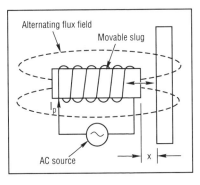

Fig. 11.8. As ferromagnetic member moves closer to coil, inductance in-creases so primary current goes down. Inductance can be calibrated to mea-sure the distance between the movable member and the coil.

increase in primary current I_p, Figure 11.7, indicates the conductor's presence. The eddy-current principle is used in metal detectors. Note that the conducting material need not be ferromagnetic; it only need be a conductor.

Because the the distance between the coil and the conductor affects the amount of current in the primary winding, it is possible to calibrate the primary current-change to distance and the device then constitutes a usable position transducer. Commercial versions have been developed that can measure a distance of less than 0.100 in. They have been used to measure paint thickness as well as main-spool position of a servovalve during frequency-response testing of the valve. Such a transducer is called an *eddy-current detector*.

A similar application of magnetism for sensing, Figure 11.8, uses the fact that when a ferromagnetic material is placed in an alternating magnetic field, net inductance of the primary winding increases. As this inductance increases, primary current I_p decreases. This current can be calibrated against the distance between the coil and the ferromagnetic material and the device becomes a position transducer. These are called *variable reluctance* transducers, because the reluctance or resistance to magnetic flux is the physical quantity that varies.

A variation of the variable-reluctance transducer has two coils whose magnetic fields aid one another, Figure 11.9. In the gap between them is a movable, detectable magnetic material that, when perfectly centered between the two coils, results in equal inductances, $L_A = L_B$. Note that these coils are connected as a bridge circuit, with R_A and R_B forming the other two legs of the bridge.

R_A and R_B are selected to be equal and when the two inductances are equal, the bridge is balanced and output voltage V_o is zero. Should the magnetic material move closer to one coil than the other, one inductance will increase while the other will decrease, unbalancing the bridge. This imbalance results in a non-zero output voltage which can be calibrated against the position of the magnetic material.

This principle has been successfully applied to make a variable-reluctance differential-pressure transducer where the magnetic material is a diaphragm subjected to the pressure differential. Pressurized deflection of the diaphragm unbalances the bridge, resulting in usable output voltage. Calibration completes the process.

Two basic schemes of inductance changes can convert transformers into transducers. The first inductance-change scheme uses fixed-position primary and secondary coils and relies upon a moveable ferromagnetic

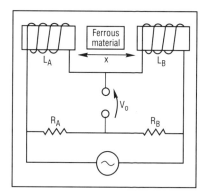

Fig. 11.9. Variable-reluctance transducer measures amount of AC bridge unbalanced voltage V_o as function of the position of a ferromagnetic material moving between two coils.

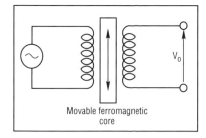

Fig. 11.10. Changing slug position changes the amount of magnetic coupling between primary and secondary windings; output voltage depends upon slug position.

core to vary the magnetic coupling, Figure 11.10. As the transformer core or *slug* moves into and out of the alternating magnetic field, the amount of coupling changes. Consequently, secondary output voltage V_o varies as well. It is apparent that upon proper calibration, the device is a position transducer. Furthermore, there is nothing to stop a user from mounting the core on the end of a Bourdon tube, for example, to create a pressure transducer.

The commercial version of the moving-core variable transformer, called a *linear-variable-differential-transformer* or LVDT, uses two secondary windings, Figure 11.11. The secondary windings are connected so that with the slug positioned precisely at the magnetic center of the flux field, the two secondary voltages will be equal but of opposite phase for zero output voltage. With the slug magnetically centered, output voltage of the *A* winding is the same amplitude as output voltage from the *B* winding but of opposite phase. At every instant in time, the sum of the two voltages is zero. When this is the case, the center position is called the null point.

Now if the slug moves up from center, there is greater magnetic coupling between the primary and the *A* secondary and less between the primary and the *B* secondary. This results in non-zero output V_o with the same phase as the *A*-winding voltage. On the other hand, if the slug moves down, the *B*-winding output voltage is greater than the *A*-winding output — again creating non-zero total output voltage V_o with a phase the same as that of the *B*-winding voltage.

Finally, see that the amplitude of the output voltage is a measure of how far the slug has moved from its center position, while the phase of the output indicates whether the slug has moved from center in one direction or the other. The output voltage signal undergoes a $180°$ phase change when the null is passed, Figure 11.12.

The second inductance-change scheme uses either a moving primary or secondary coil to cause a change in the degree of magnetic coupling between the two coils, Figure 11.13. Here, the variable transformer has

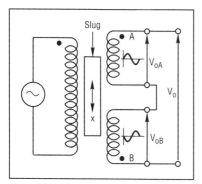

Fig. 11.11. LVDT uses dual secondary windings in series subtractively. Thus, output voltage is zero with the slug magnetically centered.

been made so one winding can move. The most common commercial version of this is the family of devices called *synchros* and *synchro re-*

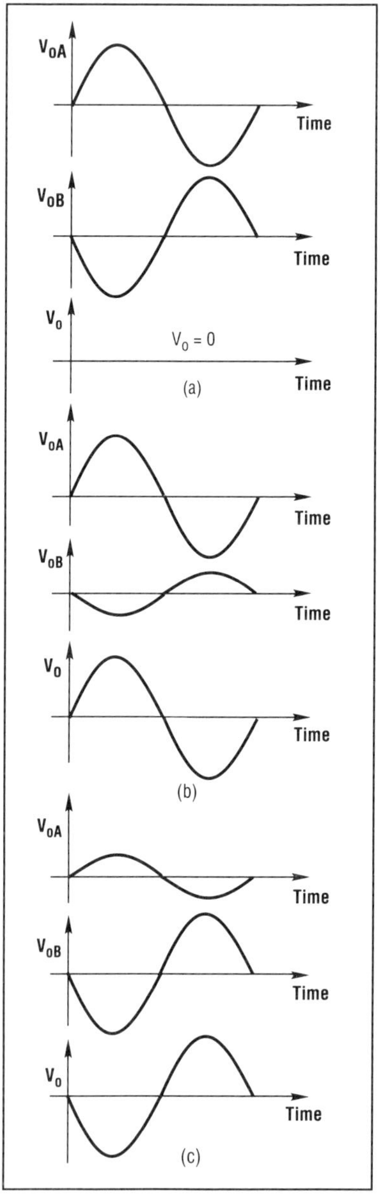

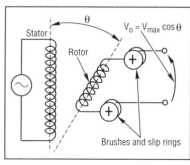

Fig. 11.12. Amplitude of output voltage indicates how far slug has moved from null. Output phase indicates which direction from center or null slug has moved, (a); slug is above center, (b), and below center, (c).

Fig. 11.13. Angular orientation of a resolver rotor is changed relative to magnetic axis of stator. RMS value of output voltage is related to the cosine of the shaft angle.

286

solvers. By varying the distance between primary and secondary windings, the amount of flux linking the two windings changes; consequently, output voltage varies with separation distance.

In the synchro, while the distance remains fixed, the angular orientation of the rotor axis changes with respect to the magnetic axis of the stator. Synchros are used as rotary position transducers, or, with rack-and-pinion gearing, as linear position transducers. Because of the trigonometric relationships between the rotor and stator and with dual windings on both, synchros can solve trigonometric problems.

Synchros find use as linear-position transducers in machine tools that require precise position measurement but this usually involves resolver-to-digital data conversion. In these systems, the resolver is the basic transducer, but instead of processing the output with another resolver as in the classical implementation, resolver output is fed into a special-purpose AC analog-to-digital converter that converts resolver output into an equivalent binary number representing the angular position of the resolver shaft. The digital signal then can be fed directly into a computer or other digital receiving device. The schematic of this system, Figure 11.14, is configured for position control.

Change in capacitance

The geometry of a capacitor, Figure 11.15, and the properties of its dielectric affect its capacitance. The basic equation for a simple, large-plate capacitor is:

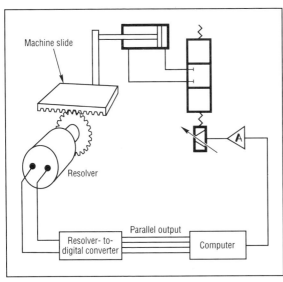

Machine slide

Resolver

Resolver- to-
digital converter

Parallel output

Computer

Fig. 11.14. Resolver with a resolver-to-digital converter can interface directly with parallel port of digital computer.

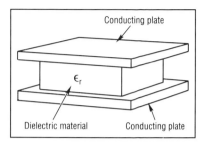

Fig. 11.15. Simple parallel-plate capacitor has two conductors separated by dielectric material.

$$C = \epsilon_o \epsilon_r A / L, \tag{11.2}$$

where C is electrical capacitance, ϵ_o is a universal constant that represents the permittivity of free space, and ϵ_r is the relative permittivity of the dielectric material. Permittivity is a property of the material which separates the capacitor's two plates. ϵ_o has the dimensions necessary to convert area A divided by plate separation distance L into coulombs/volt, the unit of electrical capacitance. In the MKS system, the units of ϵ_o are coulomb/volt-meter and the value is 8.85×10^{-12}. ϵ_r ranges from one for a vacuum to more than 150 for certain titanium alloys.

A people detector can be built using this type of transducer by exciting a large door-sized pair of capacitor plates with high-frequency AC voltage. If there is free air only between the plates the capacitance will be a certain value but when a human walks between the plates, the dielectric material changes. Because the relative permittivity of a human is higher than the permittivity of free air, the capacitance changes.

Connected into an AC bridge-detection circuit, it is possible to detect the presence of a human within the doorway and with calibration, to determine the bulk volume of the human, thus distinguishing small people from large people. This transducer would not be very good at distinguishing a small cow from a person, however. Some proximity switches use this permittivity change principle and change capacitance with the presence of a finger on a key on a keyboard. Because the switch has no moving parts, its life is unlimited.

A change in physical dimensions, that is a change in plate-to-plate separation L or plate area A also changes capacitance. One type of pressure transducer, for instance, has one capacitor plate fixed while the other is a diaphragm exposed to pressure fluid. The pressure deflects the diaphragm, reduces the separation distance and increases capacitance. The change in capacitance is calibrated against the pressure.

Summary of inductive and capacitive transducers

Note that all inductive and capacitive transduction principles require AC excitation; DC excitation does not work. This places a special requirement on signal conditioning equipment mentioned in the discussion about LVDTs. Recall that the amplitude of the AC output voltage reflected the distance that the slug had moved from center, and the phase of either 0° or 180° indicated the direction of the movement.

If it is necessary to convert AC output voltage to an analog DC voltage for a subsequent receiving device, simple rectification of the AC signal will lose track of the algebraic sign. In the case of the LVDT, we could not tell an upward displacement from a downward displacement of the slug, Figures 11.11 and 11.12. Recall the discussion in the last chapter about phase-sensitive demodulators. This demodulator rectifies AC signals, creates a proportional DC output, looks at the phase of the AC input, determines if it is 0° or 180°, and attaches an appropriate algebraic sign on the DC output.

In all transducers that use AC, the generic name for the signal that is generated is a *suppressed-carrier, double sideband amplitude-modulated signal*. The frequency of the AC source, which may be several kHz or MHz, is called the *carrier frequency*, and the information of interest changes the amplitude of the AC voltage. That is, the information is *carried* in the amplitude of the AC signal; hence oscillator frequency is called the carrier frequency.

The importance of the suppressed carrier was seen by deriving the equations for the instantaneous output signal that show there are only so-called *sum-and-difference* frequencies; the carrier frequency does not appear and is said to be suppressed. When coming across such terminology, it is helpful to know the origin of the words. In the vernacular of the day, the bottom-line information to be understood includes:

● whether AC is used by choice or necessity, the resulting output signal is suppressed-carrier, double-sideband, amplitude-modulated

● the magnitude of the measurand is reflected in the amplitude of the modulated AC output voltage, but the algebraic sign is carried in the phase of the output voltage, and the carrier voltage undergoes a 180° phase shift as the transducer passes through null or zero

● conversion of the suppressed carrier, double sideband, amplitude-modulated signal into a fully reversible (sign sensitive) analog DC signal requires the use of a phase-sensitive modulator

● when using inductive- or capacitive-transduction principles, AC excitation is imperative, and therefore the existence of suppressed carrier amplitude-modulation is assured. When using resistive-transduction principles, the use of AC excitation is optional. If it is used, the resulting output voltage will be of the suppressed-carrier double sideband amplitude-modulated type, and

● the reason for using AC excitation on resistive transducers has to do with the nature of high-gain amplifiers. With AC excitation, the amplifier's signal conditioner can easily be designed to reject low-frequency drift anywhere in the signal-processing chain. This eliminates the need to frequently re-zero the electronic equipment and yet maintains the high gain that is often necessary to process the very low level signals generated by, for example, strain-gage transducers.

It is true that many commercial strain-gage conditioning modules in use today actually excite the transducer with AC. Instructions are given for how connections are to be made, and many times the user is completely unaware of the use of AC until there is a problem which requires the use of an oscilloscope for troubleshooting. Do not be surprised, then, to find a 5- or 10-kHz AC voltage where a DC voltage was expected to be. As long as the equipment works properly, use of AC may be completely invisible to the user.

Commercial-transducer packaging at once creates a solution and another problem. The solution lies in the fact that many transducers can be purchased with on-board signal conditioning while others can be purchased without signal conditioning. The problem exists because it creates more options and confusion in the minds of non-expert users. It will be helpful if the transducer user is prepared to ask these questions when selecting a transducer. What is the:
- basic transduction principle?
- nature of on-board signal conditioning? and
- nature of the signal that is output by the package?

To be sure, there are other questions that must be asked and answered, but these three will help organize the whole scene when trying to make critical decisions about selection of the components needed to form the control chain.

ELECTRICAL GENERATION AND ENERGY CONVERSION

There are several phenomena that convert energy in one form directly to energy in another form. They have found use as transducers and their principles of operation are now addressed.

Photo-electric generation

There are two components included here that use these physical phenomena:
- the photo-voltaic cell, also called a *photocell* and/or *solar cell*, and
- the photo transistor.

Strictly speaking, the photo transistor is not a true energy converter as is the photo cell, but is included because the mathematical model of the transistor has a current generator.

Photo-voltaic cell. The photo-voltaic cell is a semiconductor device that converts light energy directly into electrical energy without an intervening thermodynamic process. The methods that accomplish this is are contained in the physics of semiconducting material, and detailed discussions are beyond the scope of this book. The user simply needs to know that the process exists. The most important aspect of the phenomenon is that no external power supply is required to obtain an electrical output response to light input. That is, if a light shines directly onto a photo-voltaic surface, Figure 11.16, the cell will generate a voltage. If a load resistance is connected between the output leads, there will be a current and, of course, power will be delivered to the load resistor. All the power comes only from the light that impinges upon the cell.

The photo transistor. This transistor, Figure 11.17, looks like a conventional NPN transistor except that no electrical connection is made to the base material. Instead, the base material is exposed to ambient light through a lens in the case. Incident light falling upon the base serves the same function as the base current in a normal transistor. That is, when the incident light increases in intensity, the reverse-biased collector-to-emitter sandwich conducts in the reverse direction.

A basic test circuit, Figure 11.18, indicates that with light energy to the base totally blocked, the collector is cut off and output voltage V_o is nearly

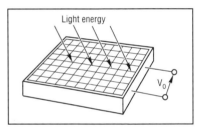

Fig. 11.16. Photo-voltaic or solar cell converts light energy directly into electrical energy.

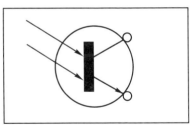

Fig. 11.17. A photo transistor uses incident light impinging on the base material to control collector-to-emitter current.

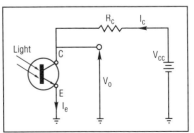

Fig. 11.18. Simple photo transistor test circuit has external resistor R_c and supply voltage V_{cc}. Incident light on base causes collector to conduct and output voltage V_o to fall.

equal to supply voltage V_{cc}. When incident light intensity increases, the collector conducts, voltage drops across collector resistor R_c which, in turn, causes output voltage V_o to decrease. The amount of current, and therefore change in output voltage, is directly proportional to the intensity of the light impinging upon the base as is suggested in the transfer characteristic, Figure 11.19.

An important distinction between the photo cell and photo transistor is that the latter requires an external DC power supply to function whereas the photo cell does not. That means, strictly speaking, that the photo transistor is not really an energy convertor in the same sense that the photo cell is. It has been lumped into the energy converter category more because the model uses a current generator to explain its function in an operational circuit. A photo transistor looks more like the photo-sensitive resistor discussed earlier.

Comparisons. Certainly, the photo transistor and the photo-sensitive resistor have similarities. They both:

● require an external power supply
● conduct more heavily with stronger incident light, and
● have two electrical leads and a lens to focus incident light.

Two significant differences are not at all apparent without detailed study:

● photo resistors will conduct in either direction with incident light,

Fig. 11.19. Photo transistor current and output voltage are affected proportionally by light intensity in the common emitter test circuit, Figure 11.18.

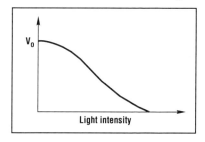

Fig. 11.20. Photo-optical shaft encoder uses rotating disc with small windows to alternately turn on and turn off phototransistor. This results in a pulse train, the frequency of which is proportional to shaft speed and whose total pulse count is proportional to incremental shaft angle.

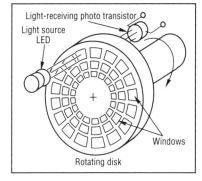

while the transistor must be connected so the collector has the correct-polarity voltage consistent with transistor type, that is an NPN transistor requires a $+V_{cc}$ and a PNP transistor requires a $-V_{cc}$, and

● photo transistors will switch from non-conducting to conducting much faster than photo-sensitive resistors.

A transistor can switch from off to on and vice-versa in a few microseconds while the photo-sensitive resistor requires from tens to a few-hundred milliseconds to fully change conducting levels. Clearly, high speed applications use a transistor instead of a photo-sensitive resistor.

The most common use of photo-voltaic cells is in solar energy conversion as an alternative energy source. Some uses also are found in the so-called *electric eyes* that detect the presence or absence of an opaque or refracting body. Provided that the processes are relatively slow, the photo cell or the photo-sensitive resistor work equally well.

For electrohydraulic purposes, the most common use of photo-sensitive devices is in the family of encoders that detect shaft and slide position.

Incremental encoders. As the windowed disk of an incremental encoder turns, Figure 11.20, it alternately passes and blocks light to the photo transistor, causing it to alternately cut off and conduct. By connecting the encoder into a circuit similar to that in Figure 11.18, the output is a train of pulses that go from zero to V_{cc} as the windows pass. The frequency is directly proportional to shaft speed according to the formula:

$$f = PN/60, \tag{11.3}$$

where f is the frequency of the pulse train in Hz, P is the number of pulses per revolution of the encoder, and N is the shaft speed in rpm. Note that if P is 60, output frequency in Hz is exactly equal to the speed in rpm, a popular way to measure shaft speed using a digital frequency meter.

With the pulse train coupled to an electronic totalizing counter, the counter records the total number of windows that have passed and is therefore directly proportional to the total angle that the shaft has turned. Be aware that in this simplistic scenario, the counter is unable to distinguish the direction of shaft rotation. To make the counter add, for example, CW pulses but subtract CCW-generated pulses, a second output called a *quadrature* signal must be generated. It is possible to use quadrature output to tell the counter to count up or count down so that the current value in the totalizing counter is an accurate reflection of the net shaft rotation.

Installing another LED light source and another photo transistor can generate the quadrature pulse. The LED-photo transistor sets are arranged so that when the first transistor is at the midpoint of its on-state, the second LED transistor set is positioned to transition from on to off. The quadrature pulse, then, is displaced 90 electrical degrees or a quarter

of an electrical cycle from the first pulse and is the reason the quadrature pulse is so named. Direction of rotation can be deduced using this logic:
● if the quadrature pulse changes from **off to on** when the main pulse is on, the shaft is turning clockwise, and
● if the quadrature pulse changes from **on to off** when the main pulse is on, the shaft is turning CCW.

Encoders that produce a quadrature output often are also equipped with circuits that perform this logic. In addition, these encoders have a third signal wire that carries direction-of-rotation information. That is, the logic is used to set a single bit which is, say, on for CW and off for CCW rotation. The three signal wires now are:
● main pulse train
● quadrature pulse train, and
● direction of rotation bit, Figure 11.21.

Note that in the normal course of events when the quadrature pulse makes its transition from off to on, the main pulse is high or on, satisfying the first logical condition — the shaft is rotating CW.

To visualize how reversing the direction of shaft rotation affects the signal, simply imagine that time increases to the left instead of to the right. Then, when the main pulse is high, the quadrature pulse goes from high to low, satisfying the second logical condition. Output of the logic circuit is used to set the CW/CCW bit appropriately. An up/down counter totalizes the **net** number of pulses that have accumulated so the counter carries an indication of actual shaft position.

A disadvantage of incremental encoders is that because of a malfunction or operation in an electronically noisy environment, they may pick up an extra count or lose a count in the totalizing counter. Then, indicated position does not agree with actual position and measurement error results. The error will remain until the encoder is forced to a home position and the counter is forcibly filled with the exact digital value which corresponds to that position.

Absolute encoders. Absolute encoders circumvent that problem by generating a parallel-bit combination which corresponds to the actual

Fig. 11.21. The main and quadrature pulse trains are displaced 90 electrical degrees. The logic for direction of rotation can be seen by imagining time increasing to the right for clockwise rotation but increasing to the left for CCW rotation.

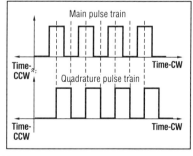

position of the shaft. There are four codes commonly in use, Figure 11.22. The first two codes are binary and have five tracks capable of resolving a revolution of the shaft into 32 parts (2^5). The last two are binary-coded decimal (BCD) codes with six tracks capable of resolving one-fortieth of a revolution. Most practical encoders have more tracks than these because with five bits, the encoder cannot resolve less than $\frac{1}{32}$nd of a revolution or about 11°. The principles remain the same.

The problem with the natural binary code occurs at the transitions from one position to the next when more than one track has to change from high to low or vice-versa at exactly the same instant. Thus, if a digital receiving device interrogates the encoder for its current position and happens to read at a transition point, and if only one of two bits scheduled to change has already done so because of say, manufacturing imperfections, an erroneous reading results.

The error will not be simply one increment of the most rapidly changing (LSB) track — it could be as much a one-half a shaft revolution, an intolerable situation. Furthermore, given that the encoder is interrogated millions of times in a day, be assured that a transition point reading error will occur frequently. Multiple-read scans with a vote for the most likely winner can be employed in the software provided the programmer has the necessary programming skills.

The Gray code was invented to circumvent ambiguity problems with the natural binary code. The genius of this code is that the natural binary code can be rearranged so that within the interval of two LSBs, Figure 11.22(b), there is no segment-to-segment transition that requires more than one bit change at a time. With this scheme, the reading error when interrogating at the transition point never exceeds the angle allocated to

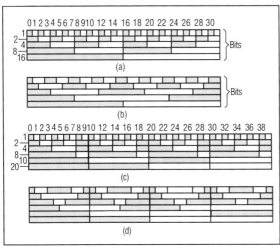

Fig. 11.22. Schematic codes: natural binary code (a) has 32 positions, five bits; natural Gray code (b) illustrates same thing; BCD — binary code (c) has 40 positions, six bits; and BCD — Gray-Excess code (d) also has 40 positions, six bits.

the LSB.

The BCD codes merely interpret the position in a BCD manner rather than in pure binary. The problem with the straight BCD is the same as with the natural binary, that is there are transitions where more than one bit must change at a time. Reading-error possibilities are the same as well. The more reliable code, Figure 11.22(d), is the BCD — Gray excess code. Note that it has only one bit changing at a time, eliminating the transition point reading ambiguity.

Thermo-electric generation

Thermocouples convert heat energy directly into electrical energy. Their simplicity gives them a particularly high value; a thermocouple is formed merely by putting two dissimilar metals into intimate contact with one another. Any time that two dissimilar metals are in contact, a voltage is generated at the junction which is affected by the internal energies of the electrons and the temperature of the junction. If both ends of the conductors are connected, Figure 11.23, there is voltage generated at each of the junctions. If both junctions are at the same temperature, the voltages are equal and they cancel one another; there is no current.

On the other hand, if one junction is at a different temperature, say junction 1 is at a higher temperature than junction 2, Figure 11.24, then E_1 will be greater than E_2 and a current will result. The power dissipated in wire resistance R_{wire} comes directly from the energy source that causes the temperature difference. The voltage difference, that is the net voltage around the loop is $E_1 - E_2$. It is a function of metal 1, metal 2, and the temperature difference, $T_1 - T_2$. The important consideration is that voltage is dependent upon the temperature difference between the two junctions. Therefore to find the temperature of junction 2 from a knowledge of the voltage, it is necessary to know the temperature of junction 1.

The traditional way that junction 1 temperature is determined is to use a reference bath of known temperature. For most measurements, this is an ice and distilled-water bath with ice and water existing simultaneously.

Fig. 11.23. Two dissimilar metals in contact will generate a voltage. When connected in a loop without a temperature difference, the voltages cancel and there is no current.

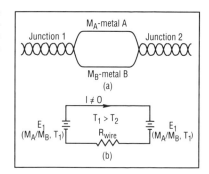

Accurate measurements require that the bath be properly maintained throughout the measurement process. Tables for commercial thermocouples list the thermally induced voltage for each thermocouple junction as a function of temperature difference and the materials of the two wires. Therefore, the voltage is a measure of how far the junction temperature is above the reference junction, which is at 32° F.

Maintaining the bath is a nuisance that is unnecessary with modern commercial thermocouples; they contain *simulated-reference junctions* and eliminate the ice bath. This author recommends that these simulated junctions be purchased by the electrohydraulic practitioner any time that thermocouples are to be used for temperature measurement. In fact, any thermocouple interface device probably will come equipped with the junctions but it would not hurt to ask just to make sure.

Piezoelectric generation

The prefix *piezo* comes from the Greek word *piezein* meaning pressure, or to press. Piezoelectricity then, is electricity that results from some sort of squeeze. The phenomenon occurs with quartz and other dielectric crystals. Simply squeezing or distorting the crystal material results in a transfer of piezoelectric charge. The crystal can be thought of as a syringe filled with electrical charges; squeezing the syringe pushes out the electrons. When a capacitor is connected to the output leads, the capacitor charges to a voltage difference commensurate with the amount of force that has done the squeezing. The voltage also is affected by the size of the external capacitor.

The piezoelectric effect is used commercially to make accelerometers and certain pressure transducers noted for their extremely fast response. Bandwidths can be as high as several hundred kHz. The load on the transducer output terminals must be purely capacitive because the crystal transfers a fixed electrical charge, as opposed to generating a steady flow of charges. The capacitive load holds the charge and converts it to a

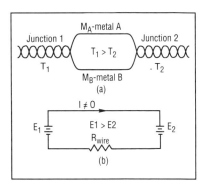

(a)

(b)

Fig. 11.24. If the two junctions are at different temperatures, one voltage exceeds the other and there is a current.

297

voltage, Figure 11.25. To the extent that there is a leakage-resistance path within the capacitor, output voltage eventually decays even with constant input force to the crystal. Thus, the quartz piezoelectric transducer is not regarded as a good steady-state performer. However it is superb for high-frequency dynamic measurements because of its quick response.

A piezoelectric transducer, Figure 11.26, is connected to a *charge amplifier*. Note that the op-amp circuit has capacitors for feedback as well as input elements. This is called the charge amplifier because output voltage is related to the charge deposited on input capacitor C_i. The voltage generated at the output terminals of the transducer is directly proportional to the force applied and inversely proportional to the capacitance which accumulates the charge. That is:

$$V_x = Kf/(C_i + C_c), \tag{11.4}$$

where V_x is the voltage across the terminal of the transducer, K is the transducer's transfer constant determined from calibration, f is the external force applied to the crystal, C_i is the charge amplifier's input capacitance, and C_c is the parasitic capacitance of the interconnecting cable.

The output voltage of the charge amplifier can be shown to be:

$$V_o = - V_x C_f/C_i. \tag{11.5}$$

After substituting Equation (11.4) into Equation (11.5), see that

$$V_o = -KfC_f/[C_i(C_i + C_c)]. \tag{11.6}$$

Fig. 11.25. Subjecting a quartz crystal to an external force causes an electric charge to be transferred from the crystal to external capacitance C_p, establishing a voltage difference across the capacitor.

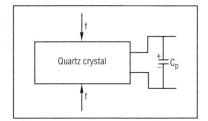

Fig. 11.26. A piezoelectric transducer uses a charge amplifier as the immediate interface at the sending end.

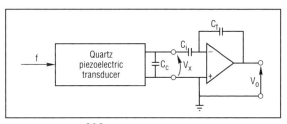

Equation (11.6) is important to those who use piezoelectric transducers because it shows that the transfer constant for the crystal plus the charge amplifier is affected by cabling capacitance C_c. The important consequence is that if one calibrates the transducer-plus-amplifier system, determines transfer constant K empirically, and then uses the transducer with a different cable, the calibration is in error. It is essential that these transducers always be used with the same cable and amplifier used during calibration. All transducers are affected by cabling, but none so severely as piezoelectric transducers.

These devices are more commonly used as accelerometers and high-speed pressure transducers. For a pressure transducer, a diaphragm mounted to the crystal is exposed to the unknown pressure, and pressure acting on an area creates the force of transduction. In a accelerometer, a small mass is mounted on the crystal and as the mass undergoes acceleration, it imparts a reaction force to the crystal.

Note that the charge amplifier with its feedback capacitor is really an integrating amplifier. As with all integrating amplifiers, it is impossible to absolutely zero the op-amp. Therefore, the output always drifts very slowly and after a few minutes of operation, DC output from the amplifier no longer reflects the DC level of the input pressure or acceleration. Signal-conditioning amplifiers are outfitted with a zeroing switch, which must be pressed every few minutes to maintain a reasonable knowledge of the DC input level.

Of course, the superior dynamic response of piezoelectric transducers makes them ideally suited to look at fluid-borne noise, pump ripple, and other such high-frequency events. If there is interest in the DC pressure level, it also is advisable to use one of the more conventional pressure transducers whose performance has been optimized to measure this. Both dynamic and steady-state performance can be monitored reliably.

Hall effect

In 1879, E. H. Hall showed that a current-carrying conductor immersed in a magnetic field, Figure 11.27, produces electron motion that

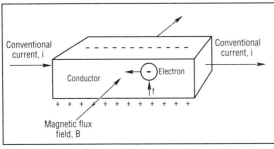

Fig,. 11.27. Hall effect explains that an electron moving in a magnetic field will be pushed up in the conductor because of force f. Electrons pushed to the top generate transverse Hall voltage V_H which will be positive as shown.

interacts with magnetic flux field B in such a way that there is a force acting on the electrons that pushes them to the top of the conductor for the conditions shown. The charge separation results in a voltage difference from the top to the bottom of the conductor with the bottom being more positive for the conditions shown. This voltage difference is the Hall voltage and is directly proportional to conventional current i and magnetic-field density B. That is:

$$V_h = KiB. \tag{11.7}$$

This is an important relationship in the modern electronic world because, unlike the Faraday voltage (described next) that requires a time-changing magnetic flux to induce a voltage, the Hall-effect voltage is generated with a stationary magnetic field and a stationary conductor. Hall-effect transducers have been made commercially in a number of ways. Some, without going into great detail, are:
● non-contacting switches
● magnetic-field strength meters
● clamp-on ammeters for DC current
● position sensors that generate a voltage based upon the relative position of a magnet compared to the Hall-effect sensor, and
● shaft encoders that function down to zero shaft speed.

Faraday-induced voltages
In 1831, Michael Faraday discovered that the induced electromagnetic voltage was directly proportional to the time rate of change of flux. We know it today as:

$$V = -d(N\Phi)/dt. \tag{11.8}$$

In using Faraday's EMF Law as it is called, the existence of a voltage requires that either the
● number of turns N be time varying, or
● amount of flux Φ linking with the N turns be time-varying.
The law has produced such diverse devices as transformers, generators, tachometers, alternators, and the like. For transduction purposes, the two uses that are important are tachometers and alternators.
DC tachometer. In its basic form, a DC tachometer is a special-purpose DC generator that has a steady magnetic field (usually created by a permanent magnet) with a commutated armature immersed within the field to measure shaft speed. As the armature turns, an AC voltage is induced in the armature winding but brushes in contact with commutator segments convert the internal AC into an external DC voltage in a way analogous to the function of port plate and pistons in a piston pump.

The reciprocating pistons produce an alternating flow but the port plate assures that the external plumbing sees only a unidirectional, albeit pulsating, flow.

Similarly, the commutator and brushes also produce a ripple voltage in a DC tachometer. These pulsations limit the minimum speed that can be effectively transduced or controlled. The more precise the tachometer, the greater the number of commutator segments. Most commercial tachometers have only five commutator segments, adequate for high-speed applications but problematic when used below about 100 rpm.

One of the major advantages of DC tachometers is their ability to generate high output voltages over their intended speed ranges. It is not unusual to find one that generates 10 volts per 1000 rpm. In most applications, this voltage is sufficiently high to be useful without any amplification. Another characteristic is that they continue to generate a voltage down to zero speed and with some limitations and perhaps some filtering, output voltage is still usable although pulsations can be a problem. Additionally, DC tachometers are very linear because the amplitude of the output voltage is directly proportional to shaft speed. They are popular rotary speed transducers.

Drag-cup tachometer. A drag-cup tachometer is an AC device that lacks the linearity of its DC counterpart and has no commutator and brushes, Figure 11.28(a). A local oscillator generates an AC voltage — usually 400 Hz but sometimes higher. The stator has two windings physically displaced 90°. One winding is connected to the local oscillator and becomes the power input. Current in the powered winding induces a circulating current (eddy current) in the aluminum drag cup. With the

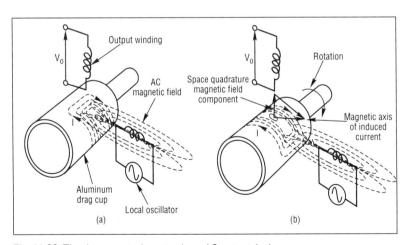

Fig. 11.28. The drag-cup tachometer is an AC output device.

301

rotor stationary, the orientation of the magnetic field of the induced current is directly in line with and opposes the causative magnetic field. As a result, there is no flux linkage with the output winding and output voltage is zero.

But when the drag cup turns, Figure 11.28(b), an eddy current is induced in the drag cup because of the alternating magnetic field of the powered coil. Due to the cup's motion, however, a *speed current* also is induced as the conductor (the drag cup) passes through the magnetic field. The combination of the induced current and the speed current causes the axis of the combined magnetic field to shift so that it has a horizontal and a vertical component. The vertical component is in line with the output coil's magnetic axis, hence there is a voltage induced therein whose amplitude is in direct proportion to the rotating speed of the drag cup, but whose frequency is controlled only by the frequency of the local oscillator.

It is important to know that drag-cup AC output voltage has:

● a frequency equal to that of the local oscillator

● an amplitude directly proportional to and nearly linear with rotational speed, and

● output voltage, like that of the LVDT and synchro, is a suppressed-carrier, double sideband amplitude-modulated signal.

Therefore, if the tachometer measured rotation only in one direction and it is necessary to have a DC rather than an AC voltage, simple rectification is sufficient, Figure 11.29; but if bidirectional rotation is to be measured and algebraic sign needed, a phase sensitive demodulator is necessary,

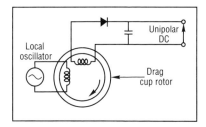

Fig. 11.29. For unidirectional rotation, a simple diode rectifier is sufficient to convert AC into useable DC.

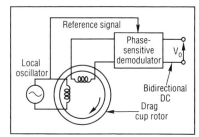

Fig. 11.30. A phase-sensitive demodulator is required for bidirectional rotation and output algebraic sign that follows the direction of shaft rotation. When all these parts are put into a single package, the result is a brushless DC tachometer.

Figure 11.30.

There are systems found in aircraft and aboard ships in which conversion of a 400-Hz output into a DC voltage is unnecessary. It is possible that these systems could be encountered in the industrial environment. More likely than not, though, the conversion to DC will be made in industrial applications because the servo or proportional amplifier requires DC input and feedback signals. In aircraft, the output actuator is often a 400-Hz servo motor which can use an amplified version of the 400-Hz signal without further modification. The AC servo motor is, at once, the actuator and demodulator.

Note that the AC device is converted into a DC device with some basic electronic signal conditioning circuits. When the drag cup tachometer, its associated phase-sensitive demodulator, and the local oscillator are all packaged within the tachometer envelope, the device is called a *brushless DC tachometer*. All the AC running around inside is invisible.

The advantage of the brushless DC tachometer is that its output is nearly devoid of ripple and the output signal is usable down to zero speed, although it is more expensive than a simple DC tachometer. Additionally, the brushless DC tachometer is slightly more non-linear than a brush-type version. Finally, when speed range is great and reliability is important, the brushless DC tachometer can be a wise choice.

Alternators, AC generators. Alternators and AC generators are machines that generate an AC voltage. The amplitude of this voltage is directly proportional to the alternator's shaft speed, and the frequency of this voltage is an exact integer multiple of the shaft speed. Alternators also are called *AC generators*, but this is technically incorrect; generators generate DC and alternators generate AC. The kinds of alternators include:

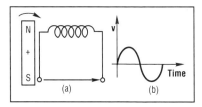

Fig. 11.31. Drawing illustrates rotating permanent-magnet alternator, (a), and output wave, (b). This waveshape is also the same for the next three types of alternators.

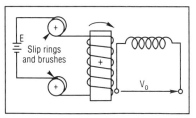

Fig. 11.32. Drawing of automotive-type rotating electromagnet alternator.

303

● rotating permanent magnets with AC voltage generated in stationary windings, Figure 11.31

● rotating electromagnets, with AC voltage generated in stationary windings, Figure 11.32. This configuration requires that electrical power be supplied to the member that turns, and so slip rings and brushes carry electrical power from the stationary, exterior world to the rotating interior world. This machine is used in automotive electrical systems; the machine is not used as a transducer because the brushes and slip rings add cost with no increase in capability

● permanent or electromagnetic stationary magnetic fields with AC voltage generated in rotating coils, Figure 11.33. This device also requires slip rings and bruhes but is not used industrially because it has no advantages over other configurations, and

● stationary magnetic fields and stationary pickup coils. This variable-reluctance alternator generates voltage by changing the reluctance of the rotating member, Figure 11.34. The most common commercial machine that uses this principle is the *magnetic pickup*, popular as a shaft speed transducer. For transduction purposes, the magnetic field is always a permanent magnet, and for construction simplicity as well as for maximum sensitivity, the stationary coil is always wound directly around the permanent magnet. The amplitude of alternator output voltage and its frequency vary in direct proportion to the speed of the input shaft, but frequency is the variable of interest when measuring data.

This is true because there is an exact integer relationship between shaft speed and frequency; no errors arise in the transduction process. When measuring shaft speed, all errors occur because of the resolution of the read-out device. The transducer itself cannot be calibrated or adjusted. Only the read-out device needs such attention. For transduction pur-

Fig. 11.33. Drawing of stationary magnetic field alternator.

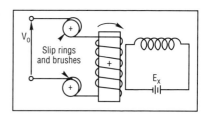

Fig. 11.34. Variable-reluctance alternator or magnetic pick-up is a popular speed transducer.

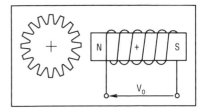

poses:

$$f = PN/60, \tag{11.3}$$

where f is the frequency of the AC signal in Hz, P is an integer that represents the number of poles in the alternator, and N is the shaft speed in rpm.

In the case of the variable-reluctance transducer, Figure 11.34, that integer is the number of irregularities around the periphery of the rotor, usually a ferromagnetic gear. Furthermore, the rotor typically has 60 teeth, which converts Equation (11.3) into:

$$f = N, \tag{11.9}$$

which means that shaft speed in RPM exactly equals the output frequency in Hz. When a digital frequency meter is used for the read out, it displays the shaft speed in rpm when the frequency-meter gate time is set to 1 sec. Thus the accuracy of speed measurement is affected only by the accuracy and resolution of the frequency meter.

While frequency generation and measurement is a popular way to determine shaft speed, all other methods using frequency to measure shaft speed introduce a time lag. As soon as actual speed is interpreted by the reader, be it human or mechanical, the value read becomes out of date. The final interpretation is the speed as averaged over the time interval. If speed is relatively constant, the interpreted value will be current. But if the speed changes, the displayed value is always out-of-date. This time lag complicates the control problem when using feedback to regulate and control speed. Note, then, that in spite of other flaws, **tachometric methods do not produce the time lag that frequency methods do.**

Mechanically variable impedance devices

Potentiometers and variable autotransformers, strictly speaking, are not generating devices in the sense that they convert energy. Instead, they accept a mechanical position input signal and develop an output voltage that depends upon the input position. Potentiometers can be excited with either AC or DC current but autotransformers always must be used with

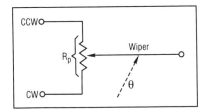

Fig. 11.35. A potentiometer is a three-terminal resistor in which one terminal is in intimate sliding electrical contact with the resistive element.

AC.

Potentiometer. A potentiometer or pot is a three-terminal variable resistance, Figure 11.35. The three terminals are labeled clockwise (CW), counterclockwise (CCW), and wiper that sometimes also is called the *slider*. Note that there is a fixed resistance between the CW and CCW terminals but the resistance between the wiper and either of the other two terminals varies as the wiper is moved. The θ notation in Figure 11.35 for the mechanical input implies that the potentiometer is a *rotary* device, the mechanical input for the vast majority of pots.

When using a pot to transduce the position of a cylinder, linear input is the obvious choice. Pot linearity refers to the constancy of the rate at which resistance changes with respect to changes in the input member. Most pots encountered in the fluid power industry are linear pots which means that nominally the slope of the resistance characteristic is constant over the entire range of the input. Of course, the resistance must be measured between the wiper and one of the fixed terminals.

Note that if the pot of Figure 11.35 is started at its full CCW position, the resistance between the CCW terminal and the wiper nominally begins at 0 Ω and increases toward total pot resistance, R_p. At the same time, resistance from the CW terminal begins at R_p and decreases toward 0 Ω, as indicated in the plot of resistance/shaft-angle characteristics, Figure 11.36. The slopes of the two curves of a pot designed to be electrically linear will be the same and will be nominally constant over the whole angular range of the shaft.

Pots designed for linear input motions also are designed to have linear electrical characteristics. Such pots are said to be *rectilinear*, which means they have linear electrical properties **and** linear input motion. When speaking of linear pots, the implication usually is that the notation applies to the electrical-resistance curves. Therefore in the parlance of the industry, *linear pot* usually refers to its electrical characteristics.

To communicate the nature of the motion, more information must be offered: rectilinear pot or linear-motion pot for example, to indicate the nature of the mechanical input movement. Furthermore, when techni-

Fig. 11.36. Resistance-shaft angle characteristics of linear, rotational-input potentiometer.

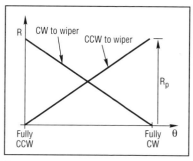

cians say *linear pot*, they probably are talking about the electrical properties and thinking of a pot with rotary mechanical input. These words cause no small source of confusion. It is wise to request clarification as to what, specifically, is meant by linear potentiometer.

Here, it is only important to know that there are two common forms of input motion for pots, they will most likely have linear resistance characteristics, and they will be called linear pots. Where the nature of the mechanical input is crucial to the point at hand, some clarifying words will remove ambiguity.

Mechanical input θ, Figure 11.35, causes the slider to travel the length of the resistive element. The resistive element could be a very fine wire (most often copper) or a conductive plastic film. This film is impregnated with tiny conducting particles so that the particles are in electrical contact with one another. The plastic thus becomes an electrical conductor. The plastic material provides a bonding agent for the conducting particles as well as a smooth, low-friction surface over which the slider can move.

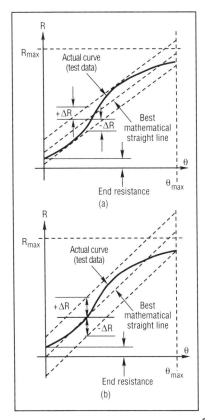

Fig. 11.37. Potentiometer independent non-linearity, (a), is reported as the deviation from best straight line independent of end resistance and measured with a mechanical input range from mechanical zero to maximum mechanical position. Terminal non-linearity, (b), is deviation for the best straight line that passes through origin. Terminal non-linearity is always greater than independent non-linearity, but only the latter is critical.

Pot linearity. Given that this discussion is limited to linear pots, we emphasize that when resistance characteristics are examined with sufficient precision, true linearity is never achieved — only approached. When potentiometers are designed and manufactured with controlled linearity, they are usually called *instrument-grade* pots, clearly implying that they can be used for instrumentation functions. All such transducers are accompanied by technical data sheets that state the expected worst-case non-linearity. Note that non-linearity actually is reported but the industry always calls it linearity.

The two methods of measuring the non-linearity of a potentiometer are the *terminal non-linearity* and the *independent non-linearity*, Figure 11.37. The difference between the two is accounted for by the *end resistance* of the pot. That is, the pot cannot be constructed so there is no resistance between the wiper arm and the respective end terminal when the arm is located at its mechanical end limit. This is not merely the resistance of the connecting wire, it is a mechanical consideration: the resistive element must always be made slightly longer than the allowed mechanical travel. The potentiometer cannot be manufactured so the physical end of the resistive element coincides exactly with the mechanical travel of the wiper.

Furthermore, when the pot is used to measure cylinder position for instance, the mechanical travel of the pot must be greater than the mechanical travel of the cylinder. To be otherwise would invite the cylinder to be stopped by the mechanical barrier in the pot, a duty for which it is not designed. The result is that even if the pot could be manufactured with zero end resistance, application considerations demand there be end resistance in the system.

The common mechanical method used to compensate for end resistance is to place the potentiometer in a pot-pot bridge circuit. The scheme, Figure 11.38, graphically indicates how end resistances in the transducer side of the bridge are placed because the wiper of the transducer pot cannot mechanically reach the true electrical end of the resistive element. In reality, end resistances R_{E1} and R_{E2} are physically part of the

Fig. 11.38. End resistances R_{E1} and R_{E2} of the transducer pot can be compensated in a pot-pot bridge circuit by deliberately introducing adjustable trimmer resistors R_{T1} and R_{T2}.

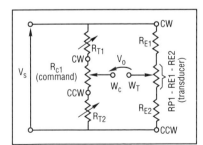

transducer pot's resistance element but are drawn as discrete resistors for analytical clarity. On the other hand, trimmer resistors R_{T1} and R_{T2} are discrete, adjustable resistors that have been deliberately introduced into the command-pot side of the bridge.

By way of explanation, consider that supply voltage V_S is applied to the circuit. For each setting of the command pot, a corresponding setting of the transducer-pot wiper results in zero output voltage V_o, end resistances notwithstanding. If it were not for the end resistances, it would be possible to position the wiper of the transducer pot so that it electrically *touches* either the CW or CCW terminal. If the command pot likewise had no end resistances, it too could be positioned at its electrical limits. Thus, fully CCW on the command pot for example, would require the transducer pot to be positioned fully CCW to set output voltage V_o to zero. Similarly, a completely CW setting of the command pot would require a fully CW setting of the transducer pot to acquire zero output voltage.

Now consider the actual situation where the end resistances are not zero. To compensate for them, the transducer pot must be moved to its mechanical limit in the CCW direction. That limit is a function of the potentiometer **and** the mechanical constraints of the load and the fluid power actuator. At the same time, the command pot must be moved to its CCW limit. If output voltage then is measured, it **will not** be zero because of end resistance on the CCW end. Next, trimmer resistor R_{T2} is adjusted until output voltage is zero.

To set conditions for the other extreme, the transducer pot is moved to its CW mechanical limit while the command pot also is moved to its CW limit. Output voltage will not be zero, and trimmer resistor R_{T1} is then adjusted until the output voltage is again zero. Because the two adjust-

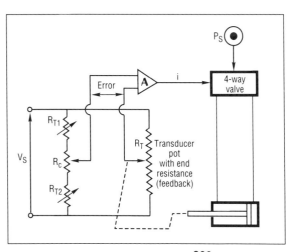

Fig. 11.39. A pot-pot servomechanism uses command and transducer pots in a bridge configuration. An error voltage causes the valve to shift, porting fluid to the actuator. The actuator moves the feedback wiper until the error goes to zero.

ments are not totally independent of one another, it becomes necessary to check and recheck each end of the travel until they both produce zero output after repeated trials. Then, the electrical and mechanical limits of both pots have been forced to coincide with one another and the trimmers can be locked into their adjusted positions.

The circuit in Figure 11.38 has practical application in a *pot-pot servomechanism*, Figure 11.39. It will be shown later that output voltage V_o, the *error* in servo mechanism parlance, is sent to a servo amplifier. Amplifier output moves the spool of a servo or proportional valve to port fluid to an actuator. Output of the actuator is mechanically connected to the transducer pot wiper shaft, so that as the actuator moves, the wiper shaft of the transducer pot moves too. The transducer pot also is called the *feedback pot* or the *feedback transducer*. When the feedback pot has moved to a position where output voltage from the bridge is zero, the valve spool centers, the actuator stops, and the system is in an equilibrium position commensurate with the command pot setting.

Adjustable voltage dividers. In strictly technical terms, the device commonly called a potentiometer really is not. The pot described so far is simply a three-terminal variable resistor. The word *potentiometer* comes from applications of the variable resistor as an adjustable voltage source in which there is a *potential* or voltage applied to the device. The idea is presented schematically in Figure 11.40(a), where voltage source V_S is applied to the fixed terminals of the resistor and the output is taken between the wiper and one end of the resistor. Now, when the voltage is taken into account, the source plus the variable resistor constitute the potentiometer or *potential meter*.

Historically, this circuit was used to measure unkown voltages with

Fig. 11.40. The potentiometer is used as an adjustable voltage divider, (a), or as a transducer, (b), which converts mechanical input θ into equivalent voltage V_o. When used with a known, precision voltage source, the wiper dial can be calibrated to measure voltage E_x.

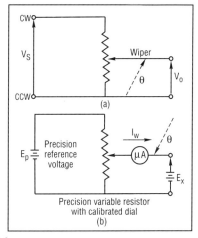

great precision. When the resistance varies linearly with the shaft setting, output voltage also varies linearly according to:

$$V_o = V_S \theta/\theta_{max}, \hspace{3cm} (11.10)$$

where θ is the actual position of the input mechanical member and θ_{max} is the maximum mechanical excursion the input shaft can make. The equation is valid only when the pot is substantially linear, and the current in the wiper is zero. If the current is not zero, output voltage will deviate from the calculation of Equation (11.10) because of loading error. Note that θ/θ_{max} is merely the fraction that the mechanical member has been moved relative to its total allowable travel. This is what gives the circuit utility as a voltage-measuring circuit.

Potential-measuring circuit. When a circuit has a supply voltage from a well-regulated source such as a *standard cell* or a precision voltage regulator that uses a zener diode, and the variable resistor has a precision-calibrated dial, the circuit becomes the so-called potential meter, Figure 11.40(b). Assuming there is some unknown voltage E_x, the circuit is placed in use by connecting the unknown voltage to the wiper arm, taking care to prevent destruction of the pot. Wiper current I_w will not be zero. The operator adjusts the wiper mechanically until the microammeter indicates zero current as closely as is practicable. At this time the circuit meets the conditions required of Equation (11.10) and the mechanical wiper arm position is, all at once, a fraction of known precision supply voltage E_p and unknown voltage E_x. Equation (11.10) can be used to calculate the unknown voltage.

Rheostats are two-terminal variable resistors connected in series with a load to provide a means to adjust the current, Figure 11.41. A limitation is that they can never completely cut off the current unless equipped with an integral switch. Rheostats are not used as transducers in the instrumentation sense. Their most common use is as automotive light dimmer controls, although the modern trend is to replace them with solid-state electronic devices. Rheostatic control of current is to electronics what valve control is to hydraulic flow. The process dissipates excess power to regulate the power consumed by the load. Self heating takes place in the

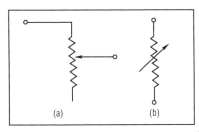

Fig. 11.41. The rheostat is a two-terminal variable resistor. Two forms for the schematic symbol imply that it is a potentiometer, (a), or a rheostat, (b).

(a) (b)

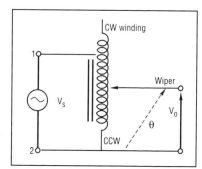

Fig. 11.42. Variable autotransformer uses a single winding for primary and secondary, and a wiper arm to provide adjustable output voltage.

electrical and the hydraulic medium.

Autotransformers. Autotransformers are similar to potentiometers in that they have a wiper and three terminals for external connections, but their operation is somewhat different. Being an inductive device, Figure 11.42, autotransformers must be supplied with AC power. They use transformer action but there is only one winding that serves as primary and secondary. It is easy to see that when the wiper is positioned at the fully CCW end of the winding, output voltage is zero. Note in Figure 11.42 that power connections are made between the CCW end of the winding and a point near but not at the CW end of the winding. In contrast, the wiper can travel beyond the upper power connection point and approach the fully CW end. Should the wiper be positioned directly across from power connection 1, output voltage obviously equals supply voltage.

But when the wiper is moved above power connection 1, output voltage will **exceed** supply voltage. This allows autotransformers to be adjustable and also provides the ability to boost the supply voltage. This voltage boost comes as a result of the flux from the powered part of the winding that links with those turns in the winding that are above power connection 1. With the wiper extended to the CW end, it effectively has more turns than the powered turns so transformer action increases the voltage by the effective-turns ratio. Autotransformers do not find use as transducers.

Chapter Twelve
Physical Principles of Transduction — Part II

We continue our investigation of transduction with an examination of light generation. When electricity flows in a conductor, some energy is converted into heat. This heat energy raises the temperature of the conductor and, if the power is sufficiently high, conductor temperature can increase to a point where the conductor glows. Its temperature is affected directly by the amount of power it dissipates. The intensity and wavelength of the resulting light is directly affected by its temperature.

This transducer converts electrical energy into heat energy and then into light energy. The process is called *incandescence* and was first made practical by T. A. Edison. The most common device that uses this principle is the household incandescent light bulb. Of the total power that enters the conductor, less than 1% is converted to light energy; most becomes heat, so as an electrical-to-light energy converter, the incandescent bulb's inefficiency makes it less than ideal. Instead, certain solid state electronic devices that avoid heat generation are favored in modern electronic equipment. There are certainly a lot of light bulbs still in use today, but use of the incandescence principle is unpopular in electronic control system designs.

Gas ionization

When certain gases are subjected to a high potential difference, the gas ionizes, becomes a conductor, and emits visible light. Two of the more popular gases used for this type of transduction are neon and xenon. Gas ionization provides a more efficient electric-to-light conversion because the temperatures are lower than in the incandescent process.

LEDs

Light emitting diodes (LEDs) are gallium-arsenide PN semiconductor junctions that emit visible light. Their unique characteristic is that they directly convert electrical energy into light energy without an intervening thermal process. The action within the junction is the direct opposite of that which changes the resistance of a junction when light energy impinges upon it.

Current through the junction in the forward direction of an LED causes the electrons to jump to higher energy bands within the atom. When they subsequently return to their original bands, the energy so expended is emitted in the form of visible light. LEDs are popular as indicators in electronic equipment because they operate at low temperature, are very small, and are efficient because there is no intermediate thermal energy conversion process.

ELECTRICAL RESISTANCE AND CURRENT

Electrical current in a resistive conductor is converted from electrical to thermal form. The amount of power, a measure of heat energy flow, is given by

$$P = I^2R, \tag{12.1}$$

where P is the power in watts, I is the current in amperes, and R is the resistance in ohms.

In the field of instrumentation, the principle is put to work to create a true RMS voltmeter. In a true RMS voltmeter, voltage is applied to a calibrated and thermally insulated resistor. The voltage and its attendant electrical current result in a power dissapation that elevates the temperature of the resistor. Then, the temperature rise of the resistor is measured and related to the unknown voltage. Of course RMS, a measure of equivalent heating, is the basis for the correlation. The advantage of the instrument, in addition to being a true RMS-measuring device, is that it yields the RMS value of any waveshape even though the instrument can be calibrated with DC.

Thermoelectric cooling

In 1834, French watchmaker Jean Peltier was duplicating Thomas Seebeck's 1821 thermocouple experiments, when Peltier discovered that putting an electrical current into a thermocouple junction resulted in a temperature difference. Seebeck's thermocouple effect caused a current in a two-metal loop when the extreme ends of the loop were at different temperatures; he discovered the direct electric-to-thermal energy conversion process.

Peltier, on the other hand, discovered that the process is entirely reversible; by inputting electrical energy, the junction can be cooled. Commercial use of the Peltier effect is limited to small, non-moving-part refrigerators that operate from a DC source. If the aim is to create a refrigerator, it is important that the amount of input current not be excessive. That is, there is a current level for the thermocouple where the amount of cooling is greater than the heating because of electrical current in the junction resistance. If the current is excessive, heating overpowers the cooling.

MECHANICAL REACTION

All solid materials are elastic, a phenomenon indicated by their modulus of elasticity. When these materials are subjected to external stress, they deform. This well-known physical principle has been put to work in transducers. The most common implementation in fluid power is the Bourdon tube pressure gage, Figure 12.1. The instrument is made by bending a piece of tubing into semicircular form. When pressure is applied at the input port, the internal pressure causes the tube to straighten, deflecting the tip. Calibrating tip movement to known pressures, the device becomes a useful pressure transducer. Note that input is fluid pressure while output is mechanical displacement.

Other types of transducers use the material modulus of elasticity princi-

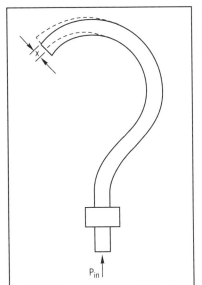

Fig. 12.1. When internal pressure in a Bourdon-tube pressure gage stretches the tube, the tip moves in direct proportion to the amount of pressure.

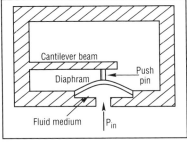

Fig. 12.2. In one version of a diaphragm pressure tranducer, the pressure-deflected diaphragm imparts motion through a push-pin to a cantilever beam. Deflection of the cantilever is calibrated against inlet pressure.

ple as well. To measure pressure, diaphragms, bellows, and simple hollow tubes are used. Pressurized fluid, introduced into the fluid cavity of a simplified diaphragm pressure transducer, Figure 12.2, acts upon the diaphgram. The diaphragm deflects because of the force generated by pressure and the deflection is imparted to a cantilever beam through a small push pin. Deflection of the cantilever can be calibrated against known pressures to create a useful pressure transducer.

The commercial version of this concept converts cantilever deflection to an electrical output by mounting strain gages on the beam. Note in Figure 12.2 that the top of the raised cantilever beam is in compression while the bottom of the beam is in tension. With two strain gages bonded to the top and two bonded to the bottom of the cantilever, the gages can be interconnected electrically to form a bridge circuit. The two tensioning gages are diagonally opposite one another in the bridge while the two compressing gages occupy the complimentary diagonals. Thus, all four gages are active and all are affected by P_{in}. This construction offers maximum sensitivity.

Force transducers are called *load cells*. One type has a *proving ring* that carries and transduces the unknown force, Figure 12.3. Applied external load force f_L causes the ring to become elliptical. Cross-center distance x is

Fig. 12.3. The proving ring is a metal ring that deforms upon application of external load force f_L. Once deflection x has been calibrated against known load forces, other x deflections are transduceable reflections of unknown loads.

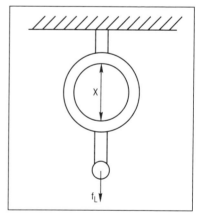

Fig. 12.4. Applied torque causes the shaft to twist, resulting in an angular difference between the input and output ends of the shaft. The amount of twist can be calibrated against known torques.

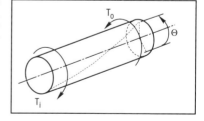

316

a function of the amount of applied force and can be calibrated. x may be converted to an electrical signal with an LVDT or with strain gages mounted on the inside and outside surfaces of the ring and on the axis which is transverse to the direction of applied force f_L.

Torque transducers, also called torque shafts, are used to measure the torque transmitted in a rotating shaft. The metal of the shaft twists in the presence of the transmitted torque, causing an angular displacement between the input and output ends of the shaft, Figure 12.4. During the calibration process, the amount of angular twist or wind-up is measured for each known torque and can then be used in a measurement situation to infer the amount of an unknown torque. In commercial versions of torque tubes, the angular deflection has been transduced using strain gages or LVDTs. Earlier we saw that magnetic pickups have been installed at both ends of the torque tube and the phase shift between the two output voltages is a reflection of applied torque. The latter method produces a phase-modulated signal because the torque data is carried in the electrical phase shift.

Thermal expansion

When materials undergo a change in temperature, a change in the physical dimensions of the body accompanies that change. It is usually an expansion with a temperature increase, and occurs in liquids, gases, and solids. This principle has been employed in temperature transducers; such bi-metal thermometers consist of two dissimilar metals bonded together, Figure 12.5. Their major dissimilarity is their respective temperature coefficients of expansion. When the bonded pair is exposed to a change in temperature, one expands more than the other to bend the assembly. The degree of bending can be calibrated for use as a temperature indicator.

The advantage of bonding two materials is that the amount of bending is greater than the simple expansion or contraction of either material alone. Thus the effect of the temperature change is apparent more readily in the bending of the assembly than it would be with only one material. Mounting strain gages on either side of the bi-metal strip and then

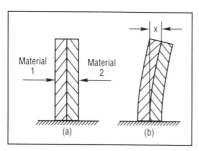

Fig. 12.5. Two materials with different temperature coefficients of expansion form the bi-metal thermometer assembly. During manufacture, (a), the assembly is straight but when exposed to an elevated temperature, (b), greater expansion of material 1 causes the assembly to bend. Tip movement x is a measure of temperature change.

forming them into a four active-gage bridge circuit converts mechanical instrument output to an electrical signal. An LVDT or other position-sensing transducer might be connected to the tip.

Liquid expansion is used in the familiar household liquid-in-glass thermometers. Alcohol-based solutions and mercury are liquids of choice because they have very low freezing temperatures; this gives the thermometer a large temperature range. The expansion liquid is contained in a relatively large bulb at the bottom of the transducer. The bulb is attached to a thin capillary tube that has been evacuated and sealed. The amount of liquid used in the manufacture of the instrument exceeds the volume of the bulb by a slight amount at room temperature so the liquid reaches up into the capillary at that temperature. When the bulb is exposed to, say, an elevated temperature, the expanding liquid rises farther in the evacuated capillary tube, and with calibration, becomes a useful temperature transducer, Figure 12.6.

Although it is difficult to convert this output to an electrical signal, it has been done by immersing a resistive element into the capillary. Then the liquid shorts out a portion of the resistor so that resistance changes with temperature. This is not a popular means of transducing temperature in fluid power systems. Gases also expand in the face of rising temperature and this principle has been put to work to make temperature transducers. Construction consists of filling an evacuated bulb with a gas (usually nitrogen because of its low freezing temperature), then connecting the bulb to a pressure transducer through a capillary tube. As the temperature of the gas changes, the internal pressure changes, reflecting the temperature of the bulb.

ELECTROMECHANICAL ENERGY CONVERSION

In electromechanical energy conversion, electrical energy is first stored in an electromagnetic or electrostatic field. Then, movement of an output member extracts some of the field energy to do useful mechanical work. The electromagnetic field surrounds a current-carrying conductor and is commonly called a magnetic field. In the electromechanical energy conversion process, this is the most commercially predominant method of energy conversion. Note also that the energy contained in the magnetic field is directly proportional to the amount of magnetic flux in the field, and that the amount of flux can be increased by forming the current-carrying conductor into a coil so that the flux produced by one wrap of the coil adds to that of the next wrap, and to the next, and so on. The flux can be further increased by providing it with a path that has a low reluctance (resistance) with the most common path material being iron. The resulting device is an iron-core inductor, but somewhat complex in that at least one part of its iron core is able to move.

Electrostatic fields for the most part are invisible to non-technical observers and are mostly misunderstood even when their effects can be seen. These fields exist because a positive electrical charge is separated from a negative charge — a charged capacitor. The electrostatic field exists in the dielectric between the capacitor plates and is substantially confined to that region. One plate is positively charged and the other is negatively charged, creating the necessary and sufficient condition for an electrostatic field.

This kind of field also exists after walking across a carpet when the humidity is low. The arc and shock that occur when a metal object is touched are palpable evidence of the energy that is stored in the electrostatic field. The shock arises because of the current that results from the electrical charges being redistributed between the charged body and the neutral metal. The heat of the arc dissipates the energy that was stored because of charge separation.

Passing a comb through your hair also picks up electric charges and the comb is able to attract small pieces of paper. Lifting the paper against gravity constitutes an electromechanical energy conversion because work is done on the paper. It is possible to harness the energy of the electrostatic field to make workable motors but they have not met with commercial success because the ability to:

- store sufficient energy requires a large number of capacitor plates, and
- generate sufficient force and torque requires extremely high voltages.

When making the calculations needed to build machines of a practical speed, torque, and power capacity, the machine either becomes very large, the voltage becomes excessive, or both. Electromagnetic energy conversion, therefore, has become much more popular than electrostatic energy conversion and is certainly more important to practitioners of electrohydraulics.

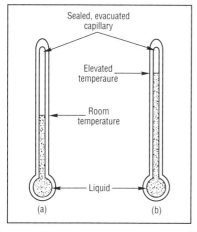

Fig. 12.6. When the thermally expandable liquid in the liquid-in-glass thermometer, (a), is exposed to an elevated temperature, the liquid rises in the sealed-and-evacuated capillary tube giving an indication of temperature change, (b).

Quartz crystals generate an electrical charge when subjected to an external force. The process is reversible. That is, when subjected to an external voltage, the crystal will change its shape or generate a force if its motion is constrained. To apply this phenomenon, the quartz is formed into a helical coil which produces a useable motion of the tip and provides a force on the order of a few pounds. Quartz motors have been used as valve operators, but are not commercially popular.

Of the electromagnetic energy convertors, there are many in regular use in today's industrial environment. Motor types include induction, synchronous, DC, stepper, brushless DC, and torque. Linear machinery includes AC, DC, and proportional solenoids, linear-force and linear-induction motors. All have found use in fluid power applications, but the few that are significant in the electronic control of hydraulic systems are torque motors, proportional solenoids, and linear force motors. These three are the links between the electronic world and the hydraulic world.

Torque motors, with only 1° or 2° of angular rotation, are popular on servovalves and also can be found on some proportional valves. Proportional solenoids got their name from their application to that class of continuously variable, electrically modulated control valves commonly called proportional valves. Linear force motors are used on both servo and proportional valves.

MECHANICAL REACTION TO FLUID MOTION

From an instrumentation and measurement point of view, mechanical reactions to fluid motion can indicate the rate at which a volume of fluid passes the measurement point. The generic name for the instruments that do this is *flowmeter*. A wide variety of physical principles has been put to work to create commercially viable flowmeters. Each has its strengths and weaknesses, its advocates and detractors. In spite of, or perhaps because of, the great number of different kinds of flowmeters, precise flow measurement remains a challenge. The state-of-the-art in flow measurement accuracy (actually, the correct term is error) is about $\pm 0.05\%$. That is, no one in the entire world can measure flow any more accurately than that and even if they could, there is as yet no way to prove it.

Contrast this with the ordinary quartz crystal-controlled wrist watch that routinely is capable of measuring time within 1 second per month, an error of only about one part in 2.6 million! State-of-the-art time measurement error is about 1 part in 10^{12}. Flow measurement is done routinely in the laboratory but is not widely incorporated in the industrial control of fluid power machinery. Cost is one deterrent and physical size is another. Of course, insertion of a flowmeter into a system requires that the plumbing be disassembled, the flowmeter plumbed in, and the plumbing reassembled. However, as electronic controls become more widespread and commonplace, there will undoubtedly be increased use of flow transducers in fluid power machinery. Each of the wide variety of flow-transduction principles generates its own kind of signal, has its own response, and requires its own kind of signal-conditioning equipment.

Positive displacement

Positive displacement is the basic means of energy conversion in fluid power. The term describes the process in which motion of a rigid member *sweeps* or positively expels fluid when making its motion, such as a piston that slides within a close-fitting cylindrical bore. Conversely, when fluid is forced into a cylinder the piston moves positively This is the basis of a positive-displacement motor. In fact, positive-displacement hydraulic motors can be successfully used as flow transducers after appropriate calibration.

The positive-displacement process can be achieved using several mechanical schemes, namely pistons within bores, meshing gears, vanes, nutating discs, and/or abutments. All have been used in fluid pumps, motors, and flowmeters. A positive-displacement flowmeter is actually a hydraulic motor designed to have low internal leakage and low starting torque relative to its torque capability. The nutating disc is another design principle. It accomplishes its positive displacement by virtue of a disc which nutates (like the nodding of the head), alternately accepting influent on one side and expelling it on the other. The nutation or wobbling is imparted to a shaft that turns so the total angular excursion of the output shaft is a reflection of the total volume of fluid that has passed during some metering time interval. Output-shaft speed, on average, is a measure of the volumetric rate of fluid transfer (flow) between the inlet and outlet ports.

A tachometric transducer at the output shaft produces an output voltage or a frequency proportional to flow. When frequency data are fed

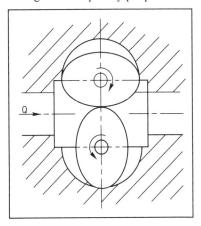

Fig. 12.7. The gear shape of a positive-displacement, oval-gear flowmeter provides a large displacement in a small package.

into an electronic counter, the counter will hold a digital value indicative of the total amount of fluid that has passed through the meter since the electronic counter was last reset. This meter-counter combination is commonly called a *totalizing meter* or an *integrating flowmeter*. The most common use of nutating-disc flowmeters is in home water-metering systems. In most older homes, the totalizing counter is a geneva mechanism that mechanically displays the total gallons of water that has passed through the meter.

Spur gear sets also have been used to implement the positive-displacement function. An oval gear set, Figure 12.7, is the internal mechanism in some flowmeters. The meshing gears, along with the small clearances at the gear tips and along their faces, produce the positive displacement. The reason for the oval-gear shape is that displacement per gear-shaft revolution is larger than it would be with a circular gear. In fact, the oval gear set can be viewed as two gears, each with only two effective teeth. The actual gear teeth, which are relatively small, merely serve to keep the two gears synchronous. A drawback of this instrument arises from the fact that the rate of volume transfer (instantaneous volume change per degree) varies considerably with gear position. This results in a non-uniform instantaneous shaft speed even when the inlet flow is perfectly constant.

If one is interested only in total volume metered over a substantial time interval or the average flow, the pulsating speed is inconsequential. On the other hand, if you need to know the instantaneous or dynamic flow, the instrument is deficient. A simple spur-gear hydraulic motor is a better dynamic flowmeter provided that it has a tolerably small internal leakage and low running pressure.

Positive-displacement flowmeters should always be used in the low-pressure lines of a hydraulic system. One reason is that most of them have a low case-pressure capability. High-pressure hydraulic motors are not

Fig. 12.8. When P_A is greater than P_B, there are resistances to leakages through paths R_{LAC} (A port-to-case) and R_{LPP} (port-to-port) that do not pass through the positive metering elements. These result in measurement error.

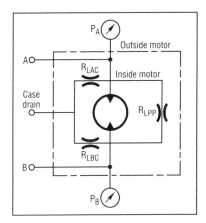

necessarily limited by their case pressures but they still must be used in the low-pressure lines because there is always an internal component of leakage that finds its way from the high-pressure inlet port to the motor case without passing through the positive-displacement elements within the motor. Figure 12.8 shows a simplified schematic of a typical hydraulic motor which is constructed of an ideal positive-displacement section plus some leakage paths. If the differential pressure across the meter (motor), P_A to P_B, is small, then the leakage component through port-to-port leakage path R_{LPP}, (leakage resistance, port to port) is similarly small. Of course, the running torque of the motor controls this differential pressure.

Thus, the best positive-displacement flowmeter will have low friction, low running torque, negligible load on the output shaft and because of this, a low differential pressure drop. This keeps the port-to-port bypass leakage small. However, if the differential pressure is low, it is still possible that P_A and P_B could be high. In that instance, there can be a substantial leakage component through the R_{LAC} (leakage resistance, A port to case) path, assuming the case drain pressure is low. The component of leakage through R_{LBC}, (leakage resistance, B port to case) has been metered so it does not matter. The case drain port can be maintained at a high pressure simply by blocking the port, but that requires a high-pressure case and shaft seal. That type seal could induce undesired friction on the shaft and require a higher differential pressure. It is better to put the flowmeter in the low-pressure lines, because any flow which enters the flowmeter but does not have to pass through the displacement elements constitutes a measurement error in the amount of the bypass flow.

Turbines and propellors

When moving fluid engages the pitched blades of a turbine flowmeter, Figure 12.9, a torque is created that turns the turbine. The turbine blades usually are made of a magnetic material to facilitate transduction. It is common industrial practice to include a magnetic pickup coil that generates a voltage pulse each time a turbine blade passes and alters the

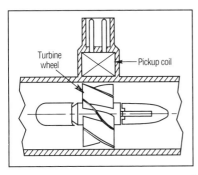

Fig. 12.9. When moving fluid impinges on the turbine blades of this flowmeter, it creates a torque that turns the turbine. A magnetic pickup generates a voltage each time a turbine blade passes.

reluctance of the magnetic path. Output voltage frequency varies in an integer relationship to the rotational speed of the turbine. The speed of the turbine is directly related to the volumetric flow through the meter but that relationship must be determined by calibration.

The calibration curve for a turbine flowmeter, Figure 12.10, is typically presented as the *K factor*, a function of independent variable f/v, on semilog graph paper. This Universal Viscosity Curve is typical of most turbines. The range on the horizontal axis is about two decades (100:1), stretching from about 20 to about 2000. The horizontal-axis limits correspond to K-factor limits of about 6580 pulses per gallon to a peak of about 6800 pulses per gallon. That is, as the user of this instrument changes the f/v ratio in the application from 20:2000, the turbine will deliver 6700 pulses for each gallon that passes through it, within ±110 pulses.

We would say then that the meter has a constant K factor of 6700, within ±110 counts (±1.5%) over the 100:1 range on the horizontal axis. On the other hand, if use of the instrument is confined to the range of 10:100 horizontally, then the K factor is constant within perhaps ±0.1%. On some turbines, the range on the f/v axis may be as high as 1000:1, or three decades. The user must determine the proper interpretation when using these graphs because the simplistic conclusion is that the flowmeter has a useful flow measuring range of 100:1 for the instrument whose curve is given in Figure 12.10.

This is not the case, which best can be understood by considering the test procedure. The test is done at several different flows, and at two, three, or perhaps as many as four different viscosities. That is, a test is run at some high viscosity and a 10:1 flow range. This describes the curve say, from 7 f/v to about 70 f/v. Then the viscosity is reduced (by using a different fluid) and the test is run again with a 10:1 flow range which will be used to describe the curve from 70 to 700 f/v, and so on. The correct interpretation of the curve is that it is a measure of the sensitivity of the instrument to changes in viscosity, not the useful flow rangeability.

The flowmeter industry uses the term *turn-down ratio*. This refers to the

Fig. 12.10. The universal viscosity curve for a turbine flowmeter shows how the K factor varies with the ratio of turbine frequency f to kinematic viscosity v. A logarithmic horizontal axis is needed to cover the entire range. Note that the K factor axis has a broken scale.

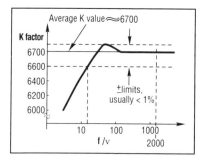

ratio of the maximum flow that can be measured to the useful minimum value of measurable flow. When making tests at a single viscosity, the turn-down ratio of a typical turbine flowmeter is about 10:1 in the best instruments, and may be as low as 5:1 in some others. When operated outside that range, the *constant* K factor is not constant at all, and can lead to measurement error if not corrected. This limitation is not at all apparent from the graph of Figure 12.10.

Turbine flowmeters are popular instruments in fluid power systems and laboratories because they offer advantages over other types. First, they can be used in high-presssure lines up to the pressure rating of the envelope; second, they are much smaller than many of the other choices; and third, they are inexpensively adapted to electrical output with the magnetic pickup coil. To the extent that the integrity of the bearings is maintained, a turbine flowmeter will maintain its calibration very well. Turbine blade shape must also be maintained, therefore their use in contaminated fluids can lead to serious data errors because of blade and bearing deterioration.

The major disadvantage of turbine flowmeters is that the output data is always frequency. Electronically, it is impossible to convert from frequency to either digital or analog values without a time delay. Therefore, even though the turbine may be very fast to respond to changes in flow, the electronic signal conditioning always adds delays to the read out value of flow. The time delay in a feedback control system always makes the control design problem more difficult.

Flow-to-pressure conversion

In flow-to-pressure conversion, the kinetic energy contained in the moving fluid is converted to potential energy. That potential energy results in a pressure difference. The measurement problem then becomes one of measuring pressure, but of course the pressure must be calibrated against known flows through the instrument — a flowmeter. The principle has been employed in a number of ways, all of which have been used in the fluid power environment.

Laminar flow tube. Any time viscous fluid passes through a restrictive passage, there is a corresponding pressure gradient as the fluid makes its way through. With a Reynolds' number below about 2000, it is generally

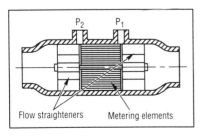

Flow straighteners   Metering elements

Fig. 12.11. The laminar flow-tube flowmeter uses a multiplicity of long, narrow passages in parallel to enhance laminarity and at the same time increase maxiumum flow capacity. Pressure taps provide access to the differential pressure drop.

accepted that the fluid motion will be laminar. In the laminar region, there is a linear relationship between the flow and the pressure gradient:

$$Q = [\pi D^4 (P_1 - P_2)]/128 \mu L, \tag{12.2}$$

where D is the diameter of the flow-carrying tube, P_1 is the gage pressure at the entry port of the tube, P_2 is the gage pressure at the tube exit port, μ is the absolute viscosity, and L is the length of the tube. Low Reynold's numbers are achieved in a number of ways, one being to make diameter D very small. But when the diameter is small, a substantial pressure drop is required to force the fluid through the tube or its maximum flow capacity is small.

To solve this problem, the designer uses many small-diameter passages and places them in parallel so that the maximum flow capacity can be made as large as needed, Figure 12.11. The major advantage of this design is the linear relationship between the flow and the differential pressure drop. It is possible to make the flowmeter so that the pressure drop at maximum flow is less than 1 psi, which causes a minimal disturbance when the meter is inserted into the test circuit. Of course the measurement problem then becomes one of measuring a relatively small pressure drop, but pressure-transducer technology allows this to be done at modest cost and with great reliability.

Another advantage is that the instrument is extremely fast compared to other types of flowmeters — such as the positive-displacement types and turbines — provided that the pressure transducer is fast. In fact, depending upon the type of differential pressure transducer, the transducer can become the limiting dynamic factor. Imagine the response if the pressure were measured in a U-tube mercury manometer. It could take seconds for the pressure indicator to settle after a flow change had taken place. On the other hand, if a variable-reluctance differential pressure transducer were used, the dynamic response could be as high as several hundred Hz, producing a steady-state output in a few milliseconds.

Disadvantages of the laminar flow tube include the dependence upon temperature (viscosity) and the limited linear range. Temperature can be accommodated by empirically deriving a mathematical model of the viscosity-temperature relationship, use of Equation (12.2), and a temperature measurement at the flowmeter to provide a correction to the differential pressure reading. These measures are problematic, however, because the point at which the pressure-flow relationship is no longer linear — the non-laminar flow regime — depends on the pressure differential and on the viscosity as well.

The mathematical model of the laminar-flow process becomes somewhat complex but not intractable. If the instrument is calibrated over the entire laminar flow range and at a representative number of viscosities, an

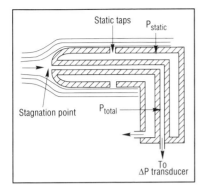

Static taps P_{static}

Stagnation point

P_{total}

To
ΔP transducer

Fig. 12.12. A pitot tube converts the kinetic energy in the moving fluid into a pressure at the stagnation point. Static taps at right angles to the flow stream measure the static pressure inside the flow-carrying envelope. The pressure differential is a reflection of fluid velocity.

empirical model for the entire meter can be derived using curve-fitting techniques. A linear pressure-flow relationship and a fast response are many times worth the effort needed to perform analysis on the data.

Pitot tube. A pitot tube, Figure 12.12, has an opening at the tip of the tube which points directly into the flow stream. The pressure at the stagnation point is the sum of the static pressure inside the fluid-carrying envelope plus the dynamic pressure created by the deceleration of the fluid at the stagnation point. A practical pitot tube therefore, is outfitted with a second pressure tap that measures the static pressure within the envelope. The axis of the static port opening is at right angles to the flow stream, and therefore does not sense a dynamic component of pressure. The differential pressure between the stagnation point and the static port is a measure of the fluid velocity. Using Bernoulli's equation, it is possible to show that the differential pressure is:

$$\Delta P = \rho v^2 / 2, \tag{12.3}$$

where ρ is the fluid's mass density and v is the fluid velocity just upstream of the stagnation point.

It should be clear that the basic sensing device measures fluid velocity. Therefore, fluid flow must be reconciled with the cross-sectional area of the flow-carrying envelope. Because the instrument is sensitive to the density of the fluid, a flowmeter thus constructed measures *mass flow* rather than *volumetric flow*. So to be of use in hydraulic fluid power applications, mass flow must be converted to volumetric flow using the mass density of the process fluid. The mass density must be known. By substituting the relationship that velocity is the volumetric flow divided by the flow area of the envelope and solving for the volumetric flow, we find that:

$$Q = A (2 \Delta P / \rho)^{1/2}, \tag{12.4}$$

327

where A is the cross-sectional area of the flow-carrying envelope upstream of the pitot tube. A disadvantage of the pitot tube is the non-linear relationship between the flow and the output pressure signal. Speed of response can be as fast as the differential pressure transducer, however. With digital processing, it is a simple software task to linearize the data using Equation (12.4).

Drag body flow sensor. The drag body flow sensor is a proprietary design

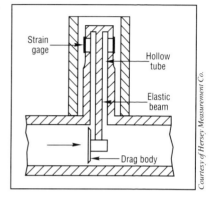

Fig. 12.13. The drag-body flow sensor converts the flow force that acts upon the target area into a beam deflection. The force is sensed and converted to an electrical output with strain gages connected in a four-active-arm bridge configuration.

Strain gage

Hollow tube

Elastic beam

Drag body

Courtesy of Hersey Measurement Co.

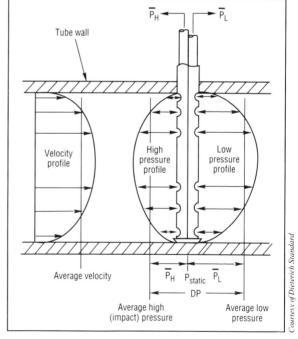

Fig. 12.14. The Annubar© flow sensor addresses the cross-sectional flow gradient problem by sensing and averaging the dynamic pressure at four points across the flow stream.

$\overline{P}_H$ $\overline{P}_L$

Tube wall

Velocity profile

High pressure profile

Low pressure profile

Average velocity

$\overline{P}_H$ P_{static} $\overline{P}_L$

DP

Average high (impact) pressure

Average low pressure

Courtesy of Dieterich Standard

which converts the force created by fluid flow into deflection of a cantilever beam, Figure 12.13. The cantilever is attached to the drag body on the end in the flow stream and to a flexure tube on the other. The flow force acting on the drag body is propagated to the flexure tube and the tube flexes because of the force. Four strain gages mounted on the flexure tube sense the strain in the tube. Connecting the gages into a four-active arm bridge circuit and powering the bridge with a supply voltage translates the fluid flow force into an electrical output voltage. The flexure tube serves as the strainable member as well as a sealed barrier that keeps process fluid away from the strain gages and other electrical elements. Output voltage is a squared function of the flow and conventional strain gage signal conditioning equipment is required.

Annubar flow sensor. The Annubar flow sensor is a modified pitot tube of proprietary design. A disadvantage of the basic pitot tube is that it actually measures the speed of the fluid at one point in the cross section of the flow-carrying envelope. To convert to volumetric flow, assumptions must be made about the nature of the flow gradient across the entire cross-section of the pipe that carries the flow. These assumptions may be correct in one case but not in another under differing flow conditions. The Annubar design attempts to solve the flow gradient problem.

An upstream element, Figure 12.14, spans the entire diameter of the flow-carrying tube and has multiple pitot openings. With different fluid-stream velocities across the cross section, there are different dynamic presssures at the openings. Within the upstream tube, the total pressure consists of the static pressure in the flow-carrying tube, plus a dynamic pressure component that is a complex function of the dynamic pressures. To obtain an average for these individual dynamic components of pressure, a second sensing tube, called the *interpolating tube* is installed inside the upstream element. The pressure at the interpolating tube is a composite of the dynamic pressures plus the internal static pressure. Mean-

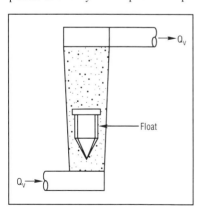

Fig. 12.15. Variable-area flowmeter uses a float inside a tapered glass tube. Flow creates a differential pressure across the float, forcing it upward to a point where increased flow area brings the differential-pressure force plus buoyancy into balance with the weight of the float.

while, a downstream element senses the static pressure so that the differential pressure between the interpolating tube and the downstream element is a measure of flow. The differential pressure reading must be processed mathematically to convert it to volumetric flow.

Variable-area flowmeter. The variable-area flowmeter, Figure 12.15, uses a float inside a tapered glass tube. The glass construction provides transparency because the readout is the position of the float. When flow enters the bottom port, differential pressure is created by the orifice formed between the float and the tapered inside diameter of the flow tube. With sufficient lift, the float rises against gravity; as it rises, orifice area increases, reducing the differential pressure.

Eventually, the float rises to a point where the differential pressure force plus the buoyancy force equals the weight of the float; it then stops rising. At that point, the meter can be read. Obviously, this instrument must be mounted in a vertical position, which can be a disadvantage. Also, because the design must reconcile the force of buoyancy, it must be calibrated for a single specific gravity. If calibrated on water, for example, use in mineral-based oil requires a correction factor for each reading.

To circumvent this problem, other designers have altered the variable-area concept by using a light-weight float operating against spring force rather than against gravity. Such instruments can be mounted in any position with a manageable shift in calibration.

Dynamic response of variable-area flowmeters is severely limited, primarily because of the physical distance that the float must move to reach the stable reading point. Although the spring-balanced design has been converted to an electrical output signal with an integral potentiometer, it remains a rather poor dynamic flow measuring instrument.

Orifice pressure drop. Because of the different flow regimes that can exist in a moving fluid, that is laminar and/or turbulent, the instrument that converts flow to differential pressure drop comes in two versions. Measure of the laminar regime has already been discussed. For turbulent flow, the orifice is deliberately designed so that it has no length along the flow path. The knife-edged orifice, Figure 12.16, forces the fluid into turbulence at flow velocities only slightly greater than zero and gives the differential

Fig. 12.16. The pressure drop across a knife-edged orifice equates to the square of the flow through it, and is substantially unaffected by the fluid viscosity.

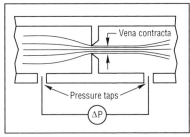

pressure drop across it a value which equates to the square of the flow through the orifice.

The knife edge also provides a degree of imperviousness to changes in temperature between calibration and use because the orifice is unaffected by changes in viscosity. The speed of response is affected by the response of the differential pressure transducer and the length of conductor that separates the two pressure taps. The non-linear pressure-flow relationship is a disadvantage, but the response time and temperature insensitivity many times outweigh the disadvantage. Linearization of the data is accomplished easily if it can be put into a digital computer.

THERMOFLUIDIC PROCESSES

Heat-transfer concepts have been put to work to create fluid power sensors and transducers, resulting in two flow sensors.

Hot-wire flow transducer

A hot-wire flow transducer, Figure 12.17, uses the heat-transfer principle that the rate at which heat energy passes from the sensor to the fluid is a measurable function of the fluid velocity at the sensor. A sensing wire lies in the path of the fluid stream and an external electronic controller supplies electrical current to the sensor's resistance that creates heat. When the surrounding fluid is stationary, sensor temperature rises to a steady-state value that is a function of the amount of current, the sensor's resistance, and the thermal conductivity from sensor to fluid. The fluid around the sensor also rises in temperature, creating a thermal gradient within the fluid. The thermal gradient acts as a barrier that retards further heat transfer. The instrument then is in thermal equilibrium in the zero flow state.

When the fluid is set in motion, heated fluid leaves and fresh, cooler fluid arrives in the vicinity of the sensor wire. This enhances transfer of heat between the sensor and fluid, causing sensor temperature to drop. Meanwhile, the electronic controller senses the rise in current caused by the drop in sensor resistance attendant with lower temperature and

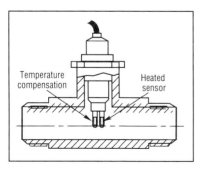

Temperature compensation

Heated sensor

Fig. 12.17. A hot-wire flow sensor measures fluid velocity by measuring the rate at which heat transfers from the heated sensor wire to the process fluid. The usual instrument maintains constant sensor temperature; the current used for this maintenance reflects fluid velocity.

increases the current until its resistance returns to the zero-flow value. The current needed to reestablish the sensor resistance is a measure of the fluid velocity at the sensor.

Now, all of this sensing and correcting takes place very quickly. In fact, it happens so quickly that the response of the instrument can be measured in kHz. This transducer has found application in laboratory hydraulic systems. The most common use is in gas-flow measurement such as measurement of the high frequency fluid flow phenomena that surround turbines and jet engines.

Heater-coil flowmeter

The heater-coil flowmeter, Figure 12.18, uses essentially the same principles as the hot wire flow transducer except the heater coil does not directly contact the process fluid. An external coil surrounds the fluid-carrying tube and heats the tube and adjacent fluid by virtue of an electrical current. At some point downstream from the heater coil, a temperature sensor is inserted into the region near the inside wall of the tube.

When the fluid is stationary, the wall and internal fluid are at the same

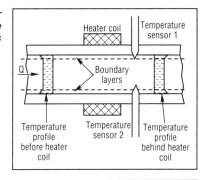

Fig. 12.18. The heater-coil flowmeter senses the change in thermal profile near the inside edge of the tube as it is inflenced by fluid velocity.

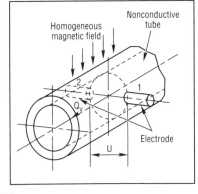

Fig. 12.19. An electromagnetic flow meter is an electrical generator where the moving fluid is the conductor. As the fluid passes through a transverse magnetic field, a potential difference is generated between electrodes 1 and 2. When the fluid is sufficiently conductive, the voltage is measurable and its value reflects average fluid velocity.

temperature. Consequently there will be no temperature difference between temperature sensor 1 and temperature sensor 2. However, when the fluid is in motion, heat energy is carried away at a different rate and the two temperature sensors will sense a gradient which can be calibrated to measure flow in the tube. This instrument has not found widespread use in the fluid power industry.

ELECTROFLUIDIC PROCESSES
Electrofluidic processes are those in which there is a direct physical interaction between electrical variables and fluid variables without a thermal or mechanical energy conversion process in between. They are found infrequently in fluid power applications, but there are two which are very interesting because of their potential and uniqueness.

Electrofluidic electrical generation
It is a well known fact that anytime a conductor moves in a magnetic field, a voltage is induced into that moving conductor. In electrofluidic electrical generators, the fluid is the moving conductor. The principle has been implemented successfully in the electomagnetic flowmeter, Figure 12.19. It is constructed with a non-conductive flow-carrying tube immersed in a strong magnetic field whose flux is oriented transversely to the fluid-flow path. The fluid constitutes a conductor moving within a magnetic field, so consequently there is a potential difference (voltage) generated between two electrodes placed along the axis that is at right angles to the plane formed by the flow stream and a magnetic flux line. The amount of voltage is a function of average fluid velocity across the flow-path cross-section and the magnetic flux density. For that statement to be true, the flux density must be uniform in the vicinity of the sensing electrodes. The usability of the output voltage is directly affected by the conductivity of the fluid.

That is, the voltage will be generated even if the fluid is essentially non-conducting, but the output impedance of the generator is so high that no signal conditioning equipment can be built that does not cause a debilitating loading error. Therefore, the device has not found widespread use in fluid power applications because of the poor conductivity of mineral-based oils and air. The meter is found in places like sewage-treatment plants because it is not adversely affected by such heterogeneous slurries. Further, the instrument has very good dynamic response and does not disrupt the flow stream.

Electro-rheological fluids
Electro-rheological fluids are those whose viscosity is affected by the presence of electric fields. It has been known for some years that certain fluids and other fluids that have been doped with certain impurities

333

behave differently in the presence of electric fields than they do in the absence of electric fields. Specifically, electro-rheological fluids experience an increase in viscosity when the magnitude of the electric field is increased. Recall that an electric field exists when charges are separated as occurs between the plates of a capacitor.

The electro-rheological control valve is implemented merely by passing the fluid between the plates of a capacitor, Figure 12.20. When electric-field intensity is increased, the fluid in its vicinity undergoes a sudden increase in viscosity. With a suffcient increase in viscosity, flow can be shut off. Removal of the electric field restores the low-viscosity state, and flow resumes as well.

State of the art in this technology has devices that operate at a few hundred psid. Clearly, this is an exciting phenomenon because the potential exists for valves with no moving parts which can respond almost instantaneously. A breakthrough in the constituent fluid could make this technology viable.

SONIC AND ULTRASONIC WAVE TRANSMISSION

Sonar gained fame in war movies which dramatized how the hunter ship located the hunted ship without visual contact. The principle is that by sending a transmitted pulse and then waiting for the return of an echo, one can determine distance, provided that the wave propagation speed in that particular medium is known. This principle has been put to practical use in several industrial transducers. There are some minor variations on the theme.

Ultrasonic position transducer

The typical function of an ultrasonic position transducer in fluid power applications is to determine the position of a piston within a cylinder. A transmitter coil receives the initiating electrical pulse from a pulse generator, forcing a deformable member to vibrate, Figure 12.21. Vibration of

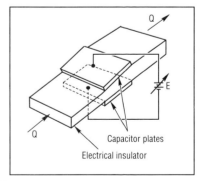

Fig. 12.20. As an electro-rheological fluid flows through an electro-rheological control valve, fluid viscosity increases because of the presence of the electrical field between the capacitor plates. With sufficient field strength and fluid sensitivity, the viscosity increase can be great enough to effectively block flow.

Q

E

Q

Capacitor plates

Electrical insulator

the member generates a wave in the fluid which propagates through the fluid at its sonic speed. When the transmitter is mounted at right angles to the piston's axis of motion, an ultrasonic reflector directs the wave along the axis of the cylinder. Eventually, the wave reaches the piston which reflects some of the ultrasonic energy; the reflected wave travels back toward the transmitter. The reflector works well in both directions so that eventually, the reflected wave reaches the deformable member.

Because the transmitter coil is wound on a permanent magnet, it works as an ultrasonic receiver as well as an ultrasonic transmitter. That is, the slight movement of the deformable member caused by the reflected wave induces a voltage in the coil. The time delay between the transmitted pulse and the returned pulse is a measure of the piston's position relative to a reference point. Meanwhile, the controller additionally measures echo time between two fixed calibration targets in the fluid. A simple mathematical ratio can determine piston position knowing the distance between the two calibration targets:

$$X_p / X_{cal} = T_{piston} / T_{cal},$$ (12.5)

where X_p is the total distance between the transmitter and the piston, X_{cal} is the known distance between the two calibration targets, T_{piston} is the measured time between the transmitted pulse and the receipt of the piston echo, and T_{cal} is the measured time interval between receipt of the two calibration echoes. X_p can be calculated and any fixed distance that occupies the first few inches where the piston is not allowed to travel can be determined and subtracted after calculation.

One of the more important fundamental concepts that arises in this example is that the waveshape thus created and shown idealized in Figure

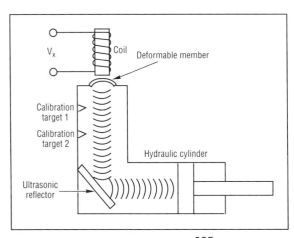

Fig. 12.21. The ultrasonic position transducer measures the distance to the piston by noting the time for an echo from the piston face to return to the transmitter. Two fixed targets of known separation are used to calibrate the speed of wave propagation every cycle.

335

12.22 constitutes a *pulse position modulated* signal. Indeed the entire system is called a *pulse position modulation system*. The constants in the system are, nominally, the receipt of the two calibration echoes and the time interval or period, T, which separates two successively transmitted pulses. The variable is the time at which the piston echo is received.

That is, the position of the piston echo in the waveshapes is a direct reflection of the physical position of the piston within the cylinder relative to the transmitter. Electronically, we say that the information we seek is carried in the position of the echo pulse. This is a pulse position modulation system because information (data) is always carried in the modulation.

This measurement can be done each and every time the transmitter pulses so that changes in fluid and temperature and other influencing variables, whatever their sources, are automatically compensated for. Unfortunately, hydraulic actuators that experience high decelerations undergo cavitation. There is a greater tendency for that cavitation to occur on the blank end of the cylinder than on the rod end. The cavitation often causes a bubble to form in the fluid because of outgassing. If the bubble reflects the ultrasonic wave, the electronic interpreter thinks the piston is closer than it really is. For this reason, ultrasonic position transducers have not found widespread acceptance in the hydraulics industry in spite of their many redeeming features.

Doppler flow transducer

When there is relative motion between the source of a sound wave and the receiver of those waves, the receiver senses a shift in frequency from the frequency that was transmitted by the source. The amount of shift correlates directly with the relative velocity between the source and receiver. When the relative motion is such as to bring source and receiver together, the receiver experiences a higher-than-transmitted frequency.

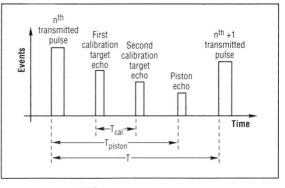

Fig. 12.22. T_{CAL}, *the time between the first and second calibration echo pulses, is* used to calibrate the sonic velocity every transmitter cycle in an ultrasonic position transducer. The system provides pulse position modulation because it is the position of the piston echo within time frame T that carries the data regarding piston position.

When the motion causes the source/receiver combination to diverge, the receiver senses a lower-than-transmitted frequency. This well-known phenomenon is called the *doppler effect*, named after 19th century Austrian researcher Christian Johann Doppler. The doppler effect has been implemented in the ultrasonic or doppler flow transducer, Figure 12.23.

As this transducer is constructed, an ultrasonic transmitter is situated on one side of the flow-carrying tube, and a mating ultrasonic receiver is on the opposite side. With the fluid at rest, the receiver experiences exactly the same frequency that is transmitted at T. When the fluid is in motion, the wave propagates diagonally across the tube at the sonic speed of the fluid medium plus a component of speed containing the fluid velocity. As a result, the receiver *hears* a wave of shorter wavelength (higher frequency) than that which was transmitted. The shift in frequency is a measure of the average fluid velocity across the tube's cross section. Note that to obtain a fluid velocity component in the wave velocity, transmitter and receiver cannot be sited directly across from one another. Instead, they must be situated diagonally as shown.

A clear advantage of the doppler flow transducer is that it causes a minimal disturbance of the flow stream. There is, for all practical purposes, no pressure drop. Additionally, the instruments can be calibrated bidirectionally, allowing flow measurement in either direction. Of course, reversal of flow direction is detected in f_r as a reduction in frequency, compared to f_t. This system generates an FM signal because the information that is sought is carried in the change in frequency from the reference frequency.

This is exactly the same principle used for FM radio transmission. In the case of the flowmeter, the wave is mechanical and the frequency is a

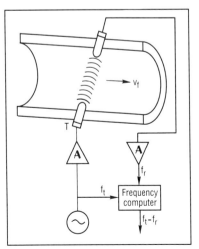

Fig. 12.23. The doppler flow transducer senses a change in frequency at the receiver when the fluid medium is in motion. The change in frequency is a measure of the average fluid velocity.

few tens of kHz, whereas in radio transmission, the wave is electromagnetic and the transmitted frequency is in the commercial FM band (several MHz). The frequency comparator in Figure 12.23 is not a basic electronic device such as those already discussed elsewhere in this book. It is an *FM demodulator* which senses the shift in frequency between the transmitted frequency (called the *carrier frequency*) and the received frequency, and outputs a comensurate voltage. That voltage, then, is calibrated against known flows through the meter to provide a useful output.

Another advantage is that the instrument is extremely fast, limited primarily by the frequency of the transmitted signal. Barring any substantial delays in the demodulator (there need not be any), bandwidths of several hundred Hz can be achieved although manufacturers will not normally quote the dynamic response of these instruments. A notable disadvantage of the doppler flowmeter is its cost. At the time of this writing, list price of these instruments is in the $6000 to $8000 range, support electronics included. The flowmeter industry refers to the doppler flowmeter as an *ultrasonic* flowmeter that happens to use the doppler principle. A variation of this is a class of instruments that use a *transceiver*, instead of the transmitter-receiver combination. It is not unusual that the transmitting member is also a good receiving member, thus with proper support electronics, one component is eliminated.

There are some limitations, however. Such instruments will work only if there is something in motion which will reflect the transmitted pulse. Therefore, the fluid must contain some impurities, or non-homogeneous elements. In the same manner as sonar, the transmitter sends out an ultrasonic burst and then pauses. The wave then propagates into the moving flow stream, until it strikes a body with a different sonic speed. That body reflects some of the ultra-acoustic energy back to the transmitter, which is now in its *listening* mode. Of course, the delay between transmission and echo receipt is a measure of position of the reflecting body, and the frequency of the echo is a measure of its velocity. These instruments have not found use in fluid power because they essentially require the fluid to be contaminated. They work well on non-homogeneous materials such as vegetable soup which has a high concentration of sonically reflective bodies; not so with hydraulic fluids.

MAGNETOSTRICTION

Magnetostriction is the principle whereby a ferromagnetic material experiences an internal stress in the presence of a magnetic field and then undergoes a subsequent change in its physical dimensions. The converse is true as well; that is, when a ferromagnetic material is strained, it undergoes a change in its permeability. Permeability is a measure of the ability to build a magnetic flux. Therefore, the presence of strain in the magnetic material causes a change in its magnetic properties. This principle has been put to work to make the ultrasonic transmitter that was described earlier for the doppler effect transducers.

When a magnetostrictive, ferromagnetic material is subjected to a high frequency (several kHz) magnetic field, the induced stress causes the material to change dimension, and the frequency of the magnetic field can be seen as a vibration of the member. That vibration constitutes the transmission of the ultrasonic wave. This vibration is contrasted with the vibration that takes place in the speaker of some audio equipment. In that speaker, which is just a special-purpose vibratory motor, the audio signal controls the current into the speaker coil that is immersed in the field of a permanent magnet. There is a force acting on the current-carrying conductor that causes the speaker coil and its attached speaker cone to vibrate at the audio frequency, creating a pressure wave which the human ear interprets as sound.

In the magnetostrictive transduction process, the pressure-wave energy is created because the material is shrinking and expanding in unison with the AC excitation frequency. Not surprisingly, the physical excursion of the speaker cone is much greater than the physical excursion of one end of the magnetorestrictive material. The former may be as high as a ¼ inch at low frequency and high power while the later excursion may be on the order of a few microinches, electrical power levels being equal. This is the reason that the magnetostrictive ultrasonic generator is more effective at the ultra-audio frequencies while the speaker is more effective in the audio range.

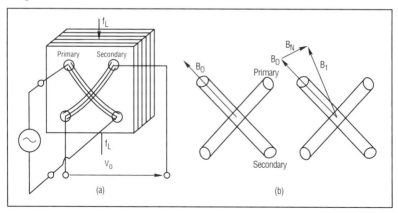

Fig. 12.24. The primary and secondary windings of a load cell are oriented in space such that normally, primary flux B_O does not link with the secondary, so there is no secondary voltage with applied load f_L. The stress reduces the magnetic reluctance in the direction of force (stress), creating flux component B_N, which links with the secondary and generates a commensurate output. B_1 is vector sum of B_O and B_N.

Magnetostriction has been used in a certain load cell for measuring force, Figure 12.24. The transducer has several layers or laminations of ferromagnetic, magnetostrictive material that have been bored to receive the four sides of a primary and a secondary coil. The spacial orientation of the coils is such that flux created by a primary current has an axis which lies in the same plane as the secondary coil, in normal or relaxed operation. With no flux linkages to the secondary, there is no induced voltage in the secondary, even though the primary is excited by some AC electrical power source. But when a load is applied, the reluctance of the magnetostrictive material changes along the axis of the applied force, but not along the axis transverse to that force. Flux build-up is enhanced along the force axis, Figure 12.24(c), creating normal component of flux B_N, which pierces the plane of the secondary coil, inducing a force-related secondary voltage. Output voltage can be calibrated in terms of applied force f_L.

Perhaps the most common application of magnetostriction in fluid power has been the development of linear-motion position transducers that easily can be buried in cylinder piston rods, Figure 12.25. In this hardware, the piston rod is hollowed out to receive the transmitting rod of the transducer. A ring magnet is fixed to the moving piston, circling the transmitting rod and moving up and down the transmitter rod in male-to-female relationship without contact. At the fixed end of the transmitter rod, attached to the blank end cap of the cylinder, a pulsing electrical generator sends a current pulse that travels into the tube at the speed of

Fig. 12.25. The interaction of the magnetic field of the interrogating pulse and the magnetic fields of the external permanent magnets causes a twist in the waveguide. This twist or torsional strain pulse is transmitted along the waveguide, damped at the end of the waveguide, and sensed in the transducer head. Two magnetic strain-sensitive tapes attached to the waveguide are coupled to sensing coils in the transducer head. The torsional strain pulse of the waveguide causes a small vibration of the tapes relative to the magnetic field of the sensing coils. This vibration induces a voltage in the coils that is amplified and conditioned in the transducer head assembly. This signal then is sent back to the analog electronics box as the return pulse.

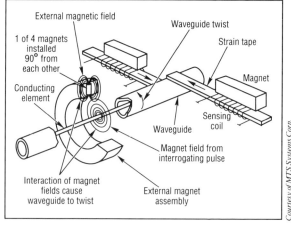

Courtesy of MTS Systems Corp.

light.

When the current pulse reaches the ring magnet, interaction of the current with the magnetic field generates a magnetostrictive strain in the rod. That strain propagates down the rod toward the transmitting end at the speed of sound in the rod material. This strain, of course, is a very tiny circumferential mechanical movement of the rod, trying to twist the rod. At the transmitting end, there are also small permanent magnets mounted so as to move as the tube twists. The movement, however small, is done very rapidly and at high velocity so a voltage is induced in a coil which surrounds the permanent magnets. The time delay between the occurrence of the transmitted pulse and the receipt of the echo pulse from the ring magnet can be calibrated in terms of distance, thus creating a viable position transducer.

Chapter Thirteen
Proportional Electrohy- draulic Interface Device Fundamentals

Because the subject of this text is electronic components and circuits as applied to hydraulic systems, little detail is included about basic hydraulic components. It is assumed that readers are familiar with this hardware. Those who are unfamiliar are encouraged to consult any of the excellent basic hydraulic textbooks and manuals for this information.

As introduction to proportional electrohydraulic valves, consider the symbol, Figure 13.1. Observe that horizontal lines just outside the schematic of a valve envelope and parallel to the longitudinal axis, indicate that the valve is continuously variable. That is, the spool can take and maintain a position anywhere within its limits of travel, precisely the kind of valve of interest — electrohydraulic valves. The two types in use today are servo and proportional valves.

Valves as bridges

Bridges are used extensively in hydraulic components and circuits. All 4-way directional control valves can be drawn as a bridge circuit, a useful

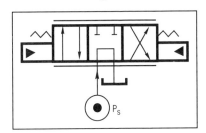

Fig. 13.1. Valve-envelope schematic with outer parallel lines indicates spool's ability to assume any intermediate position over full range of spool travel.

342

fact if one intends to mathematically model the valve for simulation and other analytical studies. Viewing the principal parts of a flapper-nozzle servovalve, Figure 13.2(a), understand that a torque applied from a torque motor to the flapper arm, say in the clockwise direction, moves the flapper closer to nozzle A and tends to close it off.

Concurrently, the flapper moves away from nozzle B to allow more flow therefrom, so the net result is a rise in pressure P_a and a drop in pressure P_b. The pressure difference, $P_a - P_b$ is felt across the two ends of the main valve spool, driving it to the right and creating communication from P port to B port and from A port to T port. Drawn schematically, Figure 13.2(b), a hydraulic bridge circuit clearly is formed.

A 4-way directional control valve also is a bridge circuit, Figure 13.3(a). When the valve spool moves to the right, $R_{p\,to\,a}$ and $R_{b\,to\,t}$ open while $R_{p\,to\,b}$ and $R_{a\,to\,t}$ close. Flow issues from the valve's A port to the load and returns via B port to tank. Left spool movement opens $R_{p\,to\,b}$ and $R_{a\,to\,t}$ so that flow issues from the valve's B port to the load, returning to tank via A port. The schematic, Figure 13.3(b), clearly shows the bridge circuit. It is balanced to stop the load and unbalanced to move it.

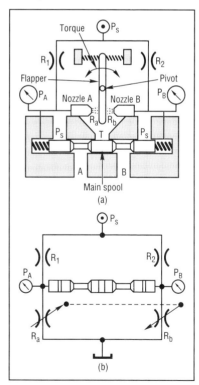

Fig. 13.2. When the flapper-nozzle pilot section (a) is drawn in schematic form, (b), it is obvious that a bridge circuit exists. By moving the flapper, restrictions R_a and R_b change in opposite directions. This unbalances the bridge and causes the spool to move against its centering springs.

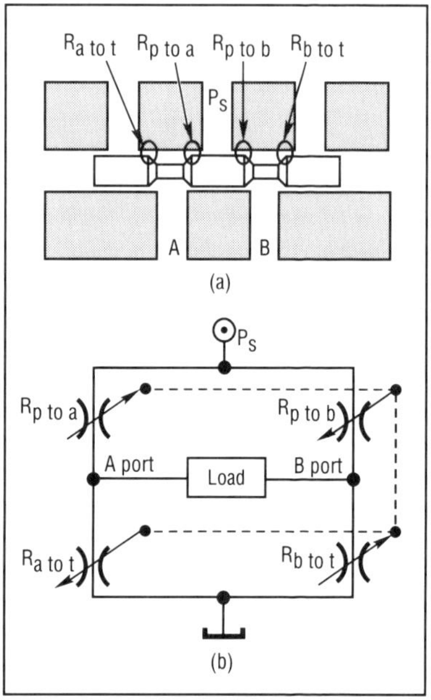

Fig. 13.3. The 4-way spool valve has four individual lands that vary in unison as the spool shifts — two lands open while the other two close. When drawn in schematic form, it is clear that the four lands constitute a bridge circuit, and spool movement unbalances the bridge one way or the other to cause a reversal in load flow.

Electromechanical actuators

It is possible to construct proportional electrohydraulic interface devices (PEHIDs, see Appendix A) only because of the invention of certain proportional electromechanical interface devices (PEMIDs). The PEMIDs commonly used in the fluid power industry include:

- torque motors
- linear force motors, and
- proportional solenoids.

The PEMIDs receive an electrical current input, convert it to mechanical force and motion, and then transform the energy into some sort of hydromechanical action. The direct mechanical action is always within a valve, although that valve may stroke a pump or directly power a load. A circuit designer would select one path or the other of the family tree, Figure 13.4, for a given application. Valve control is called the *energy-loss control* method in path *A*, because the valve, being a restrictive device, consumes excess power as a necessary part of its control function.

Path *B*, on the other hand, is called the *volume-control* or *load-demand* method that supplies only as much power as the load needs, wants, or can use. The only losses encountered using this method are those caused by the modest inefficiencies of the pump and actuator and in total, are nearly always less than those for the energy-loss, all other things being equal. This leads to these truths regarding proportioning hydraulic systems:

- path *B* is always more efficient than path *A*, and

344

● path *A* always has less initial cost because valves are less expensive than variable-displacement pumps, and one fixed-displacement pump can supply pressure fluid to more than one valve and functioning circuit branch.

Electrohydraulic valves

Continuously variable electrohydraulic valves illustrate the fact that a continuously varying control current always results in a continuously varying, controlled-output variable. That output variable could be flow, pressure, or simply the position of a spool that affects final flow and/or pressure. Broad categories of these continuously variable valves are:

● direct-acting valves where the force of the proportional solenoid acts directly upon the main spool to provide the desired degree of hydraulic control, and

● pilot-operated valves in which the PEMID acts first upon a primary hydromechanical device whose output acts on a main spool. These are also sometimes called multi-stage valves and are either 2- or 3-stage but never more. Each of the two paths of the simple family tree of all continuously variable electrohydraulic valves, Figure 13.5, can be further subdivided, but that is not elaborated on here.

Direct-acting valves

Further subdivisions include those valves that use some means of

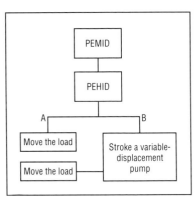

Fig. 13.4. Proportional electromechanical interface device (PEMID) causes an electrohydraulic valve (PEHID) to shift with two results: valve-control method (A), where valve output moves the load, and (B), where the valve changes the displacement of a pump with resulting pump output then moving the load, and example of the pump-control method.

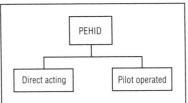

Fig. 13.5. Family tree of PEHIDs has two branches: direct-acting branch where the PEMID directly moves the main spool, and pilot-operated branch, where the PEMID shifts a pilot stage whose output moves the main spool.

345

spool-position feedback and those that do not. The non-feedback types simply take the force of the proportional solenoid and put it against a restoring spring. Thus, the main spool takes a position commensurate with the force generated by the solenoid if those were the only two forces acting on the main spool. Unfortunately, there are two other significant forces: flow forces and stiction forces.

Flow forces are a natural phenomenon in all control valves that result from the momentum change that takes place as the result of the valve's throttling effect. This occurs when potential (pressure) energy is converted into kinetic (velocity) energy in the constricting region of the valve. In spool valves, the flow force always acts to **close** the valve regardless of the direction of flow. The consequence is that when using the valve, say at low pressure drop (flow), the spool is in a position where the solenoid force is balanced by the restoring spring. As the valve's pressure drop increases, either because of a reduction in load restriction or an increase in supply pressure, the flow force increases so as to close the valve.

As a result, the spool takes a position not totally controlled by the control current (solenoid force). This does not mean the valve does not function; it does mean that the spool's exact position at any moment is harder to predict. It is true, however, that in some direct-acting valves, flow forces can be so high that they cause an automatic near-closure at high pressures and flows. Load-dependent spool position can be detected by mathematical analysis of valve pressure drop at a steady control current but varying flows. The curve, if there is no load-induced spool shift, will relate pressure drop to the square of the passing flow. If the data does not fit the square relationship, flow forces are probably causing a spool shift.

Stiction forces also act upon the spool and the solenoid's armature so that spool position does not smoothly vary as control current continuously and smoothly varies. Instead, the flow (spool position) has a stair-casing effect. Additionally, the curve trace for increasing control current is not the same as the curve trace for decreasing control current, producing *stiction-induced hysteresis*. If the valve is to be used in manually operated control systems, this hysteresis is not a major problem because a human operator can compensate easily for such performance aberrations. But when automatic controls using feedback are contemplated, hysteresis can cause a continual hunting or oscillation rather than smooth and stable operation.

Incorporating electronic dithering — that is causing the spool to be in a continuous but acceptably small state of agitation — can help significantly to reduce the detrimental effects of stiction-induced hysteresis. When properly implemented, a closed-loop feedback control system *around the spool*, called the *inner loop* in the hydraulics industry, Figure 13.6, can all but eliminate stiction and flow-force effects. This loop is

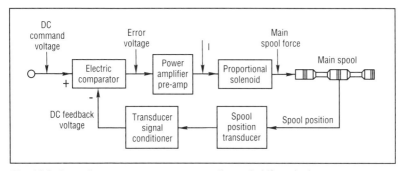

Fig. 13.6. A small current must cause a small spool shift and a large current must cause a large spool shift in continuously variable electrohydraulic valves. To assure such proportional, stepless spool positioning, some valves use a spool-position transducer to measure actual spool position. The spool is made to stop in a position commensurate with the command voltage through feedback-loop closure. This closed feedback loop often is called the inner loop.

closed by measuring actual spool position, usually with a LVTD position transducer, and comparing it to the commanded position. If the position is incorrect, the electrical current to the valve's proportional solenoid is adjusted until spool position becomes correct. Thus, the spool is always in the exact spot commanded, dynamically induced lags notwithstanding.

While not exactly true, the foregoing statement is acceptable for all practical purposes. The spool position feedback transducer of choice is nearly always a LVDT. Because LVDTs must be operated with AC voltage, they must always be accompanied by a special electronic signal conditioner that has:

● an oscillator section that generates the AC voltage to excite the transformer. This AC voltage is not derived from the 60 Hz power-company line; it is generated by a solid state electronic oscillator usually outputting a few volts at a fixed frequency, generally somewhere between 3 kHz and 10 kHz, and

● a phase-sensitive demodulator section that converts the transduced AC signal into an equivalent DC signal with the full sense of the algebraic sign of the measured position.

Pilot-operated valves

Valves with larger flow capacities need pilot stages to boost the power necessary to shift the larger spools. The electromechanical methods used for this staging are torque motors, force motors, and proportional solenoids.

Torque motors, Figure 13.7, are electromechanical rotary machines whose rotational travel is restricted, often less than 1° or 2°, and are nearly always used for a piloting function. They are fitted with permanent

Fig. 13.7. The four nominally equal air gaps of an electromagnetic torque motor each carry equal magnetic flux from the permanent magnets producing zero net torque on the armature. When current enters the coil, coil-induced magnetic flux adds to or subtracts from the four air gap fluxes creating a torque on the armature. Armature

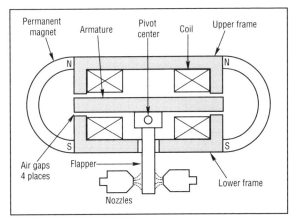

movement typically causes a flapper to move, changing resistivity of the two nozzles.

magnets as the major flux source with the flux paths arranged to form a force bridge. Their limited rotation allows the armature to be mounted on a stiff flexure spring rather than bearings, although there is one known proprietary exception which uses a soft spring. The stiff spring and lack of bearings virtually eliminate hysteresis caused by bearing restriction.

Incoming current creates a second set of magnetic fluxes that unbalance the force bridge and results in net torque. The torque causes angular rotation until the flux-induced torque equals the counter-torque of the flexing spring plus any external load. An important characteristic of the torque motor is that the direction of rotation is affected by the direction of current through the coil. The electromagnetic field caused by the current is compared to the field of the permanent magnet in the magnetic bridge circuit and rotation ensues in a commensurate direction.

In the final valve assembly, the torque-motor armature is connected to: a flapper sitting between two opposed nozzles, a jet pipe, or a swinging wand or blade. These last two steer a fluid stream, Figure 13.8, branch *B*. Basic operating principles and conceptual construction of flapper-nozzle and jet pipe servovalves are indicated in Figures 13.9 and 13.10, respectively. Torque motors almost exclusively pilot servovalves, and usually require less than 1 watt of power to fully operate although that is not a hard-and-fast rule.

Torque from the torque motor of a jet pipe servovalve steers the jet to one receiver or the other, unbalancing spool-end pressures. Movement of the main spool continues until the feedback spring between the main spool and jet forces the jet pipe back to near null. Main spool position then is commensurate with coil current.

The flapper-nozzle has two different implementations: the one already mentioned is the stiff design, wherein the force due to the impinging

348

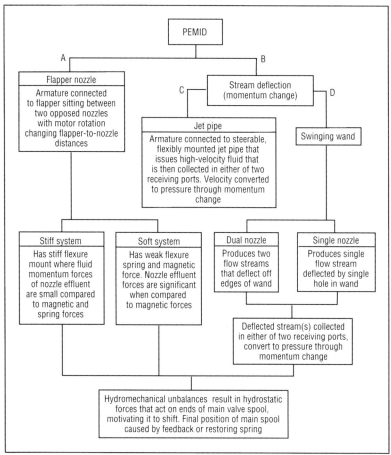

Fig. 13.8. A family tree of torque-motor electromechanical interfaces indicates all of the common piloting methods in present industrial use.

nozzle flow is small in comparison to spring and torque-motor forces. In soft designs, the torque motor and nozzles are deliberately sized so that nozzle effluent causes a significant force on the flapper. One argument concludes that this design is more tolerant of certain contamination problems. The argument goes like this: when the two fixed orifices are open fully and unclogged, the unpowered flapper will center due to a combination of fluid-momentum force acting on the flapper, restoring force on the light spring, and magnetic force in the torque motor.

Should one of the nozzles or fixed orifices become partially blocked, reduced effluent flow produces less force on the blocked side of the flapper. The flapper then moves toward the clogged bridge leg until

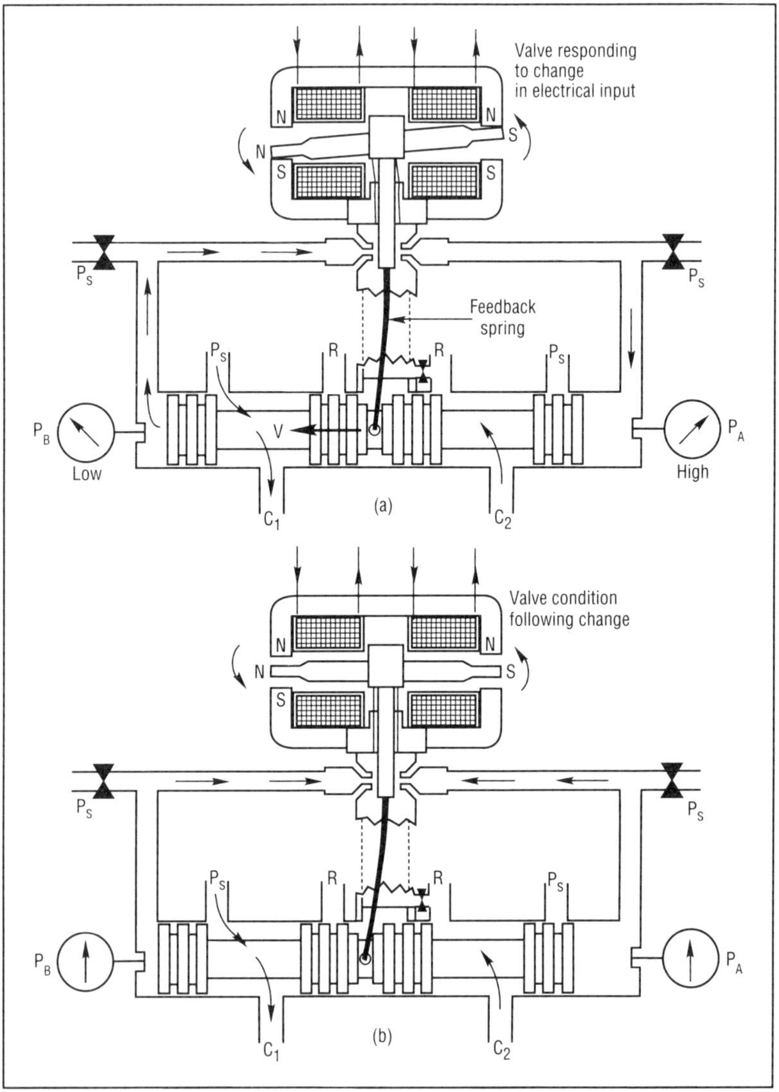

Courtesy of Moog Controls, Inc.

Fig. 13.9. Current entering the torque-motor coil, (a), causes the armature to rotate against a stiff feedback spring. The flapper, attached to the armature, blocks nozzle A and relieves nozzle B, causing pressure P_A to rise and P_B to fall. This unbalance moves the spool to the left. As the spool moves, (b), the feedback spring, anchored to the spool and the flaper, forces the flapper toward center. Eventually, the flapper and spool reach a position where the flapper is nearly centered, the pressures are nearly equal, and the spool comes to rest at a position commensurate with the amount of torque (coil current).

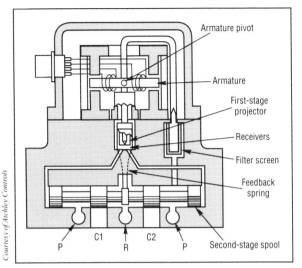

Courtesy of Atchley Controls

Armature pivot

Armature

First-stage projector

Receivers

Filter screen

Feedback spring

Second-stage spool

C1 C2
P R P

Fig. 13.10. Current in the torque motor of a jet-pipe servo-valve steers a jet nozzle, causing a pressure difference between the two collector ports. If A-port pressure is high, for example, the main spool moves to the right. Concurrently, the feedback spring drags the jet nozzle toward center and approximately equalizes collector pressures. Thus, the main spool has been positioned as directed by the coil current.

reduced force from the opposite receding nozzle equals the diminished flow force from the partially blocked nozzle. Current input to the torque motor then causes the flapper to move about a shifted neutral, but the pressure does not go to a hard-over level. The main spool might not shift fully in one direction, however.

The swinging wand, Figure 13.8 path *D*, has a mechanical-to-hydraulic interface that is proprietary to Parker Hannifin Corp. The versions of this interface include a:

● dual nozzle where the two fluid streams are deflected off the outside edges of the wand, and

● single nozzle, where a single fluid stream passes through a central hole in the wand.

Consider the dual-nozzle version, Figure 13.11. The two fluid streams issuing from the source side of the pilot head are collected in opposing receiving ports. When a current into the torque motor causes the wand to swing, one receiving port experiences a rise in pressure while the other experiences a reduction. As in the case of the jet pipe and flapper-nozzle pilots, the resulting difference in pressure shifts the valve's main spool. Parker uses this design in its industrial, 2-stage proportional valves.

The single-nozzle version has a hole laterally bored and centrally located in the wand such that the single fluid stream issuing from the single nozzle must pass through the hole. When the wand is centered, equal pressures are collected in the two receiving ports. A current into the coil causes the wand to shift and the fluid stream is deflected off the inside

351

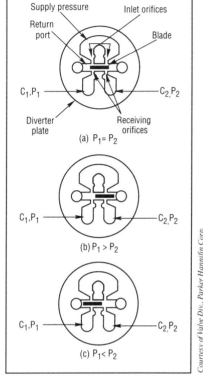

(a) $P_1 = P_2$

(b) $P_1 > P_2$

(c) $P_1 < P_2$

Fig. 13.11. The swinging-wand pilot stage generates a differential pressure in receiver ports C_1 and C_2 by deflecting two fluid streams off each edge of the wand. An unseen torque motor moves the wand in proportion to the amount of current. Thus the pressure difference between C_1 and C_2 is a reflection of coil current. Port pressures are equal, (a), C_1 pressure is higher, (b), and lower, (c).

Courtesy of Valve Div., Parker Hannifin Corp.

edge of the central hole resulting in different pressures being collected in the two receivers. The resulting differential pressure between the two receiving ports shifts the main spool.

This swinging-wand design has a supply pressure limitation in that the pilot head must be sized for a particular supply pressure range. If flow issuing from the nozzle(s) is excessive, fluid momentum force acting on the wand can pin it against the receiver side to lock-up the wand. Installing an orifice, matched with the supply pressure and the needs of the pilot stage, in series with the nozzle side remedies this problem. Approximately a 2:1 change in supply pressure is possible with a single orifice.

Force motors are the linear equivalent of torque motors in that they also have permanent magnets inside. Therefore the direction of motion depends upon the direction of input current, Figure 13.12. There is only one manufacturer of force motors in the U.S. known to the author: FEMA, Portage, Mich. The two permanent magnets each create attractive forces, each urging the armature toward it, but nominally offsetting one another

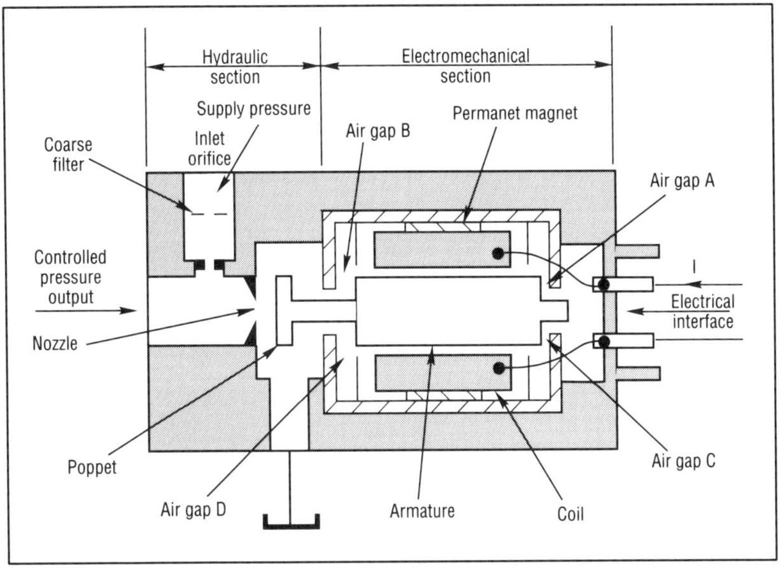

Fig. 13.12. A permanent magnet creates equal fluxes in the four air gaps of electomagnetic force motor that results in net zero force on the armature. Current into the coil in the direction shown, for example, strengthens flux in gaps B and D and weakens flux in gaps A and C. Now there is a net force to the left, pushing the poppet against the nozzle. Through control of force, the current controls output pressure.

when centered. Additionally, a stiff centering spring prevents either of the natural regenerative attractive forces from pulling the armature either way.

When a current is applied in the direction shown in Figure 13.12, the resulting electromagnetic fields act to strengthen the magnetic fields by increased flux density in air-gaps B and D while at the same time weakening the fields in air-gaps A and C. The resulting force moves the armature and poppet to the left. State-of-the-art force-motor design produces a maximum of about five pounds of stall force, about 0.02 in of travel (no load) at about 5 watts of power.

Proportional solenoids

Proportional solenoids are about 25 years old and are manufactured by a number of companies: Expert in the U. K; Ellwood Hydraulics, Oak Creek, Wis.; G. W. Lisk, Clifton Springs, N. Y.; Magnet Schultz in Germany; Parker Hannifin Corp., Cleveland, Ohio; and Vickers, Inc., Troy, Mich. The first four market their solenoids to U.S. industry, while Parker and Vickers supply themselves. All competing products have similar performance specifications. State-of-the-art proportional solenoid

Fig. 13.13. The trapezoidal air gap of a proportional solenoid is shaped to create a relatively constant force regardless of armature position when the current is constant. Because there are no permanent magnets, the force is always in one direction (to the left here), regardless of current direction. Thus, bidirectional valves always require two proportional solenoids.

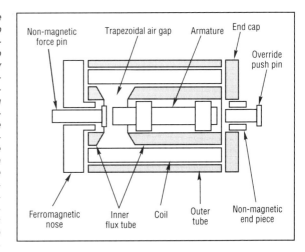

design yields these approximate *typical* specifications:

● maximum force, 20 lb

● proportioning travel, 0.10 in

● current, 12-volt coil, 1.5 to 2.5 amp, and

● power, 15 to 25 watts.

Figure 13.13 indicates approximate construction detail of a proportional solenoid. The secrets to success lie in forming the proper trapezoidal air gap dimensions and in keeping stiction low.

Figure 13.14 shows a representative force-displacement curve for a proportional solenoid. Its unique characteristics are a region of relatively constant force as the armature changes position, plus relatively linear changes in force for changes in solenoid current, both performance goals sought by the solenoid's designers. It is probably true that neither the constancy of force nor the linearity with current are as important as the manufacturers would claim. Things incorporated external to the solenoid

Fig. 13.14. Typical force vs. armature position curves show region of proportional solenoid armature travel where there is relatively constant force at constant current. Valve designers must use the solenoid so the armature operates in this proportional region. With current technology, the region is about 0.10-in wide.

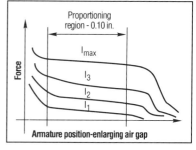

354

substantially affect performance of the total valve: use of pressure feedback or armature-position feedback, for example. Furthermore, the enormous versatility of the hardware and software of modern computers makes control and linearization a fairly straightforward task.

Device comparisons

Contrasts must be made between proportional solenoids and force/torque motors, as some differences are apparent in the specifications while others are not. Torque/force motors require lower current levels. Proportional solenoids:

● require much higher electrical output power than their motor counterparts

● produce substantially greater mechanical travel than motors

● produce higher force levels

● produce higher stiction levels

● operate with greater hysteresis, and

● generate forces in a direction independent of current direction.

Therefore, to make a 4-way directional valve operate requires two proportional solenoids but only one force/torque motor.

All of these factors make proportional-solenoid drive electronics more complex than that necessary for force/torque motors. Proportional-solenoid power requirements have caused manufacturers of proportional-valve drive electronics to adopt pulse width modulation as the power-output method of choice. The major reason for the use of PWM is to handle the high-output power required of the solenoid without overburdening the power-output transistors.

There is a second benefit of using PWM: if the PWM frequency is sufficiently low, it automatically provides a mechanical dither that helps minimize stiction-induced hysteresis. In some valves the effects of dither can only be described as dramatic when looking at the reduction in hysteresis. The correct dither frequency must be determined after the valve is designed. Furthermore, the frequency selected must be a compromise between propagating the dither pulsations imperceptibly into the hydraulic circuit and yet achieving sufficient reduction in stiction. A low frequency helps the stiction problem but if too low, the user of the hydraulic system can feel the pulsations.

U. S. industry uses PWM frequencies from about 33 Hz to about 400 Hz. At least one European manufacturer uses 40 kHz and receives no dither effects whatsoever. Their amplifier supplies dither with a separate on-board dither generator. There is an advantage to this method: dither power remains constant throughout the modulation range, whereas when relying on the PWM frequency for dithering, the dither power varies with the amount of modulation. There is none at the 0% and 100% modulation points, but maximum at 50% modulation.

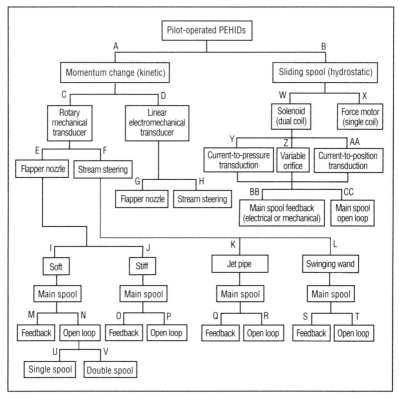

Fig. 13.15. Family tree of pilot-operated PEHIDs.

Summary of pilot-operated valves

Figure 13.15 shows a family tree of all electrically modulated, continuously variable pilot-operated valves. It is a peculiarity of the U. S. hydraulic valve-manufacturing industry that each terminus of the tree also tends to define a specific manufacturer's product. For example, the A/C/E/I/N/V path rather accurately describes the servovalve of Sauer-Sundstrand's Controls Div. in Minneapolis; its mate, U, has no supplier. In contrast though, the A/C/E/J/O path is well populated. That is where the products of Moog, Vickers, Rexroth, Dynamic Valve, and others have congregated.

Sliding-spool pilot valves

Several manufacturers of pilot-operated valves use a hydrostatic or sliding-spool scheme. They vary from the 4-way directional-control pilots of a Parker/Nichols valve, Figure 13.16, to the simple variable orifice of

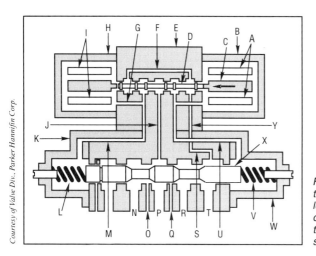

Fig. 13.16. Operation of dual-solenoid, 4-way pilot-operated proportional valve is described in text.

United Technologies Automotive/Fluid Power System's valve.

Describing the Parker Hannifin Valve Division's proportional valve, a DC current to proportional solenoid A or I, Figure 13.16, creates proportional pressure inside opposite solenoid enclosure H or B that is also propagated to 4-way end cap K or W. This pressure acts on one end of 4-way spool X and shifts it a proportional amount against centering spring L or V.

Supply pressure from supply port P in the 4-way valve is carried through channel J into pilot-valve body E. When an electrical current is fed to proportional solenoid coil A, a proportional force is generated by armature C, shifting pilot spool D to the left. The pilot spool's metering lands port supply fluid from channel J to end-cap K via internal channel M. This inflow of pressure oil into end cap K acts against 4-way spool X, moving it to the right against centering-spring V. At the same time, the metering lands of pilot-spool D connect tank port T to end cap W through channels S and U to allow fluid in end-cap W fluid to return to tank as 4-way spool X moves to the right.

Meanwhile, a force balance is obtained on pilot-spool D due to channel G which carries end-cap K pressure to left solenoid-enclosure H that acts on the left end of pilot-spool D. As the opening of pressure channel J into end-cap channel M bleeds oil into channel M and end cap K, the pressure rises in end-cap K, channel G, and solenoid-enclosure H. The force of this pressure acting on the end of pilot-spool D at some point reaches a value which barely exceeds the electromagnetic force of solenoid A and armature C.

At that point, the pilot spool moves to a position that cuts off the link between channel J and channel M. Pressure in end-cap K stabilizes, and

4-way spool X stabilizes at a position commensurate with the pressure in end-cap K, the end-area of 4-way spool X, and the effective spring rates of centering-springs L and V. Thus, the opening of 4-way spool X from the P-port to cylinder N port is controlled by the amount of current in solenoid A.

If the current in solenoid A is subsequently reduced, the force acting on armature C is proportionally reduced and the hydrostatic force generated by the pressure in solenoid-enclosure H and end-cap K is greater that the force of solenoid A. As a result, pilot-spool D moves fully to the right and the timing of pilot-spool D causes pressure-channel J to become linked to channel U. Thus, high pressure fluid is metered into opposite end-cap W and assists centering-spring V in returning 4-way spool X to its center position.

Meanwhile, note that the timing on pilot-spool D is such that when it is in the far-right position, end-cap pressure K is linked to tank-port T via channel M, bridge-channel F, and tank-channel Y. This allows fluid

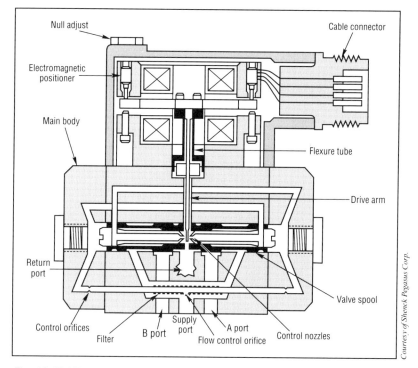

Null adjust

Cable connector

Electromagnetic positioner

Main body

Flexure tube

Drive arm

Return port

Valve spool

Control orifices

Filter

B port

Supply port

A port

Flow control orifice

Control nozzles

Courtesy of Shenck Pegasus Corp.

Fig. 13.17. With nozzles of pilot stage built into the spool, feedback spring is unnecessary. Pressures from the nozzles are ported to the opposite ends of the spool so the spool follows the flapper.

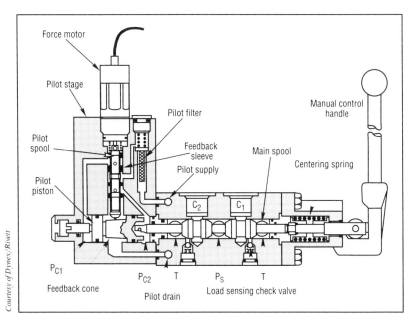

Fig. 13.18. Hollow spool and follower sleeve of pilot stage move under influence of force motor and feedback cone, respectively. As force motor positions spool relative to sleeve, it ports pressure fluid into, say chamber P_{C1}, to force feedback cone and main spool to the right. With this move to the right, the spring-loaded sleeve rides down feedback cone until sleeve position relative to the pilot spool balances the P_{C1} and P_{C2} pressures. The cone and main spool are thus positioned commensurately with amount of force-motor current.

trapped in end-cap K to return to tank when 4-way spool X moves to the left. To reverse the direction of output flow from the 4-way section P port, it is necessary to leave solenoid A deenergized and energize solenoid I instead. The entire process reverses and flow issues from port R of the 4-way section.

This valve is equipped with a special load-sensing function through relatively tiny load-sensing ports O and Q. With 4-way spool X in the position shown, load-sensing port Q is blocked, but load-sensing port O measures the load pressure in cylinder-port N. With additional circuitry not shown in the diagram, the load-sensing signal can be sent to operate a load-sensing unloading valve or load-sensing pump.

Positioning the main spool

The ultimate aim of the proportional or servovalve designer is to position a main spool in a spot commensurate with the magnitude of the control input current. This can be accomplished in either an open-loop or a closed-loop fashion. The Parker Hannifin valve is an example of open-loop positioning of the main spool. In that design, the current is converted to a pressure which acts upon the main spool ends. The main spool moves until centering-spring deflection counters the pressure force. The valve is therefore subject to the whims of stiction and flow forces acting on the main spool. As discussed earlier, feedback around the main spool counters the effects of stiction and flow force in piloted valves as well as direct-acting valves.

Feedback can be provided electrically and/or mechanically. The electrical method on pilot-operated valves uses a LVDT just as in direct-acting proportional valves. On the other hand, some clever mechanical schemes have been used in commercial products: spring feedback from main spool-to-pilot stage, nozzles in the main spool, and a feedback cone.

The concept of how the feedback spring serves to position the main spool can be seen in Figure 13.9. Note that it, like all spool-feedback schemes, helps overcome flow forces, stiction, and some contamination problems. Nozzles in the spool are used by Schenck-Pegasus, Figure 13.17, and when the hydraulic bridge circuit is properly formed, feedback *comes along free*. All of the benefits of feedback accrue to it.

A feedback cone is used in Dynex/Rivett valves, among others, Figure 13.18. Note the two piece pilot valve, consisting of a movable spool that fits into a movable sleeve. The nose of the movable sleeve rides on the feedback cone attached on the end of the main spool. When a current is sent into the force motor, the armature moves, causing oil to be ported to one end of the main spool. As the main spool moves, the feedback cone contacting the sleeve of the pilot valve allows the sleeve to re-center with the spool, stopping flow and thus stopping the main spool commensurate with input current.

Chapter Fourteen
Electrohydraulic Feed-back Control Systems

An electrohydraulic system control-loop closure is a special case of a closed-loop feedback system. In the most basic and orthodox form, any feedback system contains these essential parts or subsystems:

● some provision for entering a command into the system

● an error detector that determines the difference between the command value and the feedback signal. This error detector is also called a *comparator*, *summer*, *summing junction*, or *differencer*. Its inputs are the command and the feedback signals and it issues a single error output, the mathematical difference between the two inputs

● the plant — the generic name — that means the machine undergoing control. For our purposes, the plant is the electrohydraulic equipment less the feedback transducer, and also is called *the process* and *the forward branch*. The plant nearly always is given the symbol G which simply stands for gain. Of course in all likelihood, the plant is more complex than the simple amplifier implicit in its symbol, but whatever it is, the G indicates that it is some black box with unspecified innards

● the feedback element is nearly always symbolized using H for reasons unknown. It is almost always the feedback transducer and any necessary signal conditioning. In an electrohydraulic positional servomechanism, for example, the H element is the position transducer that measures cylinder (piston) position and generates a proportional voltage, and

● a selected output terminal or port where system output can be observed or measured. Generally, the output can represent any point in a system from which an internal variable can be observed or measured. A given system has a single output because the analyst has chosen only one of many. For example, any one of several variables in an electrohydraulic servo system can be an output. Some of them are: error voltage, coil current, feedback voltage, inlet pressure, outlet pressure, inlet flow, outlet flow, pressure drop across one valve land, speed, acceleration, force or torque, and actuator position, to name a few. The choice of output is dictated by the circumstances.

This chapter investigates how feedback systems behave. Fortunately, it is possible to study the open-loop system then predict what will happen after the loop is closed. Block diagrams are a convenient means for representing control systems without over-burdensome detail. Open-loop study really involves the study of system components: the servo/proportional amplifier, the control valve, the actuator, the feedback transducer, and the load, for example. Each component can be treated as a block or black-box component. The system designer puts the blocks together in chain-like fashion to create the system, provided that all loading effects have been taken into account.

The open-loop plant

The open loop plant is characterized by single block G, Figure 14.1. G receives command C that activates the input element. We expect that output R will respond or react in some manner dictated first, by the nature of command signal C, as well as the dynamic characteristics of the plant. Bear in mind that generally, the plant could be any machine or process that has a place to input a command and another place to measure or observe an output. If the plant is capable of responding instantaneously, then G is a simple gain block and output R is merely G times the input command. That is:

$$R = GC. \tag{14.1}$$

A good way to measure the dynamic response of a system is to input a step,

Fig. 14.1. Open-loop plant where a command is given to the plant which, in turn, produces an output response.

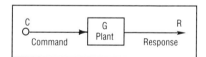

Fig. 14.2. Because output response to a step input is also a step of amplitude GC, the plant is a simple gain block capable of instantaneous response.

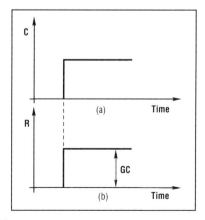

362

an instantaneous rise in command. If the output is also a step with no delay, then plant G is a simple gain block, Figure 14.2.

It should be apparent that such a plant will produce at its output an amplified reproduction of its input regardless of what the command waveshape is. The ability to reproduce an amplified version of the input is called the *fidelity* or *faithfulness* of reproduction. That is why audio amplifiers, that can produce in the output speakers an exact reproduction of the waveshape that lies on the recording, are called high-fidelity amplifiers. Servo system designers also are interested in fidelity although that term is not usually applied, and the frequencies of interest are much lower. Nonetheless, the principles are exactly the same. The system that has input/output response as shown in Figure 14.2 does not really exist.

That is, there are no real physical devices that can respond instantaneously. All real devices have some amount of dynamic-response effect that, for our purposes, appear as time lag. The time lag is usually caused by the time required to charge energy storage elements such as capacitances, whose pressures cannot change instantaneously, and masses, whose speeds cannot change instantaneously either. If the valve, Figure

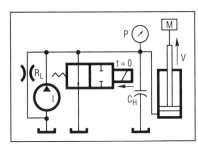

Fig. 14.3. Sudden closure of the 2-way valve creates a step flow into the system, forcing it to react and reveal its dynamic characteristics. Hydraulic capacitance C_H accounts for fluid compressibility effects.

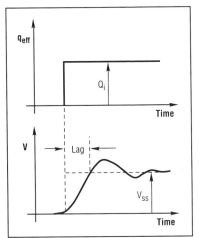

Fig. 14.4. The hydraulic capacitance and load mass not only create a resonant frequency but also produce a lag. This results in a finite time to reach steady-state speed.

14.3, is sufficiently fast and is able to shift in zero time, flow into the circuit will be a step to produce the response shown in Figure 14.4. Note that system output is cylinder velocity V.

As energy-storage elements, load mass M and hydraulic capacitance C_H; exchange energy between kinetic ($\frac{1}{2}Mv^2$) and potential ($\frac{1}{2}C_H p^2$) states, the elements account for the ringing and the time delay or *Lag*, Figure 14.4. We conclude that any time a system has energy-storage elements, time delays will ensue but not necessarily ringing. Ringing totally depends on the amount of damping or lack thereof which, in turn, is controlled by dissapative elements such as resistance, restrictivity, friction, and leakage, etc. As true as it may be that **no** real device can be free of time lag there are some so fast that they can be considered to respond instantaneously.

Consider the curves, Figure 14.5(a) and (b), that show exponential response r of a black-box system examined in two different time scales. When viewed on an oscilloscope with a sweep time of 100 msec, Figure 14.5(a), the exponential shape clearly can be seen. But if the oscilloscope sweep is slowed so that it takes 10 sec to cross the screen, Figure 14.5(b), all transient phenomena that has expired by 0.100 sec will be confined entirely to the left-most regions of the trace and will be all but invisible.

We conclude that a short time lag appears to be instantaneous to

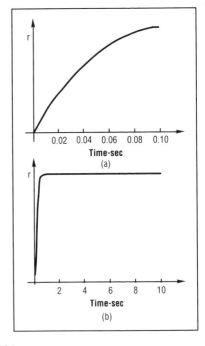

Fig. 14.5. A response of a certain black box is clearly exponential when observed in a 0- to 0.1-sec time frame (a), but looks like a step when viewed over 10 sec, (b).

another device that is much slower. In an electrohydraulic system for example, if we have a valve which can shift, say, in 0.050 sec that is connected to a cylinder-mass circuit that has a hydromechanical resonant frequency of, say, 1 Hz, the valve shift appears essentially instantaneous to the cylinder. For practical purposes, the cylinder sees a step input in flow. On the other hand, if the cylinder-mass resonant frequency is, say, 30 Hz, the valve no longer appears to be so fast. The assumption that the cylinder sees a step in flow is no longer valid. In fact in this example situation it is a very poor assumption.

The analytical methods of Laplace Transforms and Differential Equations allow the systems analyst to judge the suitability of assumptions with more quantitative precision, as compared with hunches, guesses, or intuition. Yet, assumptions **must** be made. If all the time lags in a system were taken into account, there would neither be time enough in the universe to tabulate all of them nor computer power enough to solve the problem in even the simplest system.

Simple gain block

For our purposes, be aware that two assumptions are made throughout the remainder of this book: the servo or proportional valve amplifier is so much faster than the valve and cylinder-mass systems that the amplifier will appear to be instantaneous. Mitigating this assumption is the fact that all valves are tested with the drive electronics attached, and thus any time lags present in the amplifier will be recorded and allocated to the valve. This allows the amplifier-valve combination to be represented by an instantaneous part, nominally the electronic amplifier, and a dynamically limited part, nominally the valve.

The electronic part is symbolized in block diagrams with a shaded, bold *A* to signify amplification. It is a simple gain block. The dynamically limited valve part can be treated like a gain block, but it is called a *transfer function*. Justification for use of transfer functions is contained in the theory of Laplace Transforms and Control Theory, and only a cursory summary of these subjects is within the scope of this book. The interested reader is encouraged to pursue these fascinating and powerful subjects that can be used to unlock many secrets of dynamic systems. Here, we content ourselves with a brief overview.

The second assumption is that feedback transducer *H* is instantaneous. In general, this is a dangerous assumption because some transducers have appreciable time lags. Most industrial position transducers are magnetostrictive, potentiometric, or LVDTs as was seen in Chapters 11 and 12. Many speed transducers, especially those that rely upon frequency as the data-containing method, can have substantial time lags. In most implementations, they can be treated as simple gain blocks even with the conditioning electronics included.

Combining cascaded blocks

A simple open-loop plant, Figure 14.6, has two blocks connected in chain-link fashion so the output of the first is the input to the second and so on. The blocks are said to be cascaded when so connected. It is possible to combine blocks merely by multiplying their gains and/or transfer functions. That is, since:

$$I(S) = AC(S), \tag{14.2}$$

and

$$R(S) = I(S) G_V(S), \tag{14.3}$$

it follows directly that

$$R(S) = AG_V(S) C(S). \tag{14.4}$$

The overall transfer function can be formed by recognizing that the transfer function, like gain, is merely the output divided by the input:

$$G_{AV}(S) = R(S)/C(S) = AG_V(S). \tag{14.5}$$

Here, the $_{AV}$ subscript has been adopted to connote that $G_{AV}(S)$ is the composite, combined, or overall transfer function of the amplifier-valve system. It is the new plant and now has only one block, Figure 14.7. Note the simplicity of having to deal with only one block rather than two. In more complex systems, many blocks can be combined to produce one equivalent. Such moves help to make problems more manageable.

But note that an internal variable, valve current I, has been lost. It has disappeared as a result of the combining operation: in all methods of reduction, internal variables are lost. They can be recovered merely by reversing the process, but the loss is one of the disadvantages of the block diagram-transfer function method of analyzing control systems. Modern Control Theory uses matrix methods so that all system variables can be tracked simultaneously, but the mathematical level is a notch or two

Fig. 14.6. Use of the S notation explicitly conveys the condition that dynamic limitations exist and must be accounted for.

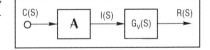

Fig. 14.7. Cascaded blocks can be reduced to a single block by multiplying all the individual transfer functions.

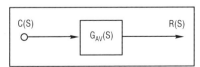

above transfer functions. Nonetheless, it is ideally suited for computer solutions.

Closed-loop plant

In a feedback-control system, the output variable is measured with a suitable transducer whose output is usually a voltage. That signal voltage is then *fed back* and compared to the input command. The discrepancy between command and feedback is an error that drives the plant, Figure 14.8. Note, that if G is the same open-loop plant shown in Figure 14.1, what was the command input to the open-loop system has moved back one step and is now the command to the input summer. Now, instead of being driven by the command input, the plant is driven by the error.

The behavior or response of the closed-loop system can be and usually is quite unlike the behavior of the open-loop system. Certainly this is true in the case of an electrohydraulic positional servomechanism. Some of the differences between open- and closed-loop can be seen by deriving the closed-loop transfer function in terms of the open-loop blocks.

The closed-loop transfer function, Figure 14.8, is taken in a very general sense because feedback element H is considered to have some dynamic limitation. We do not know the nature or extent of the limitation and only allow that the limitation may be present. Later, when a specific transducer is selected, it is a simple matter to ignore its dynamics if indeed it is sufficiently fast. Using the concept of the transfer function being like a gain block, it is true that for the system of Figure 14.8 that the feedback signal is:

$$F(S) = R(S)H(S). \tag{14.6}$$

The error is given by

$$\epsilon(S) = C(S) - F(S), \tag{14.7}$$

or

$$\epsilon(S) = C(S) - R(S)H(S). \tag{14.8}$$

It is also true that:

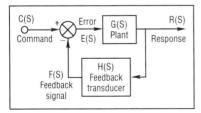

Fig. 14.8. Generalized feedback system where the plant is driven by the error. Phasing must be such that the error drives the plant in the direction that brings the feedback signal into agreement with the command.

367

MOTION CONTROL

$$R(S) = \epsilon(S)G(S). \tag{14.9}$$

Now, substituting Equation (14.8) into Equation (14.9) gives

$$R(S) = [C(S) - R(S)H(S)]G(S). \tag{14.10}$$

After expanding the right side

$$R(S) = C(S)G(S) - R(S)H(S)G(S). \tag{14.11}$$

The R terms can be collected on the left-hand side by transposition, so:

$$R(S) + R(S)H(S)G(S) = C(S)G(S). \tag{14.12}$$

It is now easy to solve for R

$$R(S) = C(S)G(S)/[1 + G(S)H(S)]. \tag{14.13}$$

But, recall that the transfer function is the ratio of output to input, which are R and C, respectively. Thus

$$G(S)/C(S) = G_{CL}(S) = G(S)/[1 + G(S)H(S)], \tag{14.14}$$

where $G_{CL}(S)$ symbolizes the closed-loop transfer function or closed-loop gain. Equation (14.14) is the usual form of the closed-loop gain of any feedback system. The configuration in Figure 14.8 is called a *feedback control system*, a *closed-loop control system*, a *closed-loop servomechanism*, or simply a *servo system* or *servomechanism*.

Feedback control

The use of servo system feedback or closed-loop control improves the degree of system control over other control methods — open-loop control, for example. It is the system designer's responsibility to ensure that the servo system delivers what it promises. The major promise of closed-loop control is seen when considering the effects of high open-loop gain; we want to know what happens if gain is increased. The open-loop gain or open-loop transfer function is defined as the term in the denominator of Equation (14.14), namely

$$G_{OL}(S) = G(S)H(S). \tag{14.15}$$

Note that $G(S)H(S)$ is simply the result of cascading $G(S)$ and $H(S)$. It suggests the open-loop configuration in Figure 14.9.

We will see shortly, if it is not already apparent, that forward-branch

368

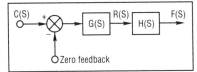

Fig. 14.9. Open-loop system configuration suggested by the so-called G (S) H (S) product, or open-loop transfer function.

transfer function G contains the servo/proportional electronic amplifier. These devices always have a servo-loop gain or amplification adjustment knob on them, whereby the user can increase or decrease amplifier gain A. That is why we refer to the $G(S)H(S)$ product as the open-loop gain rather than by its correct technical description: open-loop transfer function, because we can adjust the amplifier gain. What this means is that we control the amplitude of the $G(S)H(S)$ product, the open-loop gain by virtue of the amplifier gain. We can make that gain as big as the hardware allows.

What happens when it is made very large? That is, what happens when:

$$G(S)H(S) \gg 1? \tag{14.16}$$

If that is the case, then Equation (14.14) becomes:

$$G_{GL}(S) \cong G(S)/G(S)H(S), \tag{14.17}$$

because the value 1 can be ignored, as it is so small compared to $G(S)H(S)$. Note that $G(S)$ cancels, so:

$$G_{GL}(S) \cong 1/H(S). \tag{14.18}$$

This is the promise of feedback, and it is a profound one indeed, for it tells us that the performance of the closed-loop system depends only upon feedback transducer $H(S)$ when the open-loop gain is sufficiently high. It says that the forward branch, that is all those components that comprise $G(S)$, is unimportant in controlling closed-loop system behavior. These conclusions are approximately true only under some conditions, because the actual delivery of feedback control departs from its promise.

An important conclusion that can be reached from Equation (14.18) is that errors in the feedback transducer will propagate directly into errors in the output, 1-for-1. A 1% error in the transducer creates a 1% error in R. A 10% transducer error creates a 10% output error and so on. There is **no** tuning, **no** feedback, and **no** design ploy that corrects for transducer errors. Therefore, the transducer must be selected very carefully; it is the most critical link in the chain from an error inducement point of view. It should be the most expensive link in the chain, and in many systems, it is.

The positional servo loop induces an error in addition to the transducer error. With acceptance of that statement, it should be clear that the final positioning error will **always** be greater than the transducer error. The decisions and evaluations made when selecting the correct transducer are beyond our scope. From here on, we will consider that the transducer has been selected, evaluated, and its expected error is known for all operating conditions expected for the motion control system.

Feedback system delivery

Now it is necessary to ask whether the feedback system can deliver as promised? The answer is a resounding **no**, but system delivery can be satisfactory or acceptable. The most significant shortcoming of the feedback system is its tendency to break into oscillation with increasing open-loop gain. It was just argued that making the gain higher and higher would make system performance dependent only on the feedback transducer. If this could be accomplished, then changes in the forward-branch parameters, say, erosion of the valve metering lands, would be perfectly offset by the closure of the servo loop.

There are several other factors in the forward branch of the positional servo that contribute to degraded positioning performance, and high loop gain can indeed alleviate their adverse effects. But unfortunately, gain can never be so high that these effects are no longer felt because, at some gain value, the servo loop goes unstable. The system becomes unusable when it breaks into sustained oscillation. Instability is caused by a combination of high open-loop gain in the presence of the time lags of the constituent parts.

Consider an idealized example: because of the discrepancy between command and feedback signals in a positional servomechanism, the cylinder attempts to move to a position where feedback voltage cancels command voltage. When the error goes to zero, valve current goes to zero, the valve spool centers, and the cylinder stops. When gain is too high, the error causes an excessive valve opening that gets the cylinder moving too fast. But because there are delays in the components — the valve for example — when the cylinder moves to a position where feedback voltage exactly cancels command, we ideally would want the valve to center to stop the cylinder. Unfortunately the ideal situation does not exist. The spool is still in an open position when the error goes to zero because the spool lags the error. The cylinder overshoots its mark and reverses itself.

If the second overshoot equals or exceeds the first, the oscillation will continue ad infinitum. If gain is reduced, each successive overshoot becomes smaller than the previous one and the oscillation eventually subsides. The reduced gain setting produces a springy but stable system. We say that such a system is underdamped or lightly damped.

Conditions for instability are fairly accurately predictable with a knowledge and command of transfer functions provided that system parameters are well known. Even lacking command of the mathematical tools, it is still possible to make some reasonable estimates as to how high the gain can be before instability is reached. This knowledge is essential so that servo system design will keep positioning errors within appropriate tolerances and yet permit the system to remain dynamically stable. For now, it is sufficient to know that increasing the open-loop gain reduces closed-loop positioning error but if gain is increased too much, instability will ensue. The gain setting is always a compromise between reducing error and controlling overshoots.

There is a continuum of closed-loop responses that go from sluggish overdamped behavior, to springy underdamped, and eventually to continued and sustained oscillations as gain increases from zero. Of course as gain goes up, positioning errors go down. A graph, Figure 14.10, can explain this trend One axis tracks *Positioning* error and the other is a *Degree of instability* performance index.

In general, on the low-gain side of the graph, system response is unacceptably sluggish. At the same time, positioning error is large. There is incentive to increase the gain, and this increase reduces error and improves response. Eventually, a gain is reached that begins to produce increasing instability (springiness) and decreasing benefit of error reduction. That compromise point becomes the final resting spot for gain adjustment. The usual scenario is that gain is increased during system operation with the final setting many times reached subjectively.

Figure 14.10 can show trends but it cannot be used to quantify gain and instability values because of at least two problems. First, it is difficult to quantify *Degree of instability*. Various observers would find it difficult if not impossible to agree on a single quantitative definition. Second, the axes cannot be scaled without a complete quantitative evaluation of each individual component of each system. After doing that, there is hardly a need for the graph, which can be viewed as an aid in qualitative understanding of the gain-instability compromise.

Electrohydraulic positional servomechanism

After looking at the usual form of a generalized feedback system, Figure

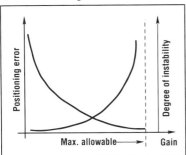

Fig. 14.10. Error goes down but instability increases with increases in open-loop gain.

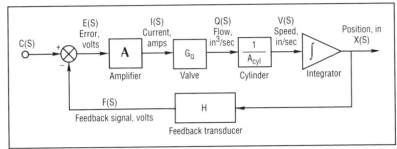

Fig. 14.11. *Basic first-order model of the electrohydraulic servo system showing engineering units in each block of inputs/outputs.*

14.8, it is time to consider the basic, first-order model of an electrohydraulic servo in a more quantitative light. The first step is to form a basic block diagram of the system, and then follow the signals through the loop to check units, Figure 14.11. The inch/pound/second system of units is used for illustration but any consistent system of units will work. The system in Figure 14.11 is a first-order system because there is only one integrator. It is necessary in quantitative assessments to convert velocity V to position X which requires an integration.

The engineering units must check and it is recommended that they always be checked in any control-system problem. Follow the case of Figure 14.11:

● input to the servo/proportional amplifier is voltage and the output is current, so the units on A are amperes/volt

● valve input is current and its output is flow, so flow gain G_Q must be in^3/sec/amp

● cylinder input is flow and output is speed, therefore the units in the box must be 1/in^2. Note that the box contains $1/A_{CYL}$ which, of course, has units of 1/in^2

● the integrator receives in/sec and outputs in, so units on the integrator block must be sec. This is true and can be recognized from the relationship between speed and position:

$$x(t) = \int_o^t v(t)dt. \tag{14.19}$$

Clearly multiplication of $v(t)$ times dt is a multiplication by seconds (dt), and

● the feedback transducer receives position and outputs a voltage. The units on it, then, are volts/in.

At the summing junction, $C(S)$ and $F(S)$ come together to form the error, $\epsilon(S)$, so all three quantities must be in volts.

The block diagram in Figure 14.11 is called a mathematical model of the electrohydraulic servo. It is a quantification of the system; when the coefficients are known, they are the gain values in each of the blocks. The block diagram is a simple model because of some of the assumptions that have been made and because some things are missing.

Note the absence of the S-operator in flow gain block G_Q. This notation implies that the valve is a simple gain block capable of responding instantaneously to any input $I(S)$. It is, implicitly, infinitely fast. This is not true, of course, and the frequency response curves in the valve's technical data sheets prove it. From those curves we would see that the amplitude falls off with increasing frequency and the phase lag increases with increasing frequency — clearly, the valve is dynamically limited.

For the moment, however, we are going to assume that the valve is sufficiently fast when compared to the other dynamic things, that its delays are negligible. The question as to how fast is sufficiently fast is answered by comparing the bandwidth of the valve to the hydromechani-cal resonant frequency and to the frequency of the motion profile. The specific details for doing so are beyond the scope of this book. For the moment, we continue with the assumption that the valve is fast without dynamic limitation.

Another point that needs to be made about the flow gain block is that flow gain depends on both cylinder areas (single rod-end cylinder) and the load placed upon the cylinder. As there is no provision for putting a load on the system of Figure 14.11, that will have to be corrected to take cylinder load and area into account. A straightforward approach to this correction is to introduce the idea of a speed gain of the valve-cylinder combination that accounts for external loading on the cylinder. This is done by combining G_Q and $1/A_{CYL}$ into one block called G_{SP}, Figure 14.12. The units on speed gain are in/sec/amp, and arrow f_L is a reminder that load force must be considered when calculating G_{SP}. Such notation is unstandard block-diagram notation.

The speed gain under load can be determined from the Valve Control of Cylinder Motion (VCCM) Equation 14.20, which relates cylinder veloc-ity to hydraulic parameters and load force. Equation (14.20) arises from

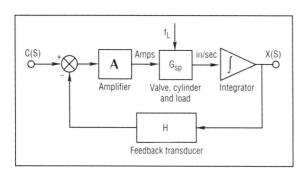

Fig. 14.12. Valve flow-gain block and cylinder area are combined to form speed-gain block G_{SP}.

hydraulic circuit analysis and is presented without proof:

$$V_{SS} = [K_{\mathrm{VPL}}^2 (P_S A_{PE} - f_L)/A_{PE}^3 (1 + \rho_V^2/\rho_C^3)]^{1/2}, \qquad (14.20)$$

Where K_{VPL} is the flow coefficient of the control valve's powered land — the land that carries flow from the pump to the cylinder, P_S is the supply pressure, A_{PE} is the area of the cylinder's powered end, that is, the piston face that is being powered by the pump. Note that it could be blank-end or rod-end area, depending upon which way the valve is shifted. f_L is the load force and has a positive value when it opposes hydraulic propulsion; ρ_V, the valve ratio, is the ratio of powered-land coefficient to the return-land coefficient; and ρ_C is the cylinder area ratio of the powered-end area to return-end area. Note that it reciprocates when going from cylinder extension to cylinder retraction.

The speed is taken as the steady-state speed with the valve wide-open, and speed gain is the speed divided by the current that caused it. For servo and proportional valves, it is saturation current I_S. Now:

$$G_{SP} = V_{SS}/I_S. \qquad (14.21)$$

Thus calculated, the speed gain is inclusive of any load f_L.

There remains the issue of extension and retraction. As a digression, it is emphasized that the models of Figures 14.11 and 14.12 are linear, and a linear model cannot simultaneously account for the two different speed gains that result from extension and retraction. It is necessary to compromise. The three possibilities are to:

● use extending speed gain $G_{SP,ext}$ only, and use the actual load while under extension

● use retracting speed gain $G_{SP,ret}$ only, and use the actual load while under retraction, and

● use average $G_{SP,ave}$ of the above extending and retracting speeds.

More research is needed for an aid when selecting one of the three, but the average seems to offer some intuitive comfort.

Rotary speed-control loops

When using feedback control, the general concept for control of a quantity is to feed it back, compare it to a command or set-point signal and let the resulting error drive the output toward the target. This is exactly what is done in speed control of a hydraulic motor. Valve control or pump control are two common methods for controlling hydraulic motor speed. .

A valve-control system, Figure 14.13, consists of a proportional or servovalve driven by an amplifier. The amplifier input stage is a simple, two-input inverting summer. This stage demands that a positive-going command voltage be off set by a negative-going feedback. Note that the

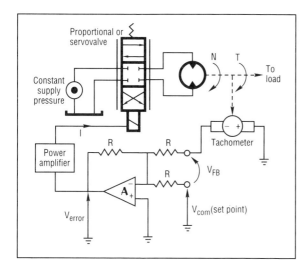

Fig. 14.13. Valve-controlled speed loop uses tachometer feedback to help regulate motor speed. This is a type-zero regulator because an error between V_{COMM} and V_{FB} is required to maintain valve opening.

tachometer that measures motor-shaft speed has its positive output terminal connected to ground to provide the correct command/feedback phasing. The closed-center, continuously variable valve is powered by a constant-pressure power unit. The valve's work ports modulate the amount of hydraulic power that goes to the hydraulic motor. When command voltage V_{COMM} is much greater than the negative value of feedback voltage V_{FB}, substantial error voltage V_{ERROR} and substantial coil current I will result. That current opens the valve, say excessively, and causes the motor to accelerate. Eventually, the negative-going feedback voltage cancels out some of the command voltage, reduces the current, decreases valve opening, and resultes in no further motor acceleration.

At this point, the motor operates in steady-state and the discrepancy between command and feedback is just enough to hold the valve open the requisite amount to sustain the loop in equilibrium. Note that the error voltage cannot go to zero, because that would shift the valve and stop the motor, clearly a paradoxical situation that cannot exist. The generic class of this control system is called a *Type-Zero Regulator*. Characteristically, type-zero regulators require an error to operate; the error cannot go to zero because that shuts down the very thing that sustains output — a contradiction.

Another characteristic of this control system is that its output speed will not recover from changes in load torque. To appreciate this, assume that the motor and control loop are operating at no-load, steady-state speed. As just explained, this results in a command voltage slightly greater than the feedback voltage (algebraic sign difference notwithstanding) to hold the valve open the required amount. Now we increase the load to see what happens. First, the additional load torque causes motor speed to drop because increased torque raises motor pressure and increases internal leakage of the motor; and the motor-pressure increase leaves a smaller pressure drop across the valve lands which further reduces flow. Clearly, the motor slows down.

At the same time, however, tachometer output voltage decreases to cause a bigger discrepancy (error) between command and feedback, that opens the valve further. This increased valve opening tends to correct for the loss in speed, but the correction is not perfect. Consider that the speed returns to the no-load value. This means that error voltage is the same as at no load so the valve spool must be back in its original no-load position. But we have already argued that the original spool position did not allow sufficient valve opening to overcome the load. Therefore the valve spool must be in some other position. Indeed, what happens is that the speed does fall off, moving the spool to a new position, but the spool cannot move far enough to correct the speed to its original value. What happens in the end is that the spool moves in the correcting direction, but the speed must drop off to sustain it. Such are the limitations of type zero control systems.

Hydrostatic-transmission control of motor speed

The hydrostatic transmission is a popular method of controlling speed of a hydraulic motor shaft. A simplified schematic of an HST speed-control loop will be discussed in two configurations. First, the swashplate position-measuring transducer, R_{SP}, will be assumed to be absent and then the addition of swashplate position feedback will be considered.

Without swashplate feedback, the control system is a type one-regulator that operates, in principle, with no error. This is true because the pump stroking pistons act as an error integrator. The circuit, Figure 14.14, consists of an electrically controlled, variable-displacement pump supplying hydraulic power to a fixed-displacement hydraulic motor. The motor output shaft drives an arbitrary load as well as a tachometer. Tachometer output forms feedback voltage V_{FB}. The amplifier input stage is a simple, two-input, inverting summer whose output voltage V_{ERROR}, is zero whenever V_{COMM} and V_{FB} are of equal amplitude but of opposite sign. This is true because all input resistors are equal. Note that the tachometer's positive terminal is connected to ground, requiring V_{COMM} be positive for correct command/feedback phasing.

At the beginning, we assumed that the motor is operating in steady-state with no acceleration. This requires the pump's stroking pistons be in some fixed position because if they were moving, the motor would be accelerating. Of course, if the stroking pistons are *parked*, the control valve must be centered. This in turn requires that valve current be zero and further requires that V_{ERROR} be zero. Finally, it is necessary that

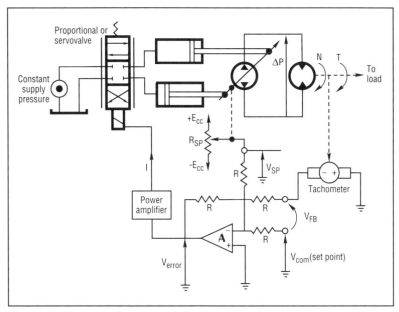

Fig. 14.14. Electronically controlled HST in a speed-control loop is a type one regulator when swashplate feedback, V$_{SP}$, is absent. Adding this feedback as shown converts system to type zero.

command and feedback voltages be equal but of opposite sign. We see no contradiction in traversing the loop.

Now consider what happens with increased load on the motor shaft. There is an immediate drop in motor speed that causes a non-zero value for V_{ERROR}. Of course, there now is a valve current that de-centers the spool, porting power to the stroking pistons that now are in motion. If the servo loop is phased correctly, stroking is in a direction that increases motor speed, and the motor accelerates. In fact, the motor continues to gain speed until such time that the stroking pistons again park. That happens only when valve current is zero, which requires that tachometer voltage and command voltage cancel each other. Obviously, the motor speed must have returned to its original speed, meaning that there is perfect speed regulation.

In summary, recognize that there was a load increase and the speed returned to its original value, although the stroking pistons are now in a new position. Increased pump displacement just offsets the load plus any increased internal HST losses. Basically, the stroking pistons have accumulated the error and compensated for it; they act as an error integrator. Type-one regulators are popular because of their ability to operate with zero error. This is an obvious advantage because the operator needs only to dial in a set-point voltage and the servo loop controls speed even when the load changes. Furthermore, output speed rises and falls in response to any required or desired change in command voltage.

Is this nirvana? Have we discovered utopia? Not quite, because as always, there is a price to pay and this price can be formidable. There is a much greater tendency for this control loop to break into sustained oscillation due to the inherent time lag in the integrating stroking pistons. Furthermore, when the loop is stabilized, it tends to be slow to change speeds upon command and also tends to be springy or underdamped when compared to the type zero speed controller. That is, the speed overshoots the target, and then settles in a springy manner. In contrast, the simple valve control-loop is very stable and responsive, but alas, it cannot regulate as well as the HST.

Swashplate feedback

When swashplate feedback is added to the circuit, the type-one characteristic is destroyed. This is most easily seen by again recognizing that steady-state exists only when the stroking pistons are parked. This, as before, requires that V_{ERROR} be zero. But now, the error is comprised of three elements:

$$V_{ERROR} = V_{COMM} + V_{FB} + V_{SP}. \qquad (14.22)$$

It is obvious that there will always be a discrepancy between V_{COMM} and V_{FB}, due to the presence of swashplate voltage V_{SP}. It cannot be type one. The reason for adding swashplate feedback is to enhance servo-loop

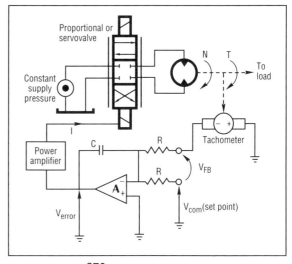

Fig. 14.15. The input operational amplifier is converted to an integrator by the use of capacitor C feedback. This ploy, called integral control, converts sytem to a type-one regulator.

stability, but unfortunately, speed regulation suffers. If type-one operation is required, it is necessary to put the integration into the electronics. Once that is done, the result is called an *integral controller*.

Valve control with integrating amplifier

Figure 14.15 shows a speed-control loop that uses a valve as the electrohydraulic interface device. The amplifier input stage uses capacitor C for feedback around the op-amp to convert it into an integrating amplifier. It is the integrator that allows this circuit to return motor speed to its set-point value even if the load changes. Recall that an important characteristic of an integrator is that its output undergoes constant change anytime its input is non-zero. Another way of stating this is that the output remains at its present value only if the input is held exactly at zero. Given this, input to the integrator is zero only when command and feedback voltages are equal but of opposite sign. Note that both input resistors R have the same value.

Assume that the system is operating in steady-state when a load is placed on the motor shaft. This causes an immediate reduction in shaft speed with an attendant drop in tachometer voltage. With reduced tachometer output, command and feedback voltages no longer cancel one another so integrator output begins to grow. As it grows, the valve opens in an attempt to increase speed. Integrator output continues to grow until the command and feedback voltages again cancel one another. The speed must, therefore, return to the same value that existed before the load was applied. There is no drop in speed, just like in the hydrostatic transmission control system. Again, it must be emphasized that as described, this integral controller does not come without penalty. The penalty is that the speed loop is just as challenging to stabilize as the HST control loop. The phase lag created by the integrator usually results in a system response that is under-damped.

To compare the effects of open-loop valve control without feedback with proportional control only, Figure 14.13, and with integral control, see Figure 14.16. Without feedback, the speed drops with increasing load along curve A, described by the flow coefficients of the valve's two

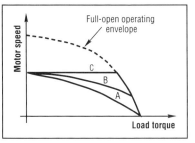

Fig. 14.16. Speed-torque curves of a valve-controlled speed loop using open loop, curve A, proportional feedback control, curve B, and integral control, curve C.

metering lands. With feedback control, curve B, the valve opening increases with increasing disagreement between command and feedback, but the opening of the valve is insufficient to fully correct the speed. Therefore, the degree of speed control is better than without feedback but certainly is imperfect. Speed regulation is perfect when integral control is used, curve C. Note that this is true only up to that load torque where the valve fully opens. At that time, the valve is incapable of further corrections.

Errors in positional servomechanisms

A study of servo-system errors is a study of servo systems. That is, one cannot credibly claim a knowledge of feedback control systems unless there is clear understanding of how errors arise and how they are controlled. The design process begins from a specification of allowable error that then becomes a design goal. The success of the final design hinges on the ability of the system to contain the errors within application limits without servo-loop instability.

In a positional servo mechanism there is an error anytime the final position disagrees with commanded position and that happens 100% of the time! That is, actual position is **never** in agreement with command position. The degree of disagreement, that is the error, can be kept within tolerable limits through the design process. To design around the inevitable error, it is necessary to know the sources of error and then size the components and tune the system to keep the error within the design goals.

Here is a list of the known error contributors in electrohydraulic positional servomechanisms. Each contributes to the total error so the final, closed-loop, positioning error becomes the sum of its contributing parts. Each item is listed here without explanation about how the contribution is made because these details are beyond our scope. At design time, each item must be dealt with quantitatively to assess its specific amount of error contribution:

● supply-pressure variations, including valve null shift and acting upon unequal areas of a single rod-end cylinder
● tank-pressure variations, including valve null shift and acting upon unequal areas of a single rod-end cylinder
● temperature affect on valve null
● valve hysteresis
● valve threshold
● valve dead zone
● load-force changes
●external magnetic influences
● cylinder and load
● break-away pressure
● backlash, inside and outside the servo loop, and

● transducer error.

The control-system industry categorizes the first eight items as system disturbances, a good term. To see why, imagine that there is a positional servomechanism that is in equilibrium. That is, the command voltage is constant and the cylinder has moved to a commensurate position and has stopped. Now, a disturbance arrives; for example, the supply pressure changes.

This causes a shift in the null of the valve because it is sensitive to supply pressure. This upsets the force-balance on the piston and requires the spool to seek a new position. Valve current must change which requires a change in input voltage to the amplifier. If command voltage remains fixed, the change in amplifier input voltage must arise from a change in feedback voltage. Of course, the feedback voltage changes only if the cylinder changes position.

This leads to the conclusion that any phenomenon that causes a null shift in the valve results in an output position error. The system designer has control over the degree that null shift propagates into position error by cylinder selection and valve selection, and later at commissioning time, by tuning loop gain. The exact quantitative methods for designing around these errors are beyond the scope of this book.

As far as backlash is concerned, it must be eliminated or minimized. Its effects are only detrimental; none are beneficial. Backlash within the loop results in hunting or oscillation that is unaffected by the servo-loop gain setting. If backlash is small, oscillation amplitude is small. Of course, if the oscillation or *limit cycle* is sufficiently small, it is invisible to the user of the servo system and does not matter. Elimination is the most effective way to deal with backlash, and the methods are beyond the scope of this book.

When backlash occurs outside the servo-loop, it does not affect stability. Instead, it results in a direct positioning error at the output — it is in fact a kind of mechanical hysteresis, and attempts have been made to correct for backlash by implementing a control method whereby the target is always approached from the same direction. The method works but the reader is cautioned: for it to work throughout the useful life of the machine, all possible randomly occurring events that could ever affect approach direction must have been brought under strict control. For example, if an operator changes the servo amplifier gain so that over-shoots occur, the direction of final approach has been changed. All previous efforts to compensate for backlash with the original gain setting now have gone for nought. Again, backlash should be eliminated so it becomes a non-problem.

We already have said that transducer selection is crucial and is outside the scope of this book. Suffice it to say that the transducer must be selected and its application analyzed so its totally expected error contribution is known or has been reasonably estimated. Total position error of a servo system is the sum of the transducer error plus the sum of those error components on the foregoing list of contributors. That is:

$$\epsilon_T = \epsilon_{SL} + \epsilon_{XD}, \tag{14.23}$$

where ϵ_T is the total error, ϵ_{SL} is the contribution caused by the servo loop and ϵ_{XD} is the contribution caused by the transducer alone. In a design situation, it is expected that total error ϵ_T will be a design specification, or target, or goal that the servo system must meet. Additionally, if the transducer has been selected and its total expected error has been evaluated, then only servo loop error, ϵ_{SL} is unknown and can be solved for:

$$\epsilon_{SL} = \epsilon_T - \epsilon_{XD}. \tag{14.24}$$

This becomes the specification to which the servo system must be designed. It should be obvious that total error, ϵ_T must be larger than the transducer error, ϵ_{XD}; that is, ϵ_{SL} must evaluate to a positive quantity. The smaller that ϵ_{SL} is, the more challenging the design. It is true that closed-loop bandwidth varies in inverse proportion to the servo-loop error. The smaller the error, the greater the bandwidth of the closed-loop system must be. As closed-loop bandwidth goes up, valve bandwidth must commensurately grow as well as the hydromechanical resonant frequency if the system is to remain stable.

It is possible for a poorly developed positioning-accuracy specification to require prohibitively expensive hardware to achieve, or perhaps even exceed the state-of-the-art in servovalve performance, a disappointing discovery. On the other hand, it is exciting to know that the design methodology exists to enable us to separate the possible from the impossible, the practical from the impractical, and the economical from the uneconomical before committing to hardware.

Systematic and random errors

Wherever measurement errors occur, they can be classified as being either systematic or random. Systematic errors are defined as errors caused by known influencing factors, are repeatable, and are therefore correctable in principle. Random errors are defined as errors that are **not** repeatable and have unknown causes. Random errors sometimes are called *residual* errors, because they are errors that remain after all systematic errors have been eliminated. Common examples of systematic errors include loading error, transducer non-linearity, and environmental factors that cause *drift*, such as temperature, atmospheric pressure, humidity, vibration, etc.

Loading error is a good example of systematic error. When electronic parts are interconnected, the terminal voltage after the connection is made always is less than the voltage with no connection. This is because the receiving device requires a bit of current from the sending device, consequently the sending device is loaded. The amount of error is directly dependent upon the relative output and input resistances (impedances) of the sending and receiving devices. The percent loading error can be estimated from:

$$\% \epsilon_L = (output\ resistance\ of\ sender)(100)/ (input\ resistance\ of\ receiver). \quad (14.25)$$

The important thing is that once the electrical connection is made, the error exists for all time. It may vary with operating parameters such as position transducer output voltage or ambient temperature, but given that the system is tested under repeatable conditions, the amount of loading error will repeat from trial to trial. Therefore, loading error in principle, is correctable and is systematic. Loading error results in a servo system positioning error **only if it remains uncorrected**, a statement that can be made of any systematic error.

Consider the error of non-linearity. It produces a servo system error only when the system designer and/or system user *assume* that the system is linear. Suppose that a position transducer, for example, has been selected that generates 1 volt/inch of piston travel and has a 10-inch stroke when fully closed. Zero volts are measured at zero inches and 10 volts are measured at 10 inches. However due to non-linearity, the transducer generates only 4.995 volts at the 5.000-inch position. If this is a repeatable result, that clue tells us that the value is not a random effect. If we put in a command to the positional servo of 5.000 volts, expecting an output position of 5.000 inches, we will be disappointed. The cylinder will have to overtravel to about the 5.005-inch position to offset the 5.000 command voltage. There is a 0.005-inch positional error.

The non-linearity error can be compensated for. There are a number of schemes but they all produce the same effect. When a final position of, say, 5.000 inches is desired, that command is entered through the input device but because of some internal logic — a math model or a look-up table — the command generator outputs only 4.995 volts. Because that value corresponds to the 5.000-inch position of the cylinder, the 5.000-inch target position is acquired, all other errors being zero. Note that for each desired target position, a corresponding voltage must be known. It sometimes is necessary to map the system over its entire operating range against independent gaging instruments to determine the precise voltage needed for each specific position. This process is called calibration and must be done in critical applications.

In the case of influencing variables such as temperature, it may be possible to develop a mathematical model of the thermal influence. The math model is a formula that calculates correction voltage that must be added to the command to correct for thermal effect. Of course the local temperature must be known, which requires its measurement and input into the correcting device. If the controller is a digital computer or programmable logic controller, an A/D converter is required plus software capability to program mathematical statements.

A number of methods can be used to correct for systematic errors and an exhaustive list would be extensive. Additionally, there are myriad application-specific considerations that affect strategy and outcome. For now, it is sufficient to understand the nature of systematic errors and that in principle, they can be corrected. If corrected, they really are not errors; they produce errors only when left uncorrected.

As far as a list of random effects is concerned, we find that the list is empty, because if we know the influencing variable, we can measure and correct for it and the effect is no longer random but systematic. It moves to the previous list. Random errors also are called *non-repeatable* errors. They arise in controlled situations where all influencing variables are held as constant as is practicable, except for the command which is repeatedly removed and reapplied, removed and reapplied for a number of trials. At the same time, output response is measured and recorded. As is the case with such experiments, even though the inputs are all the same, the outputs display a variation or scatter about a mean value. Because there is no explanation for the scatter, it is a random error. The amount of scatter determines the ultimate accuracy of the system. That is, the final error can never be less than the range described by the limits of the data scatter. The scatter defines the state-of-the-art in the process.

The purpose for distinguishing between systematic and random errors is because in some servo systems, the demands for accuracy may be such that some, if not all systematic errors must be corrected. To do so requires a knowledge of what the error contributors are, and then devising a strategy for making the corrections.

Closed-loop bandwidth of the first order model

Determining the suitability of the design to the application is done by comparing the frequency responses or bandwidths of the various components, to the required closed-loop bandwidth. The results of the comparisons are pass/fail conclusions. But first, it is necessary to be able to calculate the bandwidth of the closed-loop system in terms of its constituent parts. It is necessary to use the theory of Laplace Transforms that tells us that the integrator can be replaced by an algebraic function of S:

$$\mathcal{L} \int f(t)dt = 1/S. \tag{14.26}$$

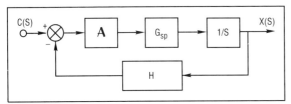

Fig. 14.17. The integrator is replaced with a gain block of 1/s.

This says that the Laplace transform of an integrator is simply $1/S$. Proof of this is possible with the theory, or by looking it up in a table of Laplace Transform pairs. At the moment, it is only necessary to accept the fact that the integrator in Figure 14.12 can be replaced by a *gain block* that contains the Laplace Transform of the integrator, $1/S$, Figure 14.17. Now, the block diagram can be treated like the orthodox feedback configuration of Figure 14.8. In making the comparison, we see that the plant consists of A, G_{SP}, $1/S$, and feedback branch H:

$$G_{CL}(S) = [(AG_{SP}/S)/(S + AG_{SP}H)/S].\qquad(14.27)$$

Clearing the denominator of the $1/S$ yields the standard form for the closed-loop transfer function:

$$G_{CL}(S) = AG_{SP}/(S + AG_{SP}H).\qquad(14.28)$$

This is the closed-loop transfer function for the simple, first-order model of Figure 14.17. Note that G_{CL} is indicated as being dynamically limited, that is it is noted as $G_{CL}(S)$. Dynamic limitation also is denoted in the fact that there is an S on the right hand side of Equation (14.27). We picked up that S because of the integrator.

That this system has dynamic limitations can be seen by imagining how the cylinder responds to servo-system commands. Those limitations exist in a physical sense as a result of the interconnection of the valve and cylinder. The valve generates a flow based on input current. The piston, trying to escape the oncoming flow, converts the flow to speed. As the piston advances to accommodate the volume of fluid, which takes time, it creates a distance as well. That distance, being the result of accumulated volume over a period of time, is the result of an integration. The S in the denominator of Equation (14.27) tells that there is one integrator and the response of this system is time dependent, or dynamically limited. To see the specific way the dynamic limitation applies, we can look at the units of the denominator of Equation (14.28). That is, the units on $AG_{SP}H$ are:

$$(amps/volts)(inches/amp\text{-}sec)(volts/inch) = 1/sec!\qquad(14.29)$$

The units on the open loop gain are $1/seconds$, a frequency! That is a profound realization of the use of Laplace Transforms. The process directly yields the time constants and the frequencies that the systems engineer needs to make intelligent choices.

There is a word of caution: the frequency represented by $AG_{SP}H$ is in rad/sec, not Hz. We now state the closed loop system bandwidth, or the closed-loop system frequency response, in Hz, is

$$f_{SYSTEM} = AG_{SP}H/2\pi \qquad (14.30)$$

If we know the amplifier gain and if we know the speed gain (and surely we should if we have selected the valve and cylinder and know the load) and if we have selected the transducer, we know H and can then calculate the expected closed-loop bandwidth.

A couple of points need to be made. First, it should be obvious that as amplifier gain increases, closed-loop bandwidth goes up in direct proportion. As bandwidth goes up, the system responds faster. In fact if we reciprocate open-loop gain, we get system time constant, τ:

$$\tau = 1/AG_{SP}H. \qquad (14.31)$$

Knowing that five time constants are required to reach steady-state, we can now calculate the time to do so. Note that as A increases, τ gets smaller and smaller, meaning that the system will respond more quickly. This is consistent with viewing Equation (14.29) as a frequency. An important principle is emerging here: it is possible to view the open-loop gain as either a frequency as in Equation (14.29), or as a time constant as in Equation (14.30).

When considering time constants, we think of time responses such as exponential rises and falls. These are things we could see on an oscilloscope if we put a step into the servo system and watched cylinder position. When considering open-loop gain as a frequency, we are considering that we are testing the servo system with sinusoidal command signals such as when performing a frequency response test, and that is the second point. If we were to test the system with a sine wave of adjustable frequency and if we used a frequency equal to that given in Equation (14.28), output position $x(t)$ would lag command $c(t)$ by 45°, and the amplitude of $x(t)$ would be 70.7% of what it was at very, very low frequency. Of course, this attenuated level (70.7%) is also the 3dB-down point, the usual benchmark for describing bandwidth.

Another word of caution: the foregoing discussion implies that gain can be increased without limit and thus the system can become faster and faster without limit. That would be great if it were true, **but it is not**. Recall that valve dynamics were ignored because the valve was assumed to be very fast. Also, we said that the hydromechanical resonant frequency was very high and could be ignored. The fallacy in the first order model is that as gain is increased, closed-loop system bandwidth begins to approach either the valve bandwidth or the hydromechanical natural frequency whichever is less. When the gain gets so high that the valve and/or load dynamics cannot be ignored, the system must take into account their delays, which increases the system order (each integrator acccounts for one order value). These are then said to be *higher-order systems*.

When this happens, the valve and load resonance begin to have a dominant influence on dynamic behavior rather than the system bandwidth given in Equation (14.29). This means that the simple first-order model fails to give us even a reasonable estimate of dynamic behavior of the servo system. Higher-order models that include dynamic effects of all components are needed if one is to estimate system response. Now it should be clear, that for the simple first order model to be valid or for estimating system behavior, the system bandwidth [Equation (14.29)] must be less than the smaller of the valve bandwidth and the hydrome-chanical resonant frequency.

For now, it is sufficient to be aware that the gain cannot be so high as to cause system bandwidth to begin encroaching upon either of the other two critical frequencies. Recall that the foregoing assumed a knowledge of amplifier gain A. As a matter of fact in a real live system, amplifier gain is usually adjusted on a subjective basis, and its actual value rarely is known in the actual system. Fortunately at design time, it is possible to relate amplifier gain directly to the amount of positioning error that can be tolerated in the servo loop and the characteristics of the valve.

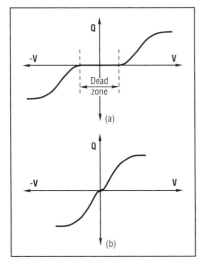

Fig. 14.18. Valve output curve (a) is be-fore dead-band correction while curve (b) is after correction.

Electronic deadband correction

Electronic designers have attempted to correct for the large spool overlap in proportional valves with electronic circuits, variously called *dead-band eliminators (DBE)* or *dead-band correctors (DBC)*, see Appendix A. The fact of the matter is that DBEs are very limited in what they can do and usually end up being worth less than they cost in all but a very few special applications. The DBE circuit can be adjusted in some amplifiers, and is designed with extremely high gain over the range of the valve's dead zone. The idea, in theory, is that the very high amplifier gain will quickly transport the spool from one side of the dead zone to the other and actually prevent the spool from ever coming to rest within the dead zone.

The idea, again in theory, is to collapse the dead zone of the valve flow-metering curve, Figure 14.18(a) to look like the corrected curve of Figure 14.18(b). But the curve of Figure 14.18(b) is deceptive on two counts. First, a finite time is required to transport the spool from one side of the dead zone to the other, so the corrected curve masks the true dynamics of the valve by implying something else.

Second, the corrected curve cannot work, because the pressure gain is so high that the servo system continues to oscillate about the target point. That this is so can be seen by considering the pressure metering curves. Recall that a cylinder stops because the forces on the piston are brought into equilibrium. When the DBE is adjusted as in Figure 14.18(b), the only places where the pressure provides the proper force balance is off-limits to the spool so-to-speak. The spool is prevented by virtue of the DBE, from occupying the balance point. As a result, the spool continues to bounce from one side of the dead zone to the other ad infinitum. Gain adjustment has no effect until it is so low that it renders the servo loop worthless.

What happens when the DBE's are adjusted in a live servo system is that they end up only partially correcting the dead zone. The one side that services the rod side of the cylinder is set only slightly above zero while the other that services the blank side is adjusted more so. When optimally tuned, there can be modest improvement in the way the cylinder acquires the target but it is not dramatic. Even when so tuned, there are problems when the load on the cylinder varies because it is possible that the adjustment made at one load covers the precise point needed by the new load. The result is oscillation or sustained, reciprocating, low-speed drift. There is no electronic compensation that truly corrects for limitations of the valve.

Phasing the positional servomechanism

Phasing refers to the process whereby the algebraic signs of the servo system are controlled so that reactions are in the proper direction. The phasing problem has two steps which must be taken, and unfortunately in a live system, the symptoms can mimic one another. The first step is to assure that the command and feedback voltages have the correct algebraic signs so they cancel one another, thus producing proper error from the input comparator. The second step is to set algebraic signs within the servo loop so that the error voltage motivates the actuator in a direction that reduces the error. To do otherwise is to have the actuator slam into one limit or the other in a runaway condition.

The phasing required of the command and feedback is dictated totally by the design of the input stage to the servo/proportional amplifier. Fortunately the only two possible designs are an inverting summer and a differential summer. In the case of the inverting summer, it is necessary that command and feedback voltages have opposite-going polarities. That is, a positive-going command voltage will be canceled only by a negative-going feedback voltage and vice-versa. Bipolar command and feedback are useful too, with $\pm$ command requiring $\pm$ feedback. The servo loop will not function if these conditions are not met. If the input stage is a differential summer, command and feedback signals must be of like polarity. Bipolar signals for both work well.

When the servo-loop is incorrectly phased, the error reinforces itself and the actuator runs away, quickly slamming into one limit or the other. The corrective action is to get one algebraic sign reversal somewhere within the loop. One of two common methods will achieve this:
● reverse the plumbing lines between valve and actuator, or
● swap the leads going to the valve coil.
Unfortunately, these avenues are not always available options. For example, the first is unworkable if the valve is mounted directly on the actuator. The second is unworkable if the valve is a dual-solenoid proportional valve with a spool-feedback loop. Swapping the solenoid leads will reverse the spool loop and create a run-away situation.

When neither option is available, there maybe electronic fixes but they require more than a passing knowledge of electronics and are always hardware specific. It may be necessary to replace the feedback transducer with one of opposite-going output polarity. In desperation, it may be necessary to install a simple, inverting unity-gain op-amp circuit to reverse the sign of the feedback signal. **Never** reverse the leads from the feedback transducer. That will cross the grounds between transducer and amplifier to create even more problems.

Chapter Fifteen
Motion Control

The positional servomechansm is at the heart of modern industrial motion control. Generally, motion-control concepts have effectively been addressed by colleagues in the electrical-drives industry. Motion control in the context here applies to presses, injection molding machines, transfer lines, conveyor systems, flying cut-offs, robots, and thousands of other applications not particularly suited to electrical drives.

In the past, the fluid power industry approached motion control in a parochial fashion, designing such stratagems as *soft-shift* valves in which an orifice was adjusted to control valve shift rate. This limitation on shift rate achieved a degree of acceleration control, but was unreliable because of a lack of repeatability. Changes in fluid temperature and metering capability while shifting were the primary causes of this non-repeatability.

The advent of proportional valves coupled control electronics with industrial-grade valves and permitted electronic velocity ramping. This at once produced wide rangeability in shift-delay tuning, on-line interactive tuning, and electronic reliability. These methods addressed the control of acceleration and shock in hydraulic systems. There are innumerable successful applications and these methods still are finding use today. The only word to describe the improved behavior when a springy hydraulic system comes under ramped control is *dramatic*.

But the ramping method addresses only acceleration and, to a lesser degree, actuator speed. Ramping is essentially open loop and does not address the positioning problem. The final stopping or reversal point is most critical in many applications. For our purposes, the following definition applies: **motion control is the simultaneous control of acceleration, speed, and position**. Typical industrial motion-control problems always can be reduced to basic specifications such as: a machine slide of stated mass must accelerate to a rapid traverse speed, then be brought to a stop within a specified time, and must achieve some final position within a specified accuracy. Design a machine that accomplishes this task.

When a machine follows the motion-control concept, it behaves in an optimum manner. That is, all at once shocks are eliminated, noise is reduced, cycle times are shortened as much as possible, final positioning is made as accurate as required, and machine life and reliability is improved at the same time. This design methodology applies motion-control concepts to hydraulic equipment and provides the applications engineer with some easy-to-use analytical tools that can assess the likelihood of success.

Understanding motion control requires a good feeling for and comfort with the relationships between acceleration, velocity, and position, Figure 15.1. Considering these acceleration, velocity, and position profiles, these points are nearly axiomatic:

● acceleration control makes shocks and noise manageable

● velocity control assures that cycle times are met and that components are neither undersized nor oversized, and

● position control assures that stopping points and transition points are precisely where they should be.

Thus, motion control can be interpreted to be total control of the machine.

The profiles of Figure 15.1 are an example of a desired motion. The process is called *constant acceleration*, but one look at the acceleration waveshape reveales that this is, strictly speaking, a misnomer. Certainly, the acceleration is **not** constant. The name derives from the fact that the waveshape is a series of vertically connected horizontal lines where the acceleration is constant within several time intervals. That is there are no sine waves, ramps, or parabolas in the acceleration waveshape.

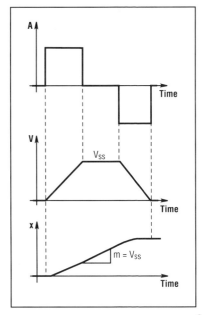

Fig. 15.1. Profiles for an idealized constant-acceleration process: (a) acceleration, (b) velocity, and (c) position.

Beginning with acceleration, it is true that velocity is its integral. Therefore in Figure 15.1, the regions of non-zero acceleration result in constant-slope ramps in the velocity profile. The velocity profile is the area under the acceleration curves and similarly, position is the integral of the velocity. Therefore, the position curve has regions where its shape is parabolic. In the design process, it is necessary that all three waveshapes be scaled such that total cycle time meets the required productivity numbers for the machine, while the machine performs to expected velocity and final position. By analyzing, creating (synthesizing), and modifying the motion waveshapes, design goals can be met — or at the least, the designer can realize early on that the design goals are *not* achievable. In the latter case, it may even be apparent that some changes can be made to bring machine and design goals into compliance. There are two unmistakable and unavoidable realities in the motion profiles. The:

● profile shape and its total time arise from the needs of the application to achieve a specified level of productivity (controlled cycle time or throughput) while also controlling shock and noise, and

● machine that is to follow the profile may or may not be able to do so. Too often, systems fail to achieve design goals because the designer did not know how to account for the dynamic limitations of the machine, such as its natural frequency for example.

Two methods of hydraulic control

It is an underlying aim here to provide a reasonably simple means to determine if a certain collection of components indeed can achieve a specified machine profile long before committing to hardware. The collection of hardware that is to achieve the design goals is called the *plant*. This, in our technology, is an assemblage of hydromechanical components, Figure 15.2. They consist of a prime mover driving a pump whose output is directed and controlled by valving whose output goes to an actuator to propel a load. The plant is equipped with several access points, labelled *Control* in the Figure. Not all control points are implemented in all machines, so the drawing must be considered a generalization. All control points are possible although they may be unnecessary. To achieve the desired action at the load, the profiled motion-control method proposed fully guides the load to its required destination. This requires some

Fig. 15.2. A hydraulic system controls the flow of energy (power) from the source to the load with access possible through several control ports.

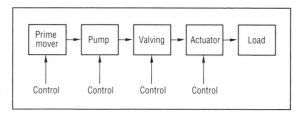

external equipment, called the *controller*.

Increasingly, controllers are electronic devices and the access points are electromechanical interfaces such as torque motors, force motors, or proportional solenoids. These interfaces allow the electronic signals to enter the hydraulic plant and act as *plant commands* that tell the plant what to do. For the controller to send the right commands, it must *know* the current status of the plant. This it does by *listening* to sensors and/or transducers which have been installed at critical points within the plant to provide feedback signals. When the assembly is put together, it is called the *system*, Figure 15.3. Note that commands to the plant are outputs of the controller and that it must receive its own set of *executive commands*.

In the design of a hydraulic plant, the designer has two methods of implementing a controllable system: *valve control*, also called the energy-loss method, because the valve(s) accomplish the control by dissipating power (converting hydraulic energy to heat energy), and *displacement control*, also called pump or motor control or volume control, wherein pump (or motor) displacement is changed to meet the demands of the load. It is apparent to all hydraulic-system designers that there are inherent advantages and disadvantages of each of these two methods of implementation.

A brief summary of the valve-control method:

● because the nature of valve control is dissipative, this method has inherent inefficiency when compared to the displacement-control method. Although efficiency has been the aim of many hydraulic system designers for decades, a system becomes worthless if it is efficient but cannot meet other design performance goals. Also in some applications, such as in a press, efficiency is a nonsensical concept

● in positioning systems that are the heart of motion control, proper motion and correct stopping points are more important than low power dissipation. In these positioning systems, valve control nearly always is superior. Efficiency is unimportant because in many instances, the load dwells for substantial portions of the cycle

● the best valve control arises when using closed-center valves that deliver power from constant-pressure sources such as pressure-compensated pumps and accumulators to meet surge demands. Such systems

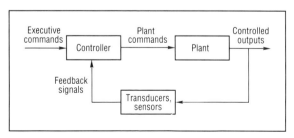

Fig. 15.3. Closed-loop feeback control uses measured values of the output, compares them to the desired values, and then issues plant commands to bring about system control.

often are alien to hydraulic designers because actuator speed is governed by control-valve spool or poppet position rather than pump output. These systems are not easily understood and are analytically more complex than their displacement-control brethren. Nonetheless, valve control is absolutely superior in these instances:

● the method provides acceleration and deceleration control; the 4-way servo or proportional valve provides both meter-in and meter-out control, and designers are not automatically left without recourse in the event of over-running loads, as is the case in open-circuit, displacement-control systems

● servo valves require fine filtration and proportional valves somewhat less. This may not be as critical an issue when comparing valve control to pump control because variable-displacement pumps also require finer filtration than, say, fixed-displacement gear pumps. However, there is a general perception that servovalves are overly susceptible to contamination fouling

● valve-control systems use a single constant-pressure supply to power a multiplicity of actuators. Of course each actuator requires a dedicated control valve but in the final analysis, the initial cost of one constant-pressure pump and several valves is less than one variable-displacement pump for each of the several actuators, and

● because of the superb control capability offered by modern valves, it is possible to program a single servo or proportional valve to perform the functions that in traditional hydraulics would require several different kinds of valves. For example, an electrohydraulic valve can control acceleration, deceleration, speed, position, pressure and force merely by giving it an appropriate command, although it is true that synthesizing the proper command is not a trivial problem.

A brief summary of the pump-displacement control method:

● because pressure-compensated and load-sensing pumps deliver only the power that the load needs at the moment, these systems have an inherent degree of efficiency, but as mentioned earlier, it does no good to build a highly efficient system if it does not meet productivity and quality requirements

● in further considering the efficiency issue, it is not the intent here to relegate the quest for efficiency to the high-tech trash heap. Indeed, efficiency can be a genuine issue in some systems. For example, if it is necessary for an actuator to be continually propelled, such as in a turret-type bottle filler or a variable-output fan, pump control may be the best choice. In such machines, the valve incessantly consumes power in doing its prescribed job. This application may be a case where control is a secondary issue. On the other hand, in positioning or motion-control applications where the actuator reciprocates such as presses, flying cutoffs, and kicker-feeders, the valve-control method is nearly always supe-

rior
- displacement control requires a variable-displacement pump. This type pump is more costly than a variable valve, and
- pump-displacement control does not work with single rod-end cylinders. There is just too much difficulty for the designer to deal with the unbalanced flows in the two ends of the cylinder.

In summary, the decision to use valve control versus displacement control is sometimes difficult. Here are some of the items to consider:
- the decision is application specific
- the need for control must be weighed against the need for efficiency
- if the application calls for linear motion, valve control may be the method of choice because, obviously, the actuator must cycle the load. On the other hand, a motor application requiring continuous or sustained periods of operation in a single direction may properly be driven by a variable-displacement pump
- duty cycle is important. If the total power needed is relatively small, such as in transfer lines with long periods of dwell, efficiency may not be important because total cost of energy also may be small
- when meter-in and meter-out flows are needed to control over-running loads, valve control may be preferred to a closed-circuit hydrostatic transmission
- if a single rod-end cylinder is the required actuator, valve control is the method of choice, and
- in those systems that require fast response, say final band-widths of more than two or three Hz, valve control is required because most pumps respond too slowly.

Use of hydraulic power to generate motion must be compared with use of other power media, specifically electrical power. Certainly, advances in electrical technology have eroded the market share held by hydraulic drives. We must review the advantages and disadvantages of hydraulic and electrical systems in light of several issues:
- linear vs rotary motion. In the linear-motion arena, hydraulics has the unmistakable advantage while continuous rotary motion clearly favors electrical machines. For linear motion, consider a hydraulic cylinder compared to the so-called electrical cylinders. The former is the essence of simplicity (cylinder designers may disagree), having only one moving part (excluding seals), while the electrical cylinder is a complex of rotary-to-linear mechanical translators. The ball screws and nuts in the latter are a continuing source of unreliability. On the other hand, an induction motor is the electrical counterpart to a hydraulic cylinder. It, too, is a model of simplicity having only one moving part (excluding bearings). Linear-motion induction motors are a reality but they have not progressed beyond a few horsepower. A breakthrough in high-temperature superconductivity could totally change that picture

• speed variability. With either valve or displacement control and rotary or linear output, hydraulic hardware provides an easy means of varying speed. This speed variability is essential to control. In contrast, variable-speed induction motors require variable-frequency controllers that are expensive above a few horsepower. Brush-type DC motors offer good speed variability with less expensive electronic-driver amplifiers but above a few horsepower, their costs are high and the driver amplifiers are not exactly cheap when compared to servovalves, hydraulic actuators, and servo amplifiers. Brushes are a source of some unreliability but that problem is overcome with brushless-DC motors. As power levels of variable-speed electrical drives increase, they can be expected to bring about further erosions into traditional hydraulic markets

• a myth about hydraulics. One of the major drawbacks facing the hydraulic industry is that it has been laboring under a false set of advantages. For years it has been touted (and the touting continues) as a medium which responds instantaneously because of the fluid's incompressibility. This myth is immediately exposed as a falsehood by anyone who has designed a hydraulic system to perform in a specified, dynamic way.

Electrical and hydraulic systems can be compared using two methods: power, and bandwidth and time constants. Considering the first: hydraulics can push more power per pound of hardware than can the electrical industry. This is true, primarily because oil simultaneously conveys power, lubricates, and removes the heat of inefficiency. Electrical system heat of inefficiency has to be carried away from its point of creation by add-on heat sinks. The oil carries the heat away from the point of creation so a simple heat exchanger can remove all heat from the system.

On the latter point, bandwidths and time constants of hydraulic systems are no better than those in equivalently powered electrical systems. When compared to a like-powered electrical motor, for example, the low-inertia advantage of the hydraulic motor usually disappears when the inevitable load inertia is taken into account.

Motion-control profiles and system response

An important part of design methodology is the beneficial effect of driving or guiding the system with a command profile. The aim of profiling is to control acceleration, which has to do with pressure acting on an actuator. If it is possible to control the pressure waveshape, it follows directly that it is possible to control shock and noise, and reliability and performance can be enhanced. But it is not assured that controlling the profile will indeed control pressure. Designers must consider the dynamic response of the electro-hydromechanical system. Overshoot and lag, Figure 15.4, measure the degree that the ideal (command profile) disagrees with actual response. Designers must consider at least four factors when matching a profile to a given machine. These factors explain why the actual response differs from the profile in an unacceptable way:

● hydromechanical resonance and damping. Hydromechanical resonance occurs because the effective load mass interacts with the compliance of the system, usually because of the compressibility of the fluid. Other causes could be beam or linking-member deflection or other springiness. This interaction results in a bouncing action, such as when an automotive suspension system hits a bump. In that instance, the mass resonates with the suspension spring. If the shock absorbers (a completely erroneous name, they really are oscillation dampers) are defective, the springy action continues for a long time. Oil compressibility is the cause of the effective spring rate in a hydraulic system. Damping is provided coincidentally by the fluid, and mechanical friction in the system however it may occur

● control-valve bandwidth or frequency response is a measure of how fast a valve can respond to input signals. If the valve has a low-frequency response and is too slow, it will contribute to the output lag relative to the command profile. Sometimes, a very fast valve seems to contribute to overshoot, but that is not a certainty in all systems

● servo-loop tuning, particularly the servo-loop gain, affects overshoot and lag. Low loop gain results in excessive lag. If loop gain is too high, overshoot is excessive. When loop gain is increased to its upper limit, overshoots never settle and an unstable system that oscillates or hunts continuously is the result. Such conditions cannot be tolerated. The accuracy with which a servo system can find its final target position (assuming the loop is stable) is directly related to gain. The higher the gain, the more accurate the target acquisition. But if gain is too high, the system becomes unstable, so the designer's job always involves the gain/

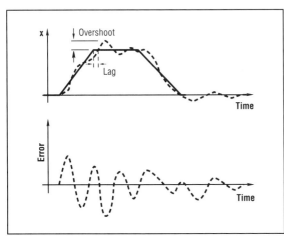

Fig. 15.4. Actual system response will lag the command profile and can overshoot depending on the nature of system dynamics.

stability compromise, and

• profile rise rate has a subtle affect on lag and overshoot. Clearly a real machine must lag the command when the profile rise is very steep. If the rise takes place over a longer time, output can very closely approximate the command profile. If the profile rise rate is great, it will excite the hydromechanical system at its resonant frequency and cause overshoots, a fact that is not so clear. The degree that this occurs is affected by the three previous factors. The designer must shape the profile to minimize lag as well as overshoot. There is always an input profile that creates the desired output profile for any desired output profile and plant. Finding this input profile is not a trivial problem.

System specification and performance

A system designer's problems are compounded by lack of an accurate and complete set of performance indexes expected of the final system. Often system sponsors do not know what performance is required or what parameters, such as friction and inertia values, exist in their processes. Yet, the systems engineer is expected to design a control system that actuates and controls the process so that the machine *works well*. Sometimes performance specifications are unrealistically demanding and when the true costs of that performance are known, machine specifications become negotiable. For instance, not knowing what the costs are, a sponsor may request positioning capabilities within 0.025 mm. When told of the commensurate high cost, and when considering what the process really needs, 1 mm might be sufficient.

Pitfalls for the unwary are many. Often the design engineer provides a system that fits within the cost framework of the customer; the designed system is as good as can be expected under the cost constraints. It is essential that the designer have a good understanding of how certain parameters affect final performance, specifically lag, overshoot, and accuracy. The following are some of the more notable items over which a designer has some control. The list is not exhaustive.

Factors affecting overshoot

Overshoot is the tendency of a system to reach its target output in a decaying, oscillatory manner. The response is said to be springy, or bouncy. Whether a system can tolerate such springiness is an application-specific question. For example, if one must control the depth of a drilling operation, overshoot can result in a hole deeper than necessary. On the other hand, the axis motion that positions the drill laterally before drill extension can withstand overshoot and actually may be faster acting and more responsive with a bit of overshoot. Systems which overshoot are also called *underdamped*.

Several factors can be identified which increasingly affect overshoot.

Knowledge of them may help a system designer when hard performance specifications do not exist.

Low hydromechanical resonant frequency. The lower the hydromechanical resonant frequency, the greater the tendency to overshoot. The question becomes how low is low? That must be taken in context of the problem at hand. In particular, it is necessary to compare the hydromechanical resonant frequency to the rise time of the command profile. Any time the reciprocal of the rise time is greater than about three times the hydromechanical resonant frequency, the likelihood of overshoots exists. It is possible to shape the profile, however, so that overshoots can be eliminated, but that subject generally is beyond our scope. Hydromechanical resonant frequency can be calculated knowing cylinder dimensions, type of fluid, and the load mass the actuator must move. Here are primary factors that work to decrease hydromechanical resonant frequency:

● large, massive loads
● large fluid volume under compression
● use of hoses and/or long connecting lines between control valves and actuators, and
● an undersized actuator.

Servo-loop gain. Increasing servo-loop gain enhances the tendency of a system to overshoot and, in the extreme, continually oscillate. By a screwdriver adjustment on the servo amplifier, gain is the simplest system parameter to change, yet has a profound affect on system performance. When gain is high, an actuator gains considerable momentum as it approaches its output target. The natural lags of the valve and other system components can allow actuator speed to be greater than necessary as the target is reached. As the target is passed, the error (difference between commanded position and actual position) reverses sign and acts to reverse the valve to bring the actuator back to the target. The result is a continuing, springy descent to the target with overshoots that decay toward zero.

Fast control valve. When valve response is slow when compared to the hydromechanical resonant frequency, the tendency to overshoot is suppressed. The situation can be as if a ramp control has been provided. The reason is simple: even though a step-input command is given to the amplifier, the sluggishness of the valve results in a gradual, gentle metering of pressure to the actuator. Similarly at deceleration time, the same phenomenon reduces the tendency to overshoot.

On the other hand, if the valve is fast, a sudden command change causes sudden pressure changes and the actuator tends to behave as though it is underdamped. This may seem to imply that a sluggish valve is preferred over a fast valve, but that is clearly not the intent or the case. Most emphatically, system designers are better served with a valve that has fast response, because any speed reduction that may be desired can easily be accomplished in the electronics. Speeding the reaction time of an inherently slow component is nearly impossible. Slow valves lead to system instability at lower servo-loop gains more quickly than fast valves. **Fast command rise rate**. For the same reason a fast-acting valve increases the tendency to overshoot, hitting the system with a fast-rising command signal excites the servo system at a spectrum of frequencies that cause overshoots. Again, the interpretation of fast and slow must be made in the context of the hydromechanical resonant frequency.

Low internal actuator leakage. Unfortunately, the parameters that enhance steady-state performance do not always enhance dynamic performance. Actuator designers have gone to great effort to reduce internal leakage. Steady-state load-holding capability is certainly enhanced when using zero-leakage cylinders. But if one is concerned about dynamic performance and minimizing overshoot, then high port-to-port leakage may be a solution to the problem, blasphemous as that may sound. The reason is that a leakage path is a restrictive element from a modeling point of view and as one of its functions, converts fluid energy into heat energy that is irreversibly carried away from the hydraulic system. Therefore, a suitably sized leakage path will convert the oscillatory (AC) energy into heat and thus help suppress the oscillations. This process provides damping for the system and always leads to a reduced tendency to hunt. Although systems have been built with some degree of success making use of a deliberately introduced leakage path, it is not the damping method of choice. With valve control, opening and closing of the valve lands can be electronically timed so that they port pump power to the actuator at crucial times, and at other equally crucial times, the lands absorb oscillatory energy to provide damping without leakage.

Factors that increase lag

Lag and overshoot interact in that the same parameters that affect one also affect the other. Sometimes, their interaction is contrary to one another.

Low hydromechanical resonant frequency. Recall that low hydromechanical resonant frequency increases overshoot and at the same time increases lag between command and output. Thus, it behooves the designer to get the resonant frequency as high as possible. Sometimes such design versatility is not possible. Then, other methods may have to be used.

Slow control valve. Valve response can sometimes be at cross purposes with lag and overshoot. If valve response is too fast, overshoot can be excessive. If too slow, lag can be excessive.

Fast command-profile rise rate. When profile rise rate is rapid, a springy system tends to overshoot. If the rise rate is too fast, it also increases lag.

Note that system lag is much like a constant value but when a steeper input occurs, output appears to lag more. Actually it is merely farther behind the input only because the input is changing faster.

Low servo-loop gain. Servo-loop gain is the overall product of all transfer factors around the loop such as valve gain, actuator area, servo-amplifier gain, and the volts/inch constant of the position transducer. After a particular system is built, only one means is avilable to designer and user to change loop gain: change of the servo-amplifier gain. It is a very simple adjustment. The system is structured so the amplifier sees the difference between command position and output position as measured by the position transducer.

It should be apparent that if servo-amplifier gain increases, then the servovalve opens more fully for a given error voltage than with a lower amplifier gain. It should be equally apparent that if the valve opens more, the load will accelerate faster and result in less lag between command and output position. The limit to increasing gain is reached when it results in excessive overshoot and ringing, or in the extreme case the output may continuously hunt. Then the system is oscillating and is said to be unstable.

High friction. Friction plays an important role in servo-system performance because it provides damping that is crucial to getting rid of unwanted ringing or springiness. On the other hand, if friction is overpowering, there may not be enough power in the actuator to accelerate the load in a timely way. This can result in excessive lag between command and output.

Solutions to the motion-control problem

The traditional method used to control motion in a hydraulic system has been to incorporate a pre-set limit switch in a position that closes an on-off control valve at a predetermined point, Figure 15.5. The idea is that if correctly set, the ballistics of the system will cause the actuator and load to stop at the precise end position just as the valve fully closes. This system has open-loop control because if the actuator does not reach its

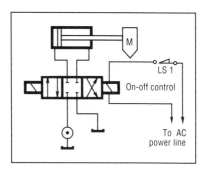

Fig. 15.5. On-off control creates shock and noise, and results in problematic stopping accuracy.

required position, there is no way to provide a correction. Similarly, an overshoot at final settling time cannot be corrected. Many of these *bang-bang* systems exist, and some provide adequate acceleration and deceleration control. Many others do not and they have given hydraulic machinery a bad name.

The bang-bang name has evolved because of their tendency to be noisy, banging and clanging at both start and stop. Accompanying the noise (actually, it is more correct to say *accounting for the noise*) is an enormous series of pressure peaks that can damage the system. They reduce seal life, create fatigue on fittings, and generally lead to the leaks that many consider to be inevitable in hydraulic circuits. All this does not mention the din and displeasure of the noise itself. Certainly, the on-off system has serious shortcomings.

Sometimes with tuning and adjustment, the stopping repeatability can be brought within tolerable limits, but in other cases, acceptable limits can never be achieved. This is because once the valve is commanded to close, the cylinder's final resting place depends only upon the system's ballistics — the cylinder and load are like free-falling objects in the same way that a baseball pitcher has no control over the trajectory of the ball once it leaves his hand.

The only element of control in this type hydraulic system is the timing of the instant when the stop signal is given. From then on, the cylinder is in free-fall. Compounding the problem are external factors — such as variations in load, in friction, and in temperature — that alter system dynamics from cycle to cycle. Repeatability is highly unlikely in these machines. To overcome some of these problems, *slow shift* or *soft shift* valves were developed with built-in orifices that slow the rate of valve shift. They resulted in a great reduction in noise and pressure peaks, leading to longer machine life, fewer shock-induced leakage problems, and overall acceptable noise level. Even so, these systems still are subject to the same

Fig. 15.6. Ramp control of a proportional valve controls acceleration and thus limits its shock, but stopping accuracy remains problematic.

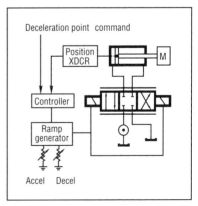

environmental variations as their bang-bang brethren in terms of repeatability.

Most notably, oil temperature affects valve shift time and thereby affects repeatability of the stopped position. In the extreme, the system may alter its dynamic response so much that it begins banging and clanging. The fix is a step in the right direction; some of the variability has been reduced by replacing the bang-bang valve with an electronically controlled proportional valve, Figure 15.6. Its electronic amplifier is equipped with a *ramp control* that sends a ramped signal to the valve's proportional coil. The rate at which the ramp changes controls the rate at which the spool moves. Thus the cylinder's acceleration and deceleration are under control of the ramp.

There are clear advantages of ramped shift over the hydraulically controlled shift rate. The time range of start and stop is increased. Commercial ramps can be altered from a few milliseconds to several seconds of ramp merely by adjusting a potentiometer. Ramp time changes with respect to environmental factors such as temperature can become minimal. Ramp shape can be altered to further enhance the dynamic behavior of the cylinder and its load even though most commercially available ramp controls use simple straight-line ramping. Use of electronically ramped proportional valves can produce downright dramatic improvements in system dynamic behavior.

One needs only to have a ramp control of some considerable range and then observe system response as the ramp is turned from minimal delay to a large value. A banging and clanging system will purr like a pussycat. Use of a proportional valve has another advantage: it usually results in a reduction in the number and complexity of other valves. The need for sequence valves, pressure-reducing valves, counterbalance valves, and the like can often be eliminated, reducing sytem cost. Without doubt, these methods enhance dynamic performance.

Unfortunately, the method is not a panacea because the system is still open loop and as such, it provides no lasting assurance that the desired final actuator position will be achieved. Controlling the degree of valve opening provides some speed control, but position control remains elusive. The final resting point of the actuator depends too much upon the ballistics and environmental factors because as before, after the signal stop has been given, no means are available to apply corrective action.

The problem is solved by building a closed-loop, positional servomechanism. A servo amplifier continuously monitors position as measured by the position transducer and compares it to the command signal. Then, based on the error, the amplifier opens the servovalve some proportional amount. When the cylinder gets into the desired position, i.e. when the command voltage equals feedback voltage, the valve closes and the cylinder stops, at least in theory.

Positional servo and profiling

Consider the operation of the system in Figure 15.7(a). If a constant voltage is applied to the summing junction of the servo amplifier, and if the feedback voltage generated by the position transducer is different, then there is an error voltage. This error voltage is amplified and a current is sent to the servovalve, shifting it to an open position. If the loop is phased correctly, the direction of valve shift ports fluid into the actuator in a direction that will cause a position-transducer output voltage of a smaller discrepancy with the command voltage. As time goes on, the motion improves the degree of agreement between command and feedback until ultimately, when command and feedback exactly offset one another, the error goes to zero, valve current goes to zero, the spool centers, and the cylinder stops. This idealized scenario depends upon proper tuning of the system.

This scene is realistic if simplistic, in describing the essential behavior of the closed-loop positional servomechanism. The end result is that with constant command voltage, proper phasing and tuning, the cylinder finds a final resting place that depends on the command voltage and the feedback transducer, not system dynamics. This is an exciting machine and one that holds great promise in solving countless industrial motion control problems.

In short, output position of the cylinder follows whatever command voltage is put into the servo system. It stands to reason then, that if a constant voltage is input, the cylinder will, in due time, achieve a com-

Fig. 15.7. Closed-loop servo machanism (a) is guided by profiled command voltage (b) to provide total motion control.

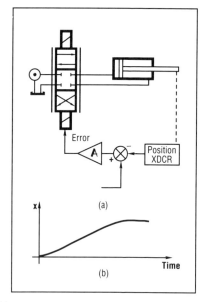

mensurate, constant position. An extension of that same argument leads to the conclusion that if a time-varying voltage is input, the cylinder motion will likewise be time-varying as it attempts to follow the command. In what way should command voltage vary with time? The profile must have a final value commensurate with the desired position, with slopes at the appropriate velocities, and changes in velocity made to conform with required accelerations, Figure 15.7(b).

Feeding this profile to the positional servo, the system achieves simultaneous control of position, speed and acceleration **if** cylinder motion faithfully follows the profile. Closure of the outer position loop with an appropriate position transducer assures that final output position is acquired within the accuracy limits of the servo loop. The shape of the profile controls the speed and acceleration.

In this scenario, total motion control is achieved in conformance with the earlier definition more so by proper design of the profile than by proper design of the servo system. That is, after specifying the acceleration, integrating it once to get the velocity and again to get the position, by default the position profile has the required characteristics. Now, **if** the servosystem is sufficiently responsive (fast, or with wide-enough bandwidth), inputting the profile as synthesized will at once result in the position, speed, and acceleration required! This is motion control. Some big *ifs* qualified that statement. That is, will the servosystem be responsive enough to faithfully follow the target profile? The answer to that question is based on the design of the servo system. A more appropriate question is, *can a servosystem be designed that is sufficiently responsive to faithfully follow the required profile?* The answer to that is a qualified yes. Theoretically, there is always some servo system that will do the job. Whether or not it can be achieved with standard commercial components or at acceptable cost is another question.

Actual design of the electrohydraulic motion control system is beyond the scope of this book. These ideas have been presented to show the reader some of the many ways in which the electronic components can be interfaced with the hydraulic components. Of course, the electronic apparatus in the motion control system consists of the servo amplifier, the transducer and its signal conditioning, and the ramp or profile generator.

Appendix A

Glossary

AC coupled — The ability to pass electrical signals only if they are above a minimum frequency.

Active region — That region in the metering characteristics curve of a valve which lies between the dead zone and the saturation region, Figure A.1.

Amplifier — A device which has a power input port and at least one signal- or control-input port. Resulting controlled power output can exceed the control input power, Figure A.2.

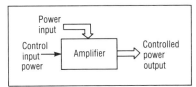

Fig. A.2. Block diagram of amplifier inputs, output.

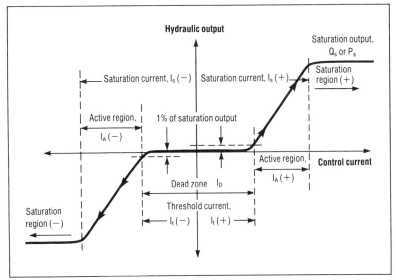

Fig. A.1. Generalized metering characteristics curve for proportional electrohydraulic interface device (PEHID).

Amplifier, operational — An electronic package consisting of several transistors and capacitors arranged to produce an output which is an amplified replica of the input. Configuring the package with user-selected input and output impedances, operational amplifiers can be used to add, subtract, integrate, and differentiate, as well as provide electronic compensation and bandpass frequency filtration, Figure A.3. Synonym: op-amp.

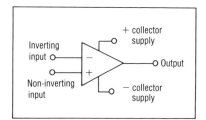

Fig. A.3. Operational amplifier symbol.

Analog — A representation of information by the amplitude of a physical variable.

Bandwidth — That band of frequencies which lies below selected points on the frequency response curve, and based on specified criteria. Two common criteria are the minus three decibel roll-off and the 90° phase lag frequency. Note that the frequency where the amplitude (gain) in dB has rolled off by three is the same as a 30% reduction in amplitude in the units

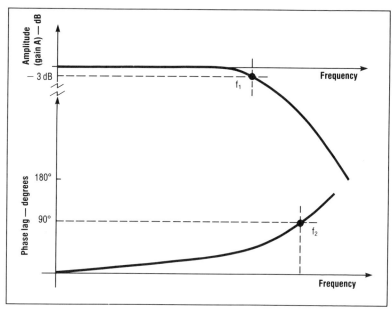

Fig. A.4. Gain and phase curves for proportional electrohydraulic interface device (PEHID); f_1 represents frequency at -3 dB bandwidth, and f_2 represents frequency at 90° phase lag bandwidth. Published bandwidth depends upon which of these two criteria a manufacturer chooses.

Table A.1 — Binary code			
3-bit binary number			Decimal equivalent
bit 2	bit 1	bit 0	
0	0	0	0
0	0	1	1
0	1	0	2
0	1	1	3
1	0	0	4
1	0	1	5
1	1	0	6
1	1	1	7

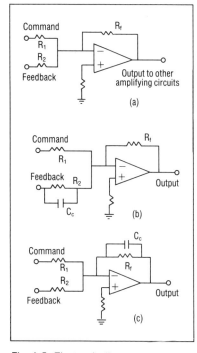

Fig. A.5. Electronically uncompensated operational amplifier circuit, (a); operational amplifier circuit with lead compensation of the feedback signal, (b); operational amplifier circuit with lag compensation of the error signal, (c). Other compensation methods are possible.

of measure, Figure A.4. See Frequency response.

Bel — A dimensionless unit that expresses the ratio of two values of power. It is the logarithm to the base 10 of the power ratio. The more commonly used decibel (dB) is 10 times the logarithm to the base 10 of the power ratio. A bel is 10 decibel. $x = \log_{10} y$; $y = 10^x$; $a^0 = 1$; $0\,\mathrm{dB} = 10^0 = 1$.

Binary code — A digital coding scheme using combinations of ones and zeros, ons and offs, trues and falses, etc., to represent quantities, Table A.1. See Gray code.

Center-lap conditions — A consideration in the design and manufacture of hydraulic valves describing the amount of spool movement needed for the pressure and tank ports to begin communicating with their respective work ports. Valves can be over, under, or critically lapped. See Dead zone and Figure A.1.

Closed loop — A commonly used term to distinguish closed control loops rather than the positional loop used to set position of the main hydraulic valve spool. This is not to be confused with the closed hydraulic circuit of a hydrostatic transmission. See Inner loop.

Command — That signal which tells a system what output level to seek. Synonym: set point.

Compensation, electronic — A process whereby an electronic circuit is especially tailored to improve the dynamic response of the overall electrohydraulic system, Figure A.5.

Compensator, unloading — A specific pressure-compensated flow control valve which also relieves a fixed-displacement pump at a low pressure when a mating directional control valve is centered, Figure A.6.

Contamination tolerance — A measure of the ability of a proportional electrohydraulic interface device (PEHID) to function within specific limits when operated with a fluid containing contaminants of a specified kind and size.

Control, closed-loop — A control concept using sensors to monitor performance or status of a machine or process output. The sensors send or feed information back to the input for automatic corrective action, Figure A.7.

Control, feedback — See Control, closed-loop.

Control, man-in-the-loop — See Control, open-loop.

Control, open-loop — A control concept in which a human observes the status or performance of a process or machine. The human makes control decisions and corrections to the system when its status or performance is unacceptable, Figure A.8. Synonym: man-in-the-loop. See Control, closed-loop.

Control, PID — A proportional, integral, and derivative control scheme that integrates or differentiates the error in a servo mechanism or scales it proportionally with a constant. The scheme is the forerunner of the state-variable controller.

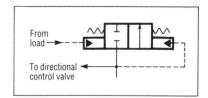

Fig. A.6. Hydraulic unloading compensator circuit.

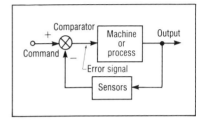

Fig. A.7. Block diagram of closed-loop control.

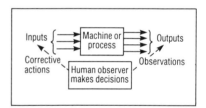

Fig. A.8. Block diagram indicates how observer makes decisions to establish closed control loop.

Control, ramp — A special electronic conditioning circuit which, when given a step input, increases or decreases the output linearly (as the case may be) until the output reaches the value of the input. Two control concepts can be implemented: constant slope, variable time to reach input level; and constant time lag, variable slope, Figure A.9.

Controller — That portion of a closed-loop control system which receives command and feedback signals and sends a command or error signal to the controlled system. See Summing junction.

Cracking pressure — That pressure needed to just begin opening a relief or counterbalance valve. See Figures A.35, A.39.

Current feedback — A design technique applied to a coil and its driver amplifier in which coil current is sensed, fed back to the amplifier, and hence is regulated. The purpose of the technique is to make current independent of coil resistance, and to increase the frequency response by raising the effective output impedance of the amplifier, Figure A.10.

Current, absolute maximum — I_r. That input current a coil can withstand at 100% duty cycle. Synonym: rated current.

Damping — A subjective term dealing with the tendency of a feedback-controlled system to diminish its overshoots as time progresses after a command change or load disturbance occurs. See Overdamping, Underdamping.

DC coupled — The ability to pass

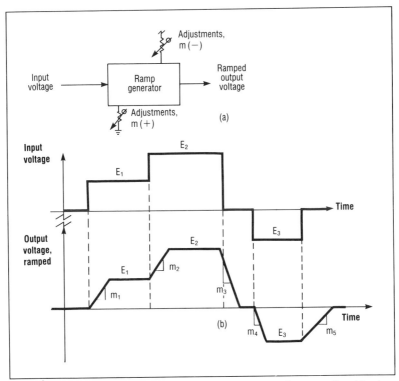

Fig. A.9. Block diagram of ramp generator, (a); graph, (b), shows relationships between input and output voltages for a ramp generator and illustrates constant slope, variable time concept; ramp slope $m_1 = m_2 = m_5$, and $m_3 = m_4$.

electrical signals at zero Hz. Synonym: direct coupled.

DCDT — See Differential transformer, DC-coupled.

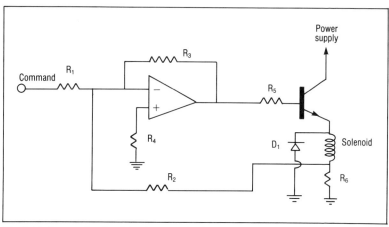

Fig. A.10. Current feedback implemented using current sense resistor R_6 and feeding it back to summing junction of R_1 and R_2. D_1 is a commutating diode.

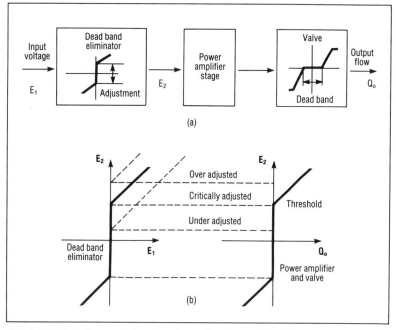

Fig. A.11. Block diagram (a), and various adjustments (b), of dead-band eliminator.

A6

Dead band — See Dead zone.

Dead-band eliminator — A special electronic circuit designed to compensate for the dead zone of a particular proportional electrohydraulic interface device (PEHID), Figure A.11. Note: The critical

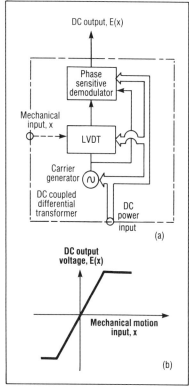

Fig. A.12. Direct-coupled differential transformer envelope diagram, (a), and (b), plot of DC output voltage vs mechanical position input to the DCDT.

adjustment may not be the optimum adjustment because that condition does not allow a loaded cylinder to be stopped. Synonym: threshold control.

Dead zone — That region at and surrounding the origin on the metering-characteristics curve in which input current causes no output. Synonym: dead band. Equations for calculation of the dead zone for bidirectional[1], and unidirectional[2] proportional electrohydraulic interface devices (PEHIDs) use letter designations described in Figure A.1.

Differential transformer, DC-coupled (DCDT) — A special packaging of a linear variable differential transformer (LVDT) in which the LVDT, carrier generator, and phase-sensitive demodulator all are contained within one envelope, Figure A.12.

Differential transformer, linear variable (LVDT) — A position transducer which produces an AC output votage with amplitude and phase (0° or 180°) dependent on core position. The transducer uses AC excitation and has a primary and two secondary windings and a moveable core (slug), Figure A.13.

Digital — Representation of information by the use of symbols, characters, or voltages in discrete, specified combinations.

Diode — An electronic device which allows electrical current to

^{1}% deadzone $= (100)[(I_t +) - (I_t -)]/[(I_s +) - (I_s -)]$

^{2}% deadzone $= (100)(I_t)/I_s$

pass only in one direction, Figure A.14.

Diode, commutating — A diode used with inductive loads and switched voltage to suppress the voltage spikes across the switch. See Figure A.10.

Dither — A process whereby an alternating signal of appropriate frequency, amplitude, and wave shape is deliberately introduced to the coil of a proportional electrohydraulic interface device (PEHID) to improve overall system performance by reducing friction-induced hysteresis and to reduce contaminant silting at the valve's metering lands.

Error — The difference between the command signal and the feedback signal used to correct the system toward a lower or zero error. See Control, closed loop; Controller.

Feathering — A subjective term which refers to the sharpness of the transition from the dead zone to the active region of a valve, Figure A.15.

Feedback — That branch in a closed-loop control system consisting of the output sensor(s) and the connections to the controller.

Flow forces — Forces created as a result of changing the direction or speed of a fluid stream.

Flow gain — (G_q) The average slope of the metering curve over 80% of its output range as recorded while operating the valve at constant pressure drop, Figure A.16.

Flow, quiescent input — (Q_z) The flow a valve consumes at a specified pressure while it is in

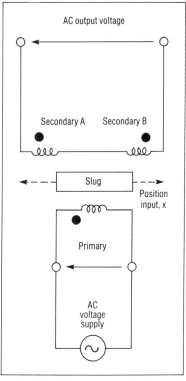

Fig. A.13. Diagram of linear variable differential transformer (LVDT) circuit.

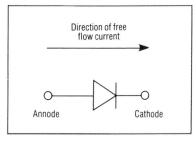

Fig. A.14. Symbol of a diode showing direction of free flow.

neutral.

Force motor — A linear motion current-to-force transducer with an integral permanent magnet, which produces a current-dependent force whose direction depends on current direction, Figure A.17.

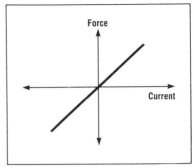

Fig. A.17. Plot of force vs. current characteristics of force motor.

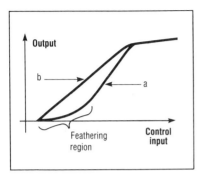

Fig. A.15. Metering characteristics curve of two different proportional electrohydraulic interface devices (PEHIDs). Device (a) has feathering capability but (b) does not.

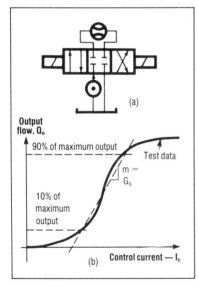

Fig. A.16. Control current applied to solenoid of valve in (a) produces output flow curve indicated in (b). Flow gain, G_q with slope m, is best mathematical straight-line fit over 80% of output flow range.

Frequency response — A graph of the ratio of output amplitude to input amplitude vs. frequency, and phase angle between input and output vs. frequency of a proportional electrohydraulic interface device (PEHID). It normally is plotted as amplitude (gain A) in dB and phase angle lag in degrees as a function of frequency in Hz (sometimes in radians/sec) plotted on a logarithmic scale. See Figure A.4.

Gain — The ratio of input amplitude to output amplitude. Synonym: amplification.

Gain margin — The gain margin of a feedback control system is a relative measure of the system's stability. Gain margin is the amount control loop amplitude (gain) can be increased to achieve unity control loop gain (0 dB = 1), measured at the frequency which causes 180° phase shift, Figure A.18.

Gray code — A special encryption

of binary code reordering common binary code so that, when moving from one value to the next, only one bit changes. This eliminates the ambiguity associated with the value-to-value transition points in binary encoders, Table A.2. See Binary code; Position transducer, absolute-encoding.

Hysteresis — The amount the output of a device with increasing input disagrees with its output as input decreases. Hysteresis usually is expressed as a percentage of total change in input between positive and negative saturation areas,

Figure A.19. Equations for calculation of hysteresis for bidirec-

3-bit binary number			Simple binary-to-decimal conversion	Gray code decimal position
bit 2	bit 1	bit 0		
0	0	0	0	0
0	0	1	1	1
0	1	1	3	2
0	1	0	2	3
1	1	0	6	4
1	1	1	7	5
1	0	1	5	6
1	0	0	4	7

Table A.2 — Gray code

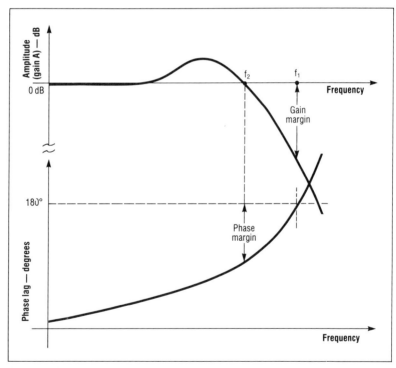

Fig. A.18. Open-loop frequency response curves show how gain and phase margins are determined; f_1 indicates frequency where phase lag = 180°; f_2 indicates frequency where gain is 0 dB.

tional[3], and unidirectional[4] proportional electrohydraulic interface devices (PEHIDs), use letter designations described in Figures A.1 and A.19.

Hysteresis current — (I_h) A projection of the widest control point of the hysteresis opening on the control input axis expressed as units of input, that is amps, milliamps, or volts, Figure A.19.

Inner loop — A common term identifying the positional servo mechanism that acquires a proportional or servovalve main-spool position, depending on the command signal, Figure A.20. See Closed loop.

Linearity — Maximum deviation between a measured input/output curve at a given point and the best-fit mathematical straight line, usually expressed as a percentage of the saturation value, Figure A.21. Note: the technically correct term is *nonlinearity* but linearity has be-

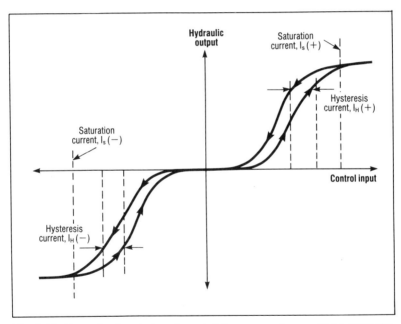

Fig. A.19. Generalized metering characteristics curve of proportional electrohydraulic interface device (PEHID) that indicates effects of hysteresis.

$$^3\% \text{ hysteresis} = (100)[(I_h+) - (I_h-)]/\Big([(I_s+) - (I_t+)]$$
$$- [(I_s-) - (I_t-)]\Big)$$

$$^4\% \text{ hysteresis} = (100)(I_h)/(I_s - I_t)$$

come industry jargon. Equations for calculation of the linearity for bidirectional[5] and unidirectional[6] proportional electrohydraulic in-terface devices (PEHIDs), use let-ter designations described in Fig-ures A.1 and A.21.

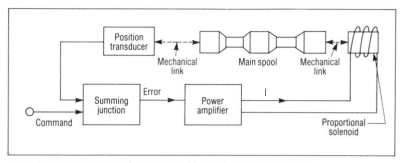

Fig. A.20. Block diagram of inner control loop of a proportional valve.

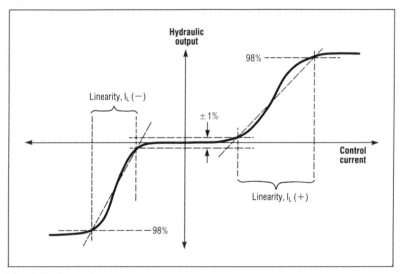

Fig. A.21. Generalized metering characteristics curve of a proportional electrohy-draulic interface device (PEHID) with the best mathematical straight line fit over 98% of output range.

$$^5\% \text{ linearity} = (100)[(I_l+) - (I_l-)] / \Big([(I_s+) - (I_t+)]$$
$$- [(I_s-) - (I_t-)] \Big)$$

$$^6\% \text{ linearity} = (100)(I_l)/(I_s - I_t)$$

Linearity current — (I_l) A projection to the current axis of the deviation between the best straight line fit over 98% of the active region and the actual metering curve, expressed as a percent. See Figure A.21.

LVDT — See Differential transformer, linear variable.

Main stage — The power-output portion of a piloted or multi-stage valve.

Metering characteristics — A graph of output flow vs. input current of a proportional electrohydraulic interface device (PEHID) at a specified applied power condition; or a family of curves, one trace for each power condition, Figure A.22.

Metering characteristics, split — A variation of the metering characteristics in which the pressure vs flow curves of: (a) the inlet pressure to the A work port and the B work port to the tank port;

and (b) pressure to the B work port and the A work port to the tank port, are tested individually because several of the metering lands are substantially dissimilar, or because pressure flow is expected to be substantially different from return flow.

Modulation, amplitude (AM) — An analog system that carries information in the amplitude of the signal.

Modulation, frequency (FM) — An analog system that carries information in the frequency of the signal.

Modulation, pulse width (PWM) — In electrohydraulics, PWM is an electronic analog power amplification scheme that the controller

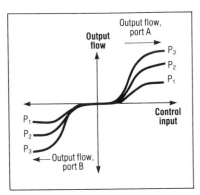

Fig. A.22. Example metering characteristics curves of proportional electrohydraulic interface device (PEHID) indicates varying output flows at supply pressures, P_1, P_2, and P_3.

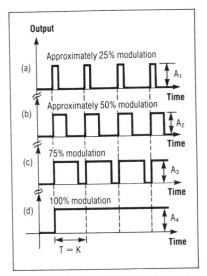

Fig. A.23. Graph of PWM voltage signals at four different modulations. (a) indicates approximately 25% modulation, (b) approximately 50%, (c) approximately 75%, and (d) 100% modulation. Amplitude $A_1 = A_2 = A_3 = A_4$.

switches ON and OFF at an appropriate frequency. Altering the amount of ON time relative to OFF time provides proportional control of valve-coil current. Thus, a slowly moving load controlled by amplifier output responds to the average value of the power signal rather than following the instantaneous PWM wave shape, Figure A.23.

Motor stroker, electrical — A proportional electrohydraulic interface device (PEHID) which accepts an input current and proportionally controls the stroke of a variable-displacement motor.

Null — A condition of zero or minimum output.

Observer — An electronic device which accepts the inputs and outputs of a system under control. The observer then delivers estimates of the state variables of the controlled system, Figure A.24.

Op-amp — See Amplifier, operational

Oscillator — A solid-state electronic generator that creates AC supply voltages for specific uses such as clock pulses, carrier supply voltages for AM carrier instrumentation systems, and pulse width modulators.

Overdamping — The tendency for a feedback-controlled system to have no overshoots. See Overshoot and Damping.

Overshoot — The phenomenon in closed-loop control wherein the system overcorrects and causes the output to exceed the desired value, Figure A.25.

PEHID — see Proportional electrohydraulic interface device.

Phase margin — Feedback control system phase margin is the number of degrees the phase angle must additionally lag the input to cause 180° phase lag, measured at

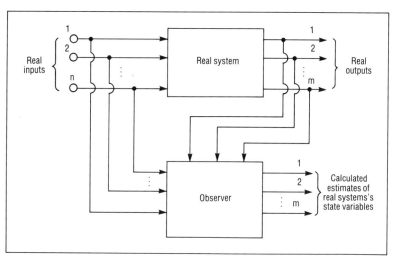

Fig. A.24. Block diagram of observer connected to real system.

A14

the point where loop gain is unity (0 dB = 1). It is a relative measure of system stability, see f_2, Figure

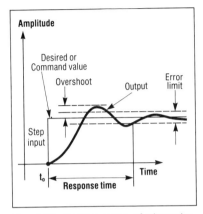

Fig. A.25. Output curve of electrohydraulic servo system shows overshoot characteristics. Time required to attain command value, and degree of overshoot are indicators of system stability; also indicates error limit, response time, and step input.

A.18.

Pilot pressure, minimum — (P_{cn}) The minimum pilot pressure or separate pilot supply pressure required to reliably control the main stage of a valve's entire range of pressures, flows, and control curves.

Pilot valve — An electric-to-hydraulic transducer/amplifier which operates a larger valve. Synonym: pilot stage.

Pilot valve, flapper-nozzle — A current-to-pressure transducer which moves a flapper to vary the flow characteristics of two opposed nozzles. With the flapper in neutral, Figure A.26, both gages indicate equal orifice pressures. As torque motor moves flappper toward nozzle A, A-side orifice pressure increases with corresponding decrease in B-side orifice pressure. This pressure differential

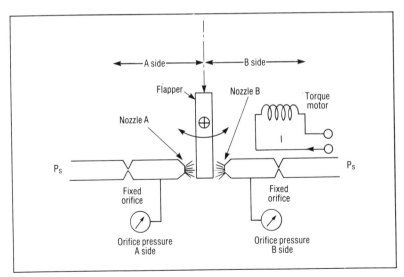

Fig. A.26. Flapper-nozzle pilot valve.

can be used to move the spool of a second stage or power valve.

Pilot valve, jet-pipe — A current-to-pressure transducer which steers a proportional fluid stream into either of two receiving ports. This generates a current-dependent pressure differential between the receiving ports used to pilot a main spool, Figure A.27.

Position transducer, absolute-encoding — A position transducer which produces a multi-bit binary code based on the position of the rotary or linear input member. Output coding may be straight binary or Gray code. Synonym: absolute encoder. See Gray code, Binary code.

Position transducer, incremental-encoding — A position transducer that accepts linear or rotary inputs and delivers a specified number of voltage pulses per unit of input, e.g. 1000 pulses/rev, 2000 pulses/in. By counting pulses, position can be tracked. Alternatively, by measuring the frequency of the output pulses, speed can be transduced. Synonym: incremental encoder.

Position transducer, magnetostrictive — A position transducer which transmits a torsional pulse along a tube and later receives an echo reflected from a purposely positioned magnet encircling the tube. The time between the transmitted pulse and the received echo is a measure of magnet position. This principle often is used to determine cylinder extension.

Potentiometer — A three-termi-nal variable resistor used as an adjustable resistor, adjustable voltage divider, or a position transducer, Figure A.28.

Power supply — That assembly of electronic components which supplies stable DC voltages to amplifying, transducing, and signal conditioning circuits. A power supply may be unipolar or bipolar.

Power supply, bipolar — A power supply which produces DC voltages of positive and negative

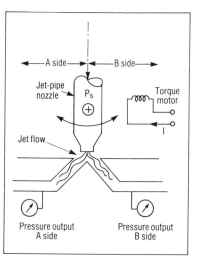

Fig. A.27. Jet-pipe pilot valve.

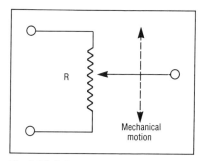

Fig. A.28. Schematic of potentiometer.

polarity with respect to ground.

Power supply, regulated — A power supply equipped with circuits which assure steady voltage(s) in the presence of varying line voltage input and varying load (output) current within specified limits.

Power supply, unipolar — A power supply which produces DC voltage of only one polarity with respect to ground.

Pressure gain — (G_p) The slope of the differential deadhead output pressure as a function of control input at a specified point, Figure A.29.

Programmable cylinder — A proportional electrohydraulic interface device (PEHID) consisting of an integrally mounted hydraulic cylinder, servo or proportional valve, and a cylinder position feedback transducer, Figure A.30.

Proportional electrohydraulic interface device (PEHID) — Any device which accepts an input voltage or current and, depending upon input signal, adjusts a hydraulic pump output flow or load pressure a commensurate amount.

Pump stroker, electrical — A proportional electrohydraulic interface device (PEHID) which accepts an input voltage or current and, depending on input signal, commensurately adjusts a hydraulic pump output flow or load pressure.

Ramp input — A specific electric signal which rises or falls in a straight line with a finite constant slope m at specified time t_o. Figure A.31.

Rated flow, pump output — The output flow delivered from a pump operating at a specified speed, output load pressure, and fluid viscosity.

Rated flow, valve output — The volumetric output flow from a valve at a specified pressure drop. For servovalves, the specified pressure drop is 70 bar (ISO 6404).

Rated voltage — (E_r) A term normally applied to ON, OFF devices to characterize nominal system voltage, e. g., 12 V DC, 120 V AC, or 220 V AC.

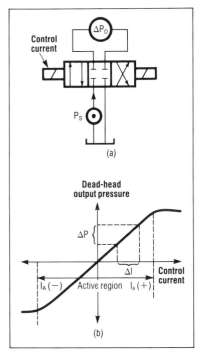

Fig. A.29. With input current to a solenoid of the PEHID (a), the pressure-metering characteristics of that PEHID (b), defines its pressure gain. $G_p = \Delta P/\Delta I$ when $P_s = K$.

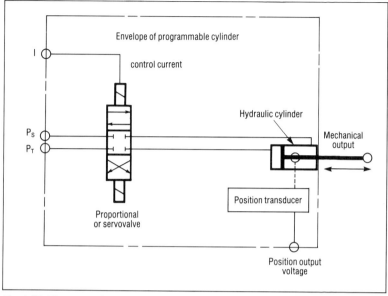

Fig. A.30. Elements of a programmable cylinder.

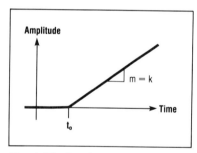

Fig. A.31. Graph shows ramp input curve with slope m=K.

Repeatability — A measure of the ability of the output of a system or device to remain the same upon repeated applications of the same input.

Resolution — Minimum discernable change.

Response time — The time a system takes to reach and remain within a specified error limit of the desired value after the input of a step function, Figure A.25.

Root mean square (RMS) — A value applied to AC currents and voltages derived from equivalent heating. That is, a 100-V DC source will produce the same heat (power) as a 100-V RMS AC source when each is impressed across a resistance of R ohms. In the defining equation[7], T is the period of the cyclic waveform, f of t is the cyclic waveform, and t is the variable of integration.

Saturation current — (I_s) That input current which, when exceeded, results in no further in-

[7]$RMS = [(1/T)\int_0^T f^2(t)dt]^{1/2}$

A18

crease in output. See Figure A.1.

Saturation flow — (Q_s) The maximum output flow at a given applied power condition. See Figure A.1.

Saturation pressure — (P_s) The maximum output pressure at a given power condition. See Figure A.1.

Sensor — See transducer.

Servomechanism — Literally, slave machine whose output faithfully follows an input command.

Signal — A physical quantity such as voltage, current, displacement, pressure, etc., which carries information regarding its source. It usually is thought of as having a low power level or is the information content of a high power-level variable.

Slew rate — The maximum output speed of a position or motion-control system.

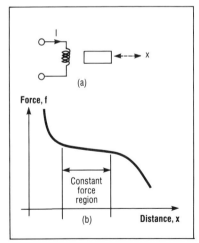

Fig. A.32 Symbol of proportional solenoid (a), and graph of its steady-state force-distance characteristics, (b).

Solenoid, proportional — A DC-operated current-to-force transducer which has a region of constant force for an armature movement, Figure A.32.

Stability — A subjective term describing the degree a system tends to hunt or oscillate about its desired output value. A continuously oscillating system is unstable. A system which overshoots but converges on the desired output in an acceptable time with acceptable overshoots is stable. See Figure A.25, Overshoot.

Stable system — See Stability.

State variable feedback — A process whereby a number of state variables in a system (as opposed to the final, controlled variable) are measured and fed back to achieve improved dynamic response.

Step input — A specific input signal which instantaneously jumps from zero to a finite value at a specific time, Figure A.25. Synonym: step.

Stiction — The tendency for a stationary object to require a higher force to start movement (breakaway friction) than the force required to continue movement (sliding friction) once it has begun. Synonym: stickslip.

Summing junction — An electrical, mechanical, or hydraulic circuit or portion thereof whose function is to compare (subtract) two signals and generate an error (difference). The error can be physical (the input resistor circuit in a two-input op-amp circuit), or abstract (a free body equation on a dancer roll). Synonym: comparator, summer, adder.

Threshold current — (I_t) The input current required to cause an output equal to 1% of saturation output. It is the current required to carry the proportional electrohydraulic interface device (PEHID) from its dead zone to its active region. See Figure A.1.

Torque motor — A current-to-torque transducer used to move a flapper, jet pipe, or wand in pilot stages of certain valves. See Figures A.26, A.27.

Transducer — A device which accepts an input of one physical variable and outputs a dependent, different physical variable; for example, a presssure-to-voltage transducer. Synonym: sensor.

Transistor, NPN — A solid-state current-amplifying device in which the emitter current leaves the emitter terminal, Figure A.33.

Transistor, PNP — A solid-state current amplifying device in which the emitter current enters the emitter terminal, Figure A.34.

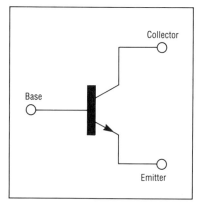

Fig. A.33. NPN transistor symbol.

Underdamping — The tendency for a feedback-controlled system

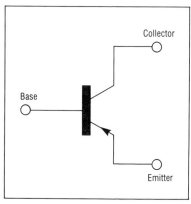

Fig. A.34. PNP transistor symbol.

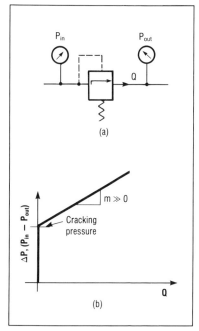

Fig. A.35. Symbol of a counterbalance valve, (a) and (b), graph of its steady-state characteristics with slope m≫0 above cracking pressure.

to overshoot its desired value. See Damping, Overdamping, Overshoot.

Unstable system — See Stability.

Valve, counterbalance — A pressure-control valve designed to provide a flow-dependent pressure above a threshold or cracking pressure, Figure A.35.

Valve, directional-control — A valve whose primary function is to direct or prevent flow through selected passages. (Extracted from American National Standard Fluid power systems and products — Glossary, ANSI/B93.2 — 1986; courtesy of the National Fluid Power Association).

Valve, electrohydraulic flow control — A proportional electrohydraulic interface device (PEHID) which accepts an input current

and controls the setting of a flow-control valve.

Valve, electrohydraulic relief — A proportional electrohydraulic interface device (PEHID) which accepts an input current and controls the cracking pressure of a relief valve.

Valve, flow-control — A variable orifice, Figure A.36.

Valve, pressure- and temperature-compensated flow-control — A variable orifice which adjusts its own opening to maintain a constant output flow in the presence of changing pressure and/or temperature, Figure A.37.

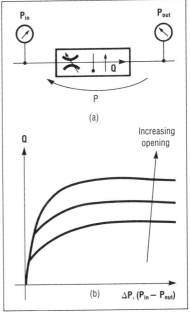

Fig. A.37. Symbol of pressure- and temperature-compensated flow control valve (a), and (b), graph of its steady-state characteristics under various larger orifice openings.

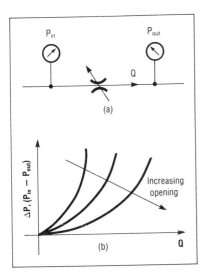

Fig. A.36. Symbol of variable flow control valve (a), and (b), graph of its steady-state characteristics as orifice area increases.

Valve, pressure-control — A valve that regulates its own input or output pressure. See Valve, relief; Valve, pressure-reducing; Valve, counterbalance.

Valve, pressure-reducing — A pressure-control valve which regulates its own outlet pressure, Figure A.38. See Valve, pressure-control.

Valve, proportional — A proportional electrohydraulic interface directional valve which has more than 3% center overlap. See Center-lap conditions; Metering characteristics; Valve, directional-control; Valve, servo.

Valve, relief — A pressure-control valve which regulates its own inlet pressure by moving a spool or poppet against a spring, Figure A.39. See Valve, pressure-control.

Valve, servo — A proportional electrohydraulic directional valve which has less than 3% center overlap. See Valve, proportional.

Voice coil — A current-to-force transducer which produces linear motion, so named because of its similarity to the electromagnetic circuit used in loudspeakers. They are used in the pilot stages of some servovalves.

Voltage regulator — An electronic device or assembly which maintains a constant output voltage regardless of input voltage or output (load) current variations within specified limits.

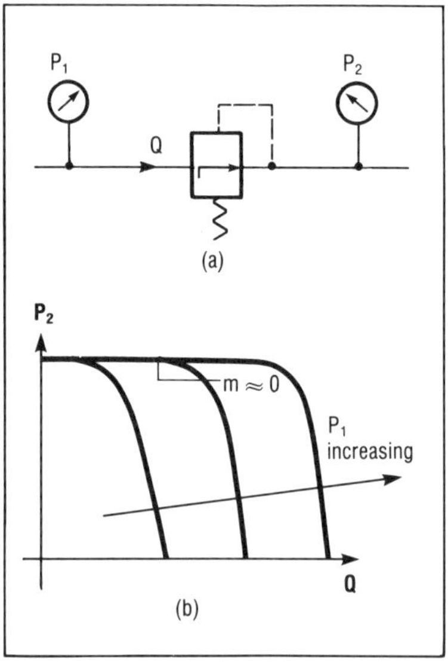

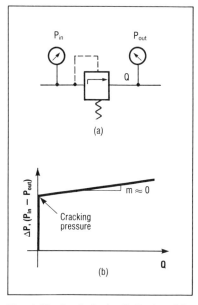

Fig. A.39. Symbol of relief valve, (a), and (b), graph of its steady state characteristics with slope m≈0 above cracking pressure.

Fig. A.38. Symbol of pressure-reducing valve (a), and (b), graph of its steady-state characteristics with increasing pressure. Slope m≈0.

Electric-Hydraulic Analogies

Electric-Hydraulic Analogies

Analogies are a powerful tool because their use builds on present understanding to learn and understand new but analogous phenomena. A danger arises when the analogy is carried to mathematical equivalence which many times does not exist.

Electric	Hydraulic

1E. Conductor — A material, usually metal, in which the mobile electrons are loosely held by their parent atoms.

1H. Conductor — A conduit through which fluid can pass with minimum obstruction; usually tubing or piping.

2E. Insulator — A material, usually non-metal, in which the electrons are tightly held by the parent atoms. Insulators are used to prevent conducting materials from contacting other materials or objects and to separate conductors from other conductors.

2H. Pressure vessel or pressure-containing envelope — Usually a metal container that totally encloses and confines a fluid in its interior while allowing it to move therein.

3E. Flow or current — (I), measured in amperes. The movement of electrons within a conductor. A measure of passing electrons per unit of time, (coulomb/sec).

3H. Flow — (Q), measured in gpm, lpm, in^3/sec. Movement of fluid molecules measured in volume per unit of time.

4E. EMF or voltage — (E or V), measured in volts. The electrical force which, when applied to a conductor, causes the electrons to move from a point of higher voltage to a point of lower voltage.

4H. Pressure — (P), measured in psi, bar, or Pa. The hydrostatic force applied to a hydraulic conductor or pressure-containing envelope which causes the fluid molecules to move from a point of higher pressure to a point of lower pressure.

5E. Positive flow source — A device which generates an output current of a certain magnitude no matter how restrictive the load. It is a contrivance, not usually a simple source; also a useful mathematical tool, Figure A.40.

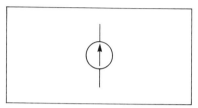

Fig. A.40. Symbol for electrical current source.

6E. Positive voltage source — The basic electrical generating device which produces a certain voltage, no matter how conductive the load. Batteries, Figure A.42(a), and generators, Figure A.42(b), are voltage sources.

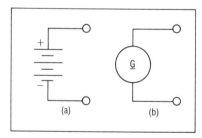

Fig. A.42. Symbol for battery, (a), and electrical generator, (b).

7E. Circuit — An assembly of electrical components which has one or more continuous flow paths, however restrictive, Figure A.44.

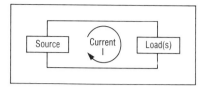

Fig. A.44. Electrical circuit provides path(s) for current flow from source through load(s) to ground.

8E. Ammeter — An instrument for measuring current. Because it *counts charges going through*, it always must be connected so that all charges to be measured pass through it, that is in series, Figure A.46.

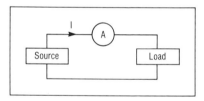

Fig. A.46. An ammeter, connected into circuit in series, is an instrument that measures current.

5H. Positive-displacement pump — The basic hydraulic power source. When the input shaft is operated, fluid is positively expelled from the output port, no matter how restrictive the load, Figure A.41.

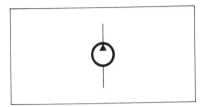

Fig. A.41. Schematic symbol of a single-direction, fixed-displacement hydraulic pump as indicated in American National Standard Y32.10 — 1979(R 1987).

6H. Positive pressure source — A contrivance such as a pressure-compensated pump which maintains its output pressure regardless of output flow. Output presssure is maintained by controlling pump displacement, Figure A.43(a). Generic pressure-source symbol, Figure A.43(b), implies that pressure remains constant from the source regardless of output flow.

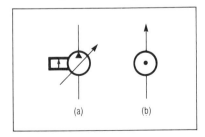

Fig. A.43. Pressure-compensated pump symbol, (a), indicates positive pressure source, as indicated in Ameri-

can National Standard Y 32.10 — 1979(R 1987). Pressure source symbol, (b), comes from International Organization for Standardization Standard ISO 1219 — 1976.

7H. Circuit — An assembly of hydraulic components that provides one or more continuous flow paths, however restrictive, Figure A. 45.

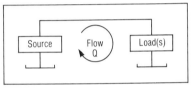

Fig. A.45. Elemental hydraulic circuit indicates that source pumps fluid around circuit path(s), expends work on load(s) and returns to tank.

8H. Flowmeter — An instrument for the measure of fluid flow. Because it *counts the molecules of fluid that pass*, it must be connected so that all molecules to be counted pass through the meter, that is in series, Figure A. 47.

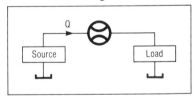

Fig. A.47. Elemental hydraulic circuit now has flowmeter to indicate volume of fluid that passes per unit of time.

9E. Voltmeter — An instrument for measuring the potential or voltage difference between any two points in an electrical circuit, Figure A.48(a). Because it has two leads or connectors and is polarity-sensitive, its reading can be positive (upscale when connected correctly) or negative (downscale when connected in reverse). Thus on circuit drawings, it is necessary to show how the voltmeter should be connected into the circuit, Figures A.48(b) and (c). The electrical corollary to the single port pressure gage is implicit in electronic and automotive electrical circuits which use a common ground reference such as the automotive chassis, Figure A.48(d). In this case, the voltage is called *the voltage at point A*. It is implied that the voltage is with resepect to chassis ground. The instrument still has two electrical leads, and one of the leads must be connected to chassis ground.

10E. Ohmmeter — An instrument that measures the resistance of an electrical device, Figure A.50.

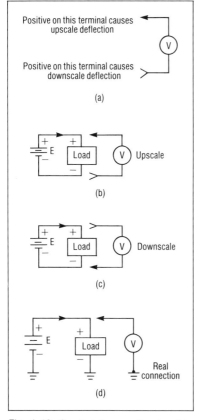

Fig. A.48. Symbol for a voltmeter, (a), and arrow shows how meter must be connected into circuit to obtain upscale reading, (b). Reverse connection, (c), gives downscale indication. Used to measure voltage at point A in automotive circuit which uses a common ground, voltmeter connection, (d), closely parallels that of single-port pressure gage.

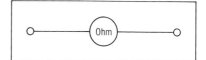

Fig. A.50. Symbol for an ohmmeter.

9H. Pressure gage, differential — An instrument for measuring the pressure difference between any two points in space. Because the gage has two ports or connection points, Figure A.49(a), and is polarity-sensitive, its reading can be either upscale or downscale depending on the way it is connected, Figure A.49(b) and (c). The symbology, therefore, should allow an indication of how the instrument is to be connected even though there is no standard in the industry. An arrow convention is used here. In the special case of a pressure gage with only one hydraulic port, Figure A.49(d), the gage still measures differential pressure. The second pressure always is atmospheric pressure. The resulting reading is the gage reading at point A, really the differential pressure between A and the atmospheric pressure.

10H. There is no analogous device to an ohmmeter in hydraulics.

11H. Resistance — A hydraulic path that allows hydraulic flow which is impeded by the cross-sectional area of the path, ie an orifice, Figure A.52(a). If there is flow through the orifice, the pressure of the flow entering the orifice is higher than the pressure of the flow emerging from the other side. Pressure drop through the orifice is non-linearly related to the flow, Figure A.52(b). In the linear flow region, $P = (K)(Q)$. In the non-linear flow region, $Q = 24(A)(P)^{1/2}$. For most hydraulic oils, when P is in psi, A is in in.^{2}, and Q is in gpm.

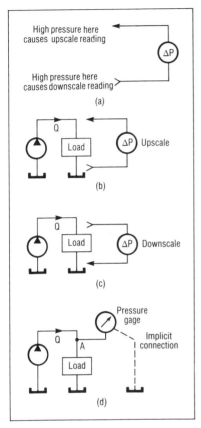

Fig. A.49. Differential pressure gage, (a) measures difference in pressure between two points in hydraulic circuit. Sometimes abbreviated psid or ΔP, differential pressure indication increases when the gage is connected in proper sequence (b), decreases when gage connections are reversed, (c). When differential pressure gage has only one port, measured pressure always is compared to atmospheric pressure, (d), through internal port within the gage case.

11E. Resistance — (R), measured in ohms. An electrical parameter which accounts for the conversion of electrical power into thermal power and represents opposition or resistance to current. If there is a current through a resistance, the polarity of the voltage drop is positive on the side of the resistor that the current enters, Figure A.51(a). Voltage is linearly related to current through Ohm's law, $E = (I)(R)$, Figure A.51(b).

tor symbols, Figure A.53(b). When charges are transferred, for example, from the lower plate to the upper plate, a voltage difference is developed, Figure A.53(c). The value of the difference depends on the number of charges transferred, and capacitance $q = (C)(v)$ where q is the charge transferred in coulombs, C is the capacitance in farads, and v is the voltage difference in volts. $i = C \, dv/dt$. Figure A.53(c).

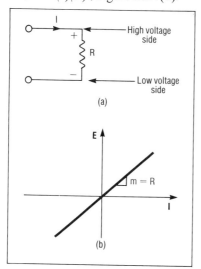

(a)

(b)

Fig. A.51. As current passes through resistor R, (a), voltage drop occurs between the side of the resistor the current enters and the side the current departs as defined by a plot of Ohm's Law, (b), which has slope m = R.

12E. Capacitor — An electrical device for storing electrical charge. It is constructed as a pair of conductors, usually plates, separated by dielectric material, Figure A.53(a), and appropriate capaci-

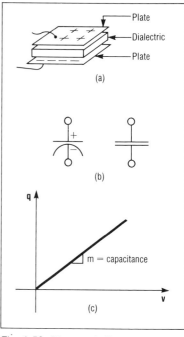

Fig. A.53. Diagram indicates construction of a capacitor, (a) with symbols, (b), polarized (left) and non-polarized. Capacitance is slope m of the curve of charge q vs. voltage v, (c).

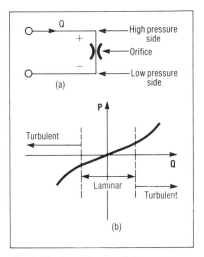

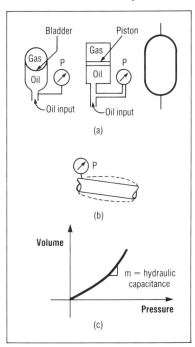

$f(P)$, where V is the volume of fluid stored and P is the pressure.

Fig. A.52. An orifice in a fluid conductor, (a), produces a pressure drop as fluid flows through the orifice. Pressure drop, ΔP or psid, is non-linearly related because of the turbulent flow that results at higher pressures and volumes (b).

12H. Accumulator — A hydro-pneumatic device which develops pressure when a volume of oil is forced into the device, Figure A.54(a). When oil is forced into the oil side, gas is compressed or a weight is raised, and pressure results. The same effect occurs because of expansion of a conductor, Figure A.54(b), when it passes high-pressure fluid, and also because of fluid compressibility. There is no accepted definition of hydraulic capacitance. If there were, it would be the slope of the pressure vs volume curve, Figure A.54(c); $q = C_H \, dp/dt$; where q is hydraulic flow; hydraulic capacitance C_H is the instantaneous slope m of the v vs P curve; $V =$

Fig. A.54. Accumulator drawings, (a) left to right, shows a bladder accumulator, which uses a synthetic membrane to separate hydraulic fluid and the gas charge, a piston accumulator with a piston separating the two media, and a schematic symbol for an accumulator. When hose expands because of interior pressure, (b), it effectively acts as accumulator. Slope m of the pressure vs volume curve, (c), indicates the non-standardized hydraulic capacitance, C_H.

13E. Inductor — A coil of wire carrying a current creates a magnetic flux around the coil. Because of current linkage, the flux induces a voltage of a polarity that oppposes the current change which originally caused the voltage, Figure A.55. The inductor opposes changes in current. Inductance is defined as the number of flux linkages per ampere, an abstract but accurate concept. Voltage $v = N \, d\phi/dt$, where N is the number of turns and ϕ is the total flux that links those turns. In practical engineering terms, $v = L \, di_L/dt$, where i_L is current in amperes and L is inductance in henries.

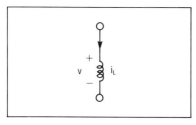

Fig. A.55. As current passes through a coil, it induces a voltage of opposite polarity which opposes the original current.

14E. Diode — A device which allows current in only one direction and little or no current in the opposite direction, Figure A.57.

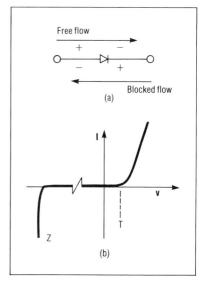

Fig. A.57. Symbol for diode, (a), includes indication of current direction. Current vs voltage plot (b) shows diode flow characteristics, Zener breakdown region Z and threshold voltage, T.

13H. Mass or inertance — The mechanical property such that when mass is placed in motion, it tends to stay in motion. This property is caused by the mass of the fluid in motion or, more extensively, by load masses being driven by cylinders, Figure A.56(a), or flywheels being driven by hydraulic motors, Figure A.56(b). There is no symbol for hydraulic inductance and no universally accepted units. Inertance is an acoustic term borrowed here to describe a hydraulic phenomenon. $p = L_H \, dq/dt$, where p is pressure, q is hydraulic flow, and L_H is "hydraulic inertance." In a cylinder circuit, Figure 56(a), the equivalent hydraulic inertance is M/A^2, while in motor circuits, Figure 56(b), the equivalent hydraulic inertance is $J4\pi^2/D^2$, where M is the load mass (lb-sec^2/in), A is piston area in in.^{2}, J is inertia in in-lb-sec, and D is motor displacement in in^3/rev.

14H. Check valve — A hydraulic device which allows free fluid flow in one direction but not in the other under certain conditions. Sometimes, the valve has a bias spring to assist closing in the blocked flow direction, Figure A.58.

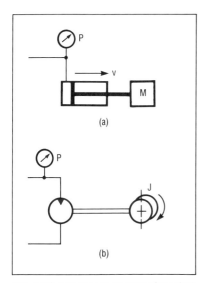

Fig. A.56. There is no accepted symbol, term, or unit for the hydraulic analogy to inductance. Some literature refers to inertance. The phenomenon arises in hydraulic circuits when accelerating masses with cylinders, (a), and inertias with motors, (b), and to a lesser degree, the acceleration of the fluid mass.

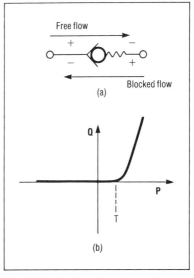

Fig. A.58. Check valve schematic symbol (a) shows free and blocked-flow directions. Pressure vs flow plot (b) gives characteristic curve of check valve. Threshold pressure T is caused by bias spring.

15E. Rectification/half-wave — A process, using a single diode, Figure A.59(a), whereby a bidirectional (AC) source current is converted to a pulsating, unidirectional current. The resulting rectified current exists only during one-half of the bidirectional source cycle, Figure A.59(b).

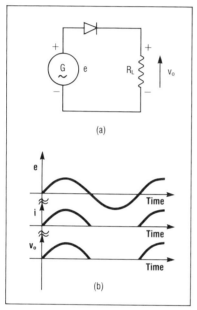

Fig. A.59. Half-wave rectification circuit (a) results in characteristic curves (b), for voltage into diode and current and voltage out.

16E. Transistor — A three-terminal device in which a relatively small input (base) current causes a much larger change in the current through another terminal, the collector; a solid state current amplifier, Figure A.61.

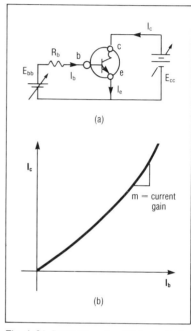

Fig. A.61. Transistor circuit (a) results in current gain through collector curve, (b). Circuit includes transistor where c represents the collector, b the base, and e the emitter. E_{cc} is collector supply voltage, E_{bb} is base supply voltage, I_c is collector current, I_b is base current, and I_e is emitter current. R_b is an external, current-limiting base resistor.

15H. Rectification/half-wave — A process whereby an alternating, bidirectional hydraulic flow source can be converted to a pulsating, unidirectional hydraulic flow to a load. The positive-displacement nature of the hydraulic circuit requires two check valves for half-wave rectification even though the analogous electrical circuit requires only one diode. This hydraulic half-wave rectifier circuit can be assembled but has no practical application, Figure A.60.

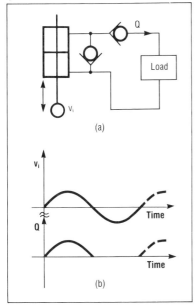

Fig. A.60. Hypothetical alternating-input hydraulic circuit (a) results in characteristic flow and pressure vs. time curves (b). This circuit has no meaning in the real world.

16H. There is no exact analog to the transistor in hydraulic componentry. However, certain contrivances can be assembled to perform an analogous amplification function, Figure A.62. See 17H.

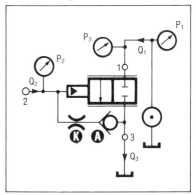

Fig. A.62. A pilot-operated proportioning valve can be made to perform analogously to a transistor. Terminals 1, 2, and 3 correspond to collector, base, and emitter, respectively. Hydraulic flow Q_1, Q_2, and Q_3 likewise correspond to collector, base, and emitter currents. The internal flow path through restriction K, along with check valve A, represent a circuit which behaves hydraulically in a manner analogous to the base-to-emitter junction of the transistor. In the hydraulic circuit, the sizing of K and the pilot-operated directional control valve can be made such that small input flow Q_2 can control and modulate much larger flow Q_1. Q_3 is the sum of Q_1 and Q_2.

17E. Transistorized voltage amplifier — The current amplification inherent in a transistor can be used to make a voltage amplifier by judicious use of resistors which convert the currents into proportional voltages, Figure A.63.

18E. Bridge rectifier — An assembly of four diodes which provide full-wave rectification, that is uni-directional load flow for both half-cycles of an alternating source, Figure A.65.

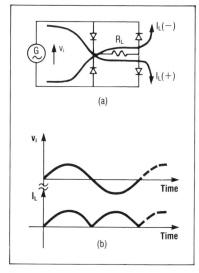

(a)

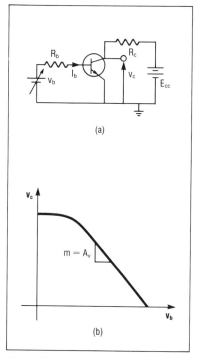

Fig. A.65. Bridge rectifier circuit (a) produces pulsating but unidirectional current (b) through the bridging load. Load current I_L is comprised of components $I_L(+)$ and $I_L(-)$ which respectively represent the current paths. The AC is alternatively positive on its upper port and then positive on its lower port.

Fig. A.63. Transistorized voltage amplifier, (a), results in voltage gain curve (b), where slope m is negative. $A_v = \Delta v_c/\Delta v_b$, where A_v stands for voltage amplification or gain, v_c represents collector voltage, and v_b is base voltage. See Figure A.61.

19E. Zener diode — A diode designed to operate in the zener breakdown region to take advantage of the very good voltage regulation in zener breakdown. The diode sometimes is used to limit voltage in one direction, and at other times used for free *flow* in reverse direction, see Figure A.57.

17H. Pilot-operated check valve pressure amplifier — A hydraulic circuit contrivance better suited to showing analogous operation than in finding a practical application, Figure A.64.

18H. Bridge rectifier — An assemblage of a cylinder and check valves which provide full-wave rectification, that produces unidirectional load flow for both half cycles of an alternating displacement source, Figure A.66.

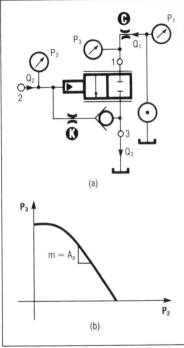

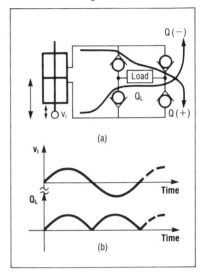

Fig. A.64. As pilot pressure increases opening of pilot-operated proportioning directional control valve, (a), pressure from constant hydraulic pressure source through orifice c, indicated by gage P_3, decreases. Plot of pressure out, P_3, vs pilot pressure P_2, (b), has negative slope m. Pressure gain $A_p = \Delta P_3/\Delta P_2$, where A_p is pressure amplification or gain, P_3 is pressure downstream of orifice, and P_2 is pilot pressure.

Fig. A.66. Hydraulic bridge rectifier circuit (a) produces pulsating, unidirectional flow (b) through the bridging load. Load flow Q_L is composed of components $Q_L(+)$ and $Q_L(-)$ which represent the respective flow paths. When the pump is stroked with sinusoidal velocity v_i, pressure flow alternates between the pump's upper and lower ports while the unpresurized port receives return flow. Bridge rectifiers have found some use in hydraulic circuits, but AC hydraulics has never been implemented to the extend AC electronics has.

Index

A

AC.............................22
   generator.....................303
A/D converter 249
Absolute-position encoder 242, 294
Acceleration
   control 204
   waveshape.....................391
Accelerometer 297, 299
Accumulator 8, 79
Accuracy.........................12
Actuator........................362
Alternating current 22, 90
Alternator.......................303
Ambient light....................201
Ammeter.........................11
Ampere..........................11
Amplification...................16, 119
   adjustment 369
Amplifier
   , charge 298
   circuit card 149, 150
   , ideal.......................120
   , integrating..................204
   , negative feedback-stabilized 155
   , proportional valve 201
   , triode......................136
Amplitude
   modulation, carrier present........250
   modulation, suppressed-carrier, double-
   sideband.....................253
   peak..........................92
Analog 207
   function 134
   summer.......................202
   -to-digital converter 242
AND............................210
Annubar flow sensor 329
Armature 348
Atoms...........................10
Attenuate 162

Attenuator circuit.................154
Autotransformer 312
Average
   value 26
   voltage.......................114

B

Backlash....................380, 381
Ball screw 395
Bandwidth 384, 386, 387, 395
   , closed-loop system 386
Band-pass filter...................241
Bang-bang systems................402
Base
   2 226
   10 226
   16 226
Bellows 316
Bias
   adjustment 206
   control 249
Biased
   , forward 110
   , reverse......................110
Binary..........................208
   coded decimal (BCD) 226, 296
   digit........................228
   equivalent....................226
   numbering system 226, 228
   register 229
   variables 207
Bipolar power supply 135, 171
Bi-metal thermometers 317
Bi-stable flip-flop 220
Bit............................228
Black box 362
Bleed-off flow control...............45
Bleed resistor 146
Block diagram 362
Bourdon-tube pressure gage . 14, 277, 315

Break-away pressure 380
Bridge
   circuit 31, 280, 284, 342
   , single active-arm. 280
   , four active-arm 280
   supply voltage. 280
Broadcast band. 259
Brushes 301
Brushless DC tachometer 303
Buffer amplifier 248
Byte. 232, 233

C

Calculus 1
Calibration 383
   curve 324
Capacitor 8, 79
   filter. 117
Capacitance 11, 79, 288
Capacitive reactance 96
Capillary tube. 318
Carrier. 249, 251
   frequency 251, 289, 338
   signal. 250
Cascaded blocks. 366
Center-tapped. 115, 116, 118
Centering spring. 357
Characteristic
   , op amp 137
   , voltage transfer. 137
Charge amplifier. 298
Circuit
   -board common 271
   card. 158
   loading 53
   , parallel 44
   , series 44
Clamp-on ammeters. 300
Clock. 257, 260
   frequency 261, 262
   pulse generator. 257
Closed-loop
   bandwidth. 384
   control system 368
   feedback 361
   plant 367
   positional servomechanism 368, 404
   system. 367
      bandwidth. 386
   transfer function. 367, 385
Coarse-fine adjustment 165
Collector saturation resistance 180

Color code, resistor 18
Command. 156
   pot. 309
   profile 399
   voltage. 156
Commutator. 300, 301
Comparator 143, 167, 361, 389
Compiler. 233
Complex
   algebra 100
   numbers 92
   operator 100
Complementary metal-oxide semiconductor (CMOS) 208
   chips 209
   logic 209
Compressibility 40
Conductors. 10
Conductive plastic film 307
Conductivity. 50
Constant
   acceleration 391
   current
      generators. 13
      source 13
   -pressure pump. 394
Contact. 276
   bounce 175
   eliminator. 174
Control
   valve 362
      bandwidth. 397
   theory 365
Control-loop closure 361
Cosine wave 94
Counter. 217
   emf 61
   is busy 257
Current 11
   , alternating 22
   amplifier. 205
   -amplifying transistor. 121
   , conventional. 12
   feedback 205
   loop. 242,
      , 4- to 20 mA. 243, 248
   , maximum 94
   -sensing resistor 205
   , short circuit. 71
   source 12
Cylinder 8
   , single rod-end. 195

D

D/A converter 236
DC
  data transmission forms 246
  tachometer 300
Damping 364, 397
Data
  form 245, 246
  ready 238
  transmission medium 241
  transmission method 243
Deadband
  corrector (DBC) 193, 388
  elminator (DBE) 193, 195, 388
  transfer characteristic 195
Dead zone 194, 388
Debouncer 174
Decimal
  equivalent 229
  system 226, 227
Deformable member 335
Deglitcher 174
Degree of instability 371
Demodulate 250, 252, 260, 289
Detector
  , level 167
  , threshold 167
  , zero-crossing 167
Diaphragm 315
Dielectric 79
Differencer 361
Differential
  amplifier 165, 274
  equations 365
  output 165
  -pressure transducer 13
  summer 389
Differentiation 1
Differentiators 8
Digital
  circuits 207
  computer 257
  , special purpose 242
  coding 207
  multimeter 249
  output, parallel 242
  -to analog conversion 235
  signal 260
  update time 238
Digitize 7, 226, 257
Digitization of frequency 260
Diode 51, 110
Direct-acting valves 345

Direction of rotation bit 294
Displacement control 393
Dissimilar metals 296
Dither 178, 355
  voltage 158
Derivative 2
Doped 110
Doppler
  effect 337
  flow transducer 336
Double
  -ended 165
  -sideband AM 250
  -sideband suppressed-carrier, amplitude-
  modulated signal 245
  sidebanded 252
Down count 226
Drag-body flow sensor 328
Drag-cup tachometer 301, 302
Driving device 149
Duality 248
Dual-voltage transformer 204
Dummy gages 280
Dynamically limited part 365

E

Echo 334
Eddy current 282, 302
  detector 283
Efficiency
  , volumetric 58
Electric
  eye 293
  fields 334
  valve 121
Electrical
  generation 290
  power 395
Electrofluidic processes 333
Electrohydraulic 31
  positional servomechanism . . . 367, 371,
  380
Electromagnetic
  energy conversion 319
  interference (EMI) 265
Electromechanical
  actuators 344
  energy conversion 318
Electromotive force (EMF) 13
Electron flow 12, 16
Electrostatic energy conversion 319
Electro-rheological fluids 333

Electron 10, 32
Electronic
   counter 218, 221, 260
   deadband correction 388
   dithering 346
   flip flop 218
   frequency meter 169
   integrator 190
   oscillator 257
   totalizing counter 293
Electronically controlled on-off switch. 180
Electrostatic
   charge 210
   interference (ESI) 265
   shielding 269
End resistance 308
Energy
   -loss control method 344
   conversion 290
   storage elements 364
Envelope 252
Error 161, 310, 380, 389
   amplifier 202
   components 382
   integrator 377
   voltage 160, 404
Exclusive OR 210, 214
Executive commands 393
Exponential
   charging curve 82
   decay 84
   rise 84

F

FM 245, 258
   band 338
   , carrier is the data 260
   demodulator 338
   deviation from center frequency 259
   modulator 259
   receivers/demodulators 242
   radio signal 241, 337
   radio transmitters 242
Faithfulness 363
False trigger 167, 169
Fan out 208
Farad 80
   , micro 80
   , pico 80
Faraday-induced voltages 300
Feedback 156

control loop 245
control systems 24, 240, 367
   , operational amplifier 125
   pot 310
   resistor 152
   signals 393
   transducer 310, 362, 404
   voltage 161
Ferromagnetic
   gear 304
   material 339
Fiber-optic cable 241, 243
Fidelity 363
Filter capacitor 117, 204
First-order model 372, 385, 387
Fixed-displacement hydraulic motor . . 376
Flapper nozzle 348
Flexure spring 348
Flip flop 217
   , JK 221, 223
   , RS 218
   , RTS 263
Float 330
Flow
   control, load-sensing 132
   forces 346, 360
   gain block 373
   , laminar 51
   , mass 40
   metering curve 193, 388
   regulation 134
   , square-law 51
   -to-pressure conversion 325
   , volumetric 40
Flowmeter 320
   , integrating 321
   , nutating-disc 321
   , positive-displacement 321
   , variable-area 330
   , totalizing 322
   , turbine 323
   , ultrasonic 338
Flow control
   , bleed-off 45
Flux
   density 90
   field 88
      energy 88
   linkage 275
   , magnetic 108
Force motor 352, 393
Form factor 23
Forward branch 361
Four active gage bridge circuit 318, 329

Frequency........................92
, angular........................91
divider circuit...................261
methods.........................305
modulation......................245
response....................384, 397
test............................386
, rotational......................90
-to-voltage convertor 169, 263, 266
Friction..........................401
Full-wave rectified................113

bridge circuit....................343
cylinder.......................8, 395
transistor.......................129
Hydromechanical
control.........................134
natural frequency...............387
resonance.......................397
resonant frequency.. 373, 382, 386, 398
Hydrostatic transmission.... 61, 376, 379
Hysteresis .. 144, 168, 169, 170, 346, 348, 355, 381

G

Gage pressure......................69
Gain.............................119
block...........................385
Gallium-arsenide..................313
Galvanometer......................12
Gas
ionization......................313
precharge........................79
Gates........................207, 210
Geneva mechanism................322
Ground
current.........................273
loop.............. 243, 265, 272, 273
Gray
code............................295
excess code.....................296

H

HST................. 61, 376, 377, 379
Hall effect............... 240, 260, 299
voltage..........................300
Handshaking............ 241, 257, 258
Heat
sink........................118, 181
-transfer principle...............331
Heater-coil flowmeter..............332
Henries...........................87
Hexadecimal......................226
numbering system...............232
High-level language...............233
Higher-order model................387
Horsepower........................66
limiting.........................134
Hot-wire flow transducer...........331
Hybrid parameters.................128
Hydraulic

I

Ice bath..........................297
Ideal
amplifier...................120, 141
load.............................54
source...........................54
Imaginary numbers................100
Impedance.............. 26, 100, 101
right triangle....................107
matching....................73, 153
Impurity.........................110
n-type..........................110
p-type..........................110
Incandescent.....................312
Incremental encoder...... 226, 260, 293
Independent non-linearity..........308
Inductance..............11, 79, 85, 86
Induction motor...................395
Inductive reactance................98
Inertia...........................86
Inner loop........................346
Input
attenuator......................153
impedance 136, 140, 141, 142, 147, 149, 152, 154, 155, 157, 162, 248
port, parallel....................242
stage...........................206
Input-to-output resistance ratio.......54
Instrument-grade pots..............308
Insulators........................10
Integral controller.............379, 380
Integrated circuit (IC)..............134
Integrating
amplifier....................204, 379
capacitor....................191, 192
Integration........................1
Integrator.........................8
Internal
leakage 57, 129, 141

resistances. 28
voltage drop .54
Interpolating tube 329
Interpreter. 233
Interstage section 204
Instability 370
Intrusiveness. 26, 28
Inverter. 210
Inverting
  amplifier. 149, 150
  input 137, 152
  summing amplifier. . 158, 161, 374, 389
  terminal 147, 151
Iron-core inductor 318

K

K factor. 324
Kinetic energy 33
Kirchoff's
  current law 31, 39
  voltage law 31, 35, 38

L

Lag 397, 398
Latching 220
Laminar flow 50, 330
  tube. 325
Laplace transform 365, 384, 386
  pair 385
Large current gain 123
Last significant digit (LSD) 218
Leading-edge triggered. 224
Leakage
  coefficient. .59
  ,internal 57
Least significant bit (LSB) . . 224, 230, 295
Lenz's law 282
Level detector. 167, 182
Light-emitting diode (LED) 219, 220, 313, 314
  -photo transistor. 293
Limit
  adjustments 197
  circuit 200
  cycle 381
  switch 143
Linear
  model 58
  position transducer 144, 297, 340

variable differential transformer
(LVDT). . . 285, 289, 302, 317, 318, 347
Linearity. 308
Liquid
  expansion .318
  -in-glass thermometer 318
Load
  cells. .316, 340
  -demand method 344
  resistance 72, 73
  -sensing function 359
Loading
  effect. 155
  error 141, 142, 147, 149, 150, 152, 155,
  157, 164, 393
Local oscillator. 259, 282, 301
Logic
  circuits 210
  families 208
  gates 210
Logical
  inverter 210
  function 210
  one 208
  oscillator. .202
  zero 208
Low-pass filter 264
Lower sideband 252
LVDT local oscillator. 202

M

Machine
  -executable code. 234
  language 233, 234
  life. 390
Magnetic
  -field strength meters 300
  flux 85, 274, 318
    field. 300
  radiation 275
Main spool 64, 345, 348
Magnetostriction 338
Magnetostrictive material 340
Mass 86
  flow. 40, 327
Master reset 2, 261, 263
Maximum power transfer. 76
Measurand 240, 243, 280
Mechanical
  flip flop 217
  reaction. 315

Memory 217
Metal detector 283
Meter-in 14, 395
Meter-out 14, 395
   lands 68
Microammeter 12, 311
Milliammeter 12
Mhos...........................128
Mobile charge carrier.............12, 32
Modern control theory..............366
Modulation......................250
Modulus of elasticity 315
Mono-stable multivibrator . 168, 174, 175
Mother earth............. 268, 271, 272
Motion
   control 1, 242, 390
     profile 396
     system.......................405
   profile 373, 392
   waveshapes 392
Motors 320, 347
Multi-stage counters 223
Multimeters 16
  , digital 26
Multiplexer......................238

N

NAND 210, 216
Natural logarithm system 84
Negative feedback 136
  , stabilized amplifier...............155
Neon...........................313
Noise...........................265
   control 265
   current 268, 270
   -free input......................167
   immunity 165, 168, 170, 171, 209, 247, 248, 274
   rejection 168
   voltage........................268
Non-contacting switches 300
Non-inverting
   input......................138, 154
   operational amplifier 151, 152, 153
   terminal 146, 147, 151
Non-linear devices 51
   -linearity......................393
   -repeatability 390
   -repeatable error................384
NOR 210, 216
Norton current 71

Norton's theorem..................71
NOT 210
Nucleus..........................10
Null............................132
   shift..........................381
Numbering systems 226
Nutating disc flowmeter.............321

O

OIR............................274
OIT............................274
Odometer 8
   automotive 1
   reading 7
Offset 249
Off state........................207
Ohmmeter 21, 29
Ohm's law.....................15, 31
Ohms/volt rating 27
On
   -off switch......................282
   state..........................207
One-shot multivibrator 174, 223, 264
Open-loop
   control 368
   gain 16, 148, 149, 152
   system....................362, 367
   voltage gain.....................138
Operand 2
Operational amplifier (op-amp) . 125, 134, 136, 137, 138, 139, 144, 146, 147, 150, 379
   characteristics...................137
   chip............................16
   comparator circuit 139, 183
   feedback 125
Operators 2
  , differential 2
  , integral 3
Opto-isolation 243, 274
Orifice
   area 50
   pressure drop 330
Oscillation . . 193, 370, 378, 381, 388, 399
Oscilloscope 249
Outer-loop analog summer 203
Output
   admittance 128
   impedance 140, 142, 149, 150, 153, 162, 248, 333
   voltage range....................236

Oval gear set 321
Overlap 193
Overshoot 397, 398
Over-running 395

P

Parallax 27
Parallel 31
  circuits 44
  digital output 242
  input port 242
Parasitic
  capacitance266, 267, 269, 270, 272, 298
  feedback path 270
Peltier effect 314
Performance specifications 398
Period 91
  digitization 262
Permanent magnet 348
Permeability 338
Permissivity 50
Permittivity 288
Phase 201
  input 160
  inversion 138
  modulation 254, 255
  -sensitive demodulator . . . 202, 241, 250,
  254, 289, 302, 347
  shift 95, 138, 255
    torque transducer 256
Phasing the positional servomechanism 388
Photo
  cell 290, 292
  detector 279
  -electic generation 290
  -optical encoding 260
  resistor 278, 279, 292
  transistor 274, 290
  -voltaic cell 290
Pickup coils 304
Piezoelectric
  effect 297
  generation 297
  transducer 298
Pilot-operated valve 345, 347
Pitot tube 347
Place weighted 227
Plant 361
  commands 393
Plug-in cards 236
Polling 258
Position

-accuracy specification 382
  error 381
  sensor 300
  transducer 145, 283, 285
    output 404
  weighted 227
Positional servo mechanism. 194, 370, 390
Positive
  feedback 169, 183
  -displacement
    flowmeter 321
    function 321
Pot-pot
  bridge circuit 308
  servomechanism 310
Potential 310
  difference 13
  -measuring circuit 311
  meter 310
Potentiometer (pot) . . . 144, 153, 164, 305,
  306
  , linear 306, 308
  -motion 306
Power 60
  accounting 62, 68
  amplifier 242
  output 242
  -output transistor 202
  rating 19
  supply 112, 202, 204, 292
    , bipolar 135
    transformer 271
  transfer, maximum 71, 76
  transforming machines 120
  transistor 179
Powered land 374
Position feedback 376
Positive displacement 321
  motor 321
Preamplifier 204
Pressure
  compensation 132
  , gage 69
  gain 130, 194, 388
  metering curves 388
  regulation 134
  transducer 285, 297, 299
  , differential 13
Process 361
Profile rise rate 398
Profile generator 405
Profiling 404
Programmable
  limit switch 143

logic controller 236, 242, 258
Proportional
  amplifier 189, 204, 242, 249
  electrohydraulic interface device (PE
  HID) 344
  electromechanical interface device
  (PEMID) 344, 345
  solenoid . 320, 345, 346, 347, 353, 355,
  355, 393
  spool 207
  valve 26, 178, 320, 342, 394
Protons 10
Proving ring 316
Pulse
  -position modulation 245, 256
    systems 336
  train, main 294
  , quadrature 294
  width modulation (PWM) 178
    circuit 179
    frequency 186
    signal 256, 355
    waveshapes 179
PWM
  modulator 187
  op-amp comparator 202
Pump
  , positive-displacement 58
  , variable-displacement 132
  transfer characteristic 132

Q

Quiescent state 175
Quadrature
  output 293
  pulse 293
  signal 293
Quartz
  crystal 320
  motor 320
  piezoelectric transducer 298

R

Radio
  frequency interference (RFI) . . . 265, 275
  signals 275
Ramp
  bypass switch 204

control 403
function 190
generator 189, 203
shape 403
Ramped control 390
Ramping 390
Random error 382, 384
Range change 236
Rated
  displacement 58
  speed 59
Ratiometric 164
Reactance
  , capacitive 96
  , inductive 98
Receiving 142
  device 242, 243, 393
Receiver signal processing 242
Rectilinear 306
Reference
  bath 296
  voltage 170, 171
Regenerative 176
  feedback 184
Register 218
  , decimal 218
Relative permittivity 288
Relay 207, 276
Reliability 391
Reluctance 318, 340
Repeatability 390
Residual error 382
Resistance 15
  input 26
Resistivity 278
Resistor color code 18
  values, standard nominal 17
Resolution 162, 236
Resolver-to-digital converter 254
Resonant frequency 365
Rheostat 311
Ringing 364
Ring magnet 340
Rise rate 400
Root-mean-square (RMS) 22, 92, 113
  voltmeter 314
Rotary
  speed-control loops 374
  speed transducer 301
Rotational frequency 90
RS flip flop 218
RTS flip flop 263
Runaway condition 389

S

Saturation 138
, negtive 170
, positive 170
resistance 183
Scaling 23, 156
command 204
the servo 162
Scatter. 384
Schmitt trigger 168, 169, 175, 262
Self heating 311
Semiconductor 278
diodes 110
Sender signal conditioning 241, 242
Sending 142
device 162, 241, 393
Sensitivity 12, 280
Sensor 240, 393
Series 31
circuits 44
Servo
amplifier 1, 204, 242, 243, 405
gain 381
-loop
gain 369, 397, 399
instability 380
phasing 148
tuning 397
/proportional amplifier 362, 365
system 368
Servomechanism 310, 368
electrohydraulic positional 367
Servovalve 29, 64, 342, 393
flapper nozzle 33, 343
jet-pipe 33, 348
torquemotor 205
Set-point summer 374
Set-reset flip-flop 218
Shaft encoder 254, 300
Shielded
cable 272
twisted pair 247
Shielding case 271
Short circuit
condition 72
current 71
Sideband 252
, double 252
, lower 252
, single 252
, upper 252
Signal

conditioner 240, 347, 404
conditioning, sender 241
processing 204, 242
-to-noise ratio 248
Simple gain block 365
Simulated reference junction 297
Sine wave 91
Single-ended
amplifier 274
to differential conversions 165
voltage 165
Sinking 209
Slider 306, 307
Sliding-spool pilot valves 356
Slow shift 402
Slug 286
Software 239
Soft shift 402
Solar
cell 290
-energy conversion 293
Solenoid 189
Solid-state devices 207
Sonar 334
Sonic speed 335, 337
Source
impedance 164
resistance 53, 73
Speed current 302
Spool transportation delay 194
Springy 378
Square-law flow 51
Standard
cell 311
nominal resistance values 17
Steady-state 386
Steering logic 189
circuit 202
Stiction 354, 355, 360
forces 346
-induced hysteresis 346, 355
Stopping repeatability 402
Strain-gage 316, 317
transducer 240, 280
Stroking mechanism 132
Summer 361
Summing junction 361
Sum-and-difference frequency 289
Superposition 171
Suppressed-carrier, double-sideband, amplitude-modulated signal 289, 302
Swinging wand 348, 351
Swashplate 376
feedback 378

position feedback 376
Synchro. 286, 287, 302
System
    time constant 386
    response 396
    specification 398
Systematic errors 382, 384

T

Tachometer. 301, 302, 375, 376
Tachometric
    methods 265, 305
    transducer. 321
Temperature
    coefficients of resistance. 17, 278
    compensation. 282
    transducer. 318
Terminal non-linearity. 308
Thermal
    conductivity 331
    energy 314
    equilibrium. 331
    gradient. 331
    sensitivity 278
Thermofluidic processes 331
Thermistor 278, 279
Thermocouple 296
Thermoelectric
    cooling 314
    generation. 296
Time
    constant 83, 205
    lag 4, 305, 363, 370
    lead 4
Titanium. 288
Toggle 222
    port 221
Tolerance on. 17
Torque
    control 134
    motors. 347, 392
    shaft 317
    transducer. 254, 317
T-port 221
Transfer function 365, 366, 368
    , closed-loop 367
    , open-loop 368
Transciever 338
Transducer 240, 243, 277, 393, 405
    , differential-pressure 284
    , doppler-flow 336
    error 369, 382

, position 285
, linear. 287
, rotary. 287, 301
pot. 309
, pressure. 285, 297
, peizoelectric 298
, quartz piezoelectric 298
sensitivity 145, 146
, strain-gage. 240
, torque 317
, variable-reluctance. 283
Transfer
    characteristic 200
    function 1
Transformer 108, 115
    , center-tap 116, 118
    core 285
Transistor 120, 134
    characteristic 128
    , current-amplifying. 121
    NPN 121
    -transistor logic (TTL) 208
Transmitted pulse. 334
Triangular wave 143, 168
    oscillator. 183, 202
Trimmer resistor. 309, 311
Triode amplifier 136
Trip-point voltage. 168
Trigger. 167, 175
    level. 169
Truth table 214
Tube
    , cathode ray 33
    , vacuum 33
Tuned circuit 252
Turbine 323
    flowmeter 277, 323, 325
Turbulent 330
Turn down ratio 324
Turns
    primary 109
    secondary 109
Twisted shielded pairs 266
Two
    -conductor shielded cable 242
    -input
        AND gate 213
        differential amplifier . . 155, 156, 157
        OR gate. 215
Two-port device 142
Type
    -one regulator. 377, 378
    -zero regulator 375

U

Underdamped 370, 378, 379, 398
Ultrasonic
   energy.........................335
   position transducer 334
   receiver 335, 337
   reflector......................335
   transmitter 334, 337
Unilateral.......................120
Universal viscosity curve............324

V

VCCM..........................373
Valve
   bandwidth frequency.............382
   , check........................111
   , control 393
   control of cylinder motion (VCCM) . 373
   electric 121
   null..........................193
   , proportional 194
      amplifier.....................201
   , servo, flapper-nozzle 33
      , jet-pipe 33
      , zero-lapped..................193
Variable-displacement pump.....376, 393
Variable reluctance
   alternator 303
   autotransformer 305
   transducer...................283, 303
Variable-speed electrical drive........396
Varistor.........................276
Velocity profile 392
Viscosity 326, 335
Visible light...................313, 314
Volt/ampere characteristic 111
Voltage 13
   amplifier conversion 122
   attenuator equation 51
   divider................ 53, 153, 170
      equation 51
   drop..........................34
   gain calculation 123
   gain, open loop..................138
   /pressure analogy.................14
   regulator.............. 30, 117, 204
   rectification 112
Voltmeter 13
Volume-control method 344, 393

Volumetric

Volumetric
   efficiency 58
   flow.......................40, 327

W

Ward-Leonard drive.................61
Watts...........................60, 66
Waveshape-squaring 168
Wheatstone bridge...............16, 21
Wiper 306
Winding
   primary........................108
   secondary 108, 109

Z

Zener diode...................192, 311
Zero crossing detector 256
Zeroing.........................249
Zero-lapped servovalve 193
Zone of ambiguity 146

To order additional copies of this book, write to:

Penton Education Division
1100 Superior Avenue
Cleveland, OH 44114-2543

or call toll-free 800/321-7003
(In Ohio call 216/696-7000)